Dear Reader,

You are about to have a secret revealed to you.

Sometimes secrets are for keeping; other times they are for sharing. Because Hannah Whitall Smith shared her very important secret, her generation and succeeding generations have found the key to a more abundant life.

That key is here extended to you.

THE CHRISTIAN'S SECRET
OF A HAPPY LIFE

Hannah Whitall Smith

SPIRE BOOKS

Fleming H. Revell Company • Old Tappan, New Jersey

THE CHRISTIAN'S SECRET OF A HAPPY LIFE

A SPIRE BOOK
Published by Jove Publications, Inc. for the Fleming H. Revell
Company

Thirtieth printing, October 1979

Copyright 1942, 1970, by the Fleming H. Revell Company

All Rights Reserved

Printed in the United States of America

SPIRE BOOKS are published by the Fleming H. Revell Company, Old Tappan, New Jersey 07675, U.S.A.

CONTENTS

The Christian's Secret of a Happy Life

CONTENTS

FOREWORD

CLASSICS IN RELIGIOUS BOOKS ARE FEW AND FAR BETWEEN; many are written which have the appearance of the classic, but few live long enough to make a lasting mark upon the lives of men. *The Pilgrim's Progress*, a Kempis with his *Imitation of Christ* and Calvin with his *Institutes of the Christian Religion* rise like mountain peaks above the trail down which man has marched, but the trail is white with the bones of lesser books cast off as excess baggage, and forgotten. The march has been a grueling one, and all too often its spiritual scribes have reflected its uncertainty and terror. Bunyan's pilgrim had a desperate time; a Kempis, an ascetic, now and then dipped his pen in tears and in the times of Calvin love strove with fire and woe.

But none of this found its way into the spirit of Hannah Whitall Smith, or into her classic and enduring *The Christian's Secret of a Happy Life*. She was a happy passenger in the chariot of God, always in the van and never a despondent straggler in the rear, calling out with an infectuous enthusiasm, "Come up and ride with us!" She had nothing in common with the disillusioned author of Ecclesiastes, to whom "all, all is vanity," and all things filled with weariness. To her, every bush along the wayside was afire with God. There is a merry mercy, a rhapsodic joy in all she hears and sees and knows, for all, all is the handiwork of a God with a happy purpose for man, of a Creator who created all in beauty and in love. Life to her was no dismal journey between the peaks of birth and death; it was the scene of a continuing Triumphal Entry into the courts of God, with Everyman marching.

Quaker, rebel, realist, she faced life as she found it, and she found it good. In a day when the shadows of human error and apostasy hung heavy on the world she wrote this book and held it forth to her generation as a key to the house of light. Her generation bought it, read it, kept

7

and treasured it next to the Book of books itself, for her generation saw in it and in her that for which they longed: the open sesame to a more abundant life.

Posterity loved it, too; printed first in 1870 (one of the first books published by Revell), nearly two million copies have been sold. That was to be expected, for man has an incurable urge to solve secrets, to find out and walk the higher hidden roads. "H. W. S." has set their feet upon those roads. She took the gloom from the Gospel (if ever there were gloom in it, which she would likely doubt) and made life an unending joy. It has not only been the common people who have heard her gladly!

The Christian's Secret of a Happy Life has outlived the years, not for its holy optimism alone, but more because there is nothing shallow or shadowy in its optimism. It is a rock of a book, solid and immovable, built upon the inexhaustibility of God and the unfolding of His everlasting truth. This is no quickly written "how-to-be-successful-and-popular" treatise, no ill-conceived experiment in "new thought." This is truth and proof of truth as she found it and lived it. She took her Bible promises literally, tested them, and found them true as tested steel. She stepped out of conjecture into certainty, and from that moment on she found no shadows on her path. Greater still, she shows us how we may do it!

She writes here, not for the spiritual genius, not for the world-forsaking saint, but for those who are in the world and of it, for the great little ones who long for God as they struggle for bread. She writes in their language—plainly; the confusing theological speech of the scholar is not here; the secret is revealed in countless illustrations from the common walk of life. It is as simple and understandable as the language of Jesus Christ.

It is practical; it deals with daily duties, deeds and decisions. It is personal; the author is no day-dreaming speculator with her head in the clouds and her feet caught in the clods of the field; she had head knowledge and heart knowledge in beautiful balance. Powerful, unmarred by petty bickerings over faith's incidentals, this book has swept men into the ministry, selfish laymen into unselfish living at the command of Christ.

As orthodox and reverent as Luke or John, every line of it is backed by Scripture, every phrase is an enlargement of the Master's "Come and see!" and "Follow me!"

No reader has ever found it fruitless; millions have found in it new wings for life.

In deep humility and profound gratitude, we present to this tired and trembling generation a book that cannot die—the latest edition of *The Christian's Secret of a Happy Life*.

The Publishers

THE CRY OF SAINT PAUL

*Brethren, my heart's desire and prayer to God
for Israel is, that they might be saved.*
                                        ROMANS 10:1

Oh, could I tell, ye surely would believe it!
    Oh, could I only say what I have seen!
How should I tell, or how can ye receive it,
    How, till He bringeth you where I have been?

Therefore, O Lord, I will not fail nor falter;
    Nay but I ask it, nay but I desire,
Lay on my lips thine embers of the altar,
    Seal with the ring, and furnish with the fire.

Give me a voice, a cry, and a complaining,—
    Oh, let my sound be stormy in their ears!
Throat that would shout, but cannot stay for straining,
    Eyes that would weep, but cannot wait for tears.

Quick, in a moment, infinite forever,
    Send an arousal better than I pray;
Give me a grace upon the faint endeavor,
    Souls for my hire, and Pentecost to-day!

Scarcely I catch the words of His revealing,
    Hardly I hear Him, dimly understand;
Only the Power that is within me pealing
    Lives on my lips, and beckons with my hand.

Whoso has felt the Spirit of the Highest,
    Cannot confound, nor doubt Him, nor deny;
Yea, with one voice, O world, though thou deniest,
    Stand thou on that side, for on this am I.

                                        F. W. H. MYERS

PART I
THE LIFE

Is It Scriptural?

NO THOUGHTFUL PERSON CAN QUESTION THE FACT THAT, for the most part, the Christian life, as it is generally lived, is not entirely a happy life. A keen observer once said to me, "You Christians seem to have a religion that makes you miserable. You are like a man with a headache. He does not want to get rid of his head, but it hurts him to keep it. You cannot expect outsiders to seek very earnestly for anything so uncomfortable." Then for the first time I saw, as in a flash, that the religion of Christ ought to be, and was meant to be, to its possessors, not something to make them miserable, but something to make them happy; and I began then and there to ask the Lord to show me the secret of a happy Christian life.

It is this secret, so far as I have learned it, that I shall try to tell in the following pages.

All of God's children, I am convinced, feel instinctively, in their moments of divine illumination, that a life of inward rest and outward victory is their inalienable birthright. Can you not remember, some of you, the shout of triumph your souls gave when you first became acquainted with the Lord Jesus, and had a glimpse of His mighty saving power? How sure you were of victory, then! How easy it seemed to be more than conquerors, through Him that loved you! Under the leadership of a Captain, who had never been foiled in battle, how could you dream of defeat? And yet, to many of you, how different has been your real experience! Your victories have been few and fleeting, your defeats many and disastrous. You have not lived as you feel children of God ought to live. You have had perhaps a clear understanding of doctrinal truths, but you have not come into possession of their life and power. You have rejoiced in your knowledge of the things revealed in the Scriptures, but have not had a living realization of the things themselves, consciously felt in the soul. Christ is believed in, talked about, and served, but

13

He is not known as the soul's actual and very life, abiding there forever, and revealing Himself there continually in His beauty. You have found Jesus as your Saviour from the penalty of sin, but you have not found Him as your Saviour from its power. You have carefully studied the Holy Scriptures, and have gathered much precious truth therefrom, which you have trusted would feed and nourish your spiritual life, but in spite of it all, your souls are starving and dying within you, and you cry out in secret, again and again, for that bread and water of life which you see promised in the Scriptures to all believers. In the very depths of your hearts, you know that your experience is not a Scriptural experience; that, as an old writer said, your religion is "but a *talk* to what the early Christians enjoyed, possessed, and lived in." And your hearts have sunk within you, as, day after day, and year after year, your early visions of triumph have seemed to grow more and more dim, and you have been forced to settle down to the conviction, that the best you can expect from your religion is a life of alternate failure and victory, one hour sinning, and the next repenting, and then beginning again, only to fail again, and again to repent.

But *is* this all? Had the Lord Jesus only this in His mind when He laid down His precious life to deliver you from your sore and cruel bondage to sin? Did He propose to Himself only this partial deliverance? Did He intend to leave you thus struggling under a weary consciousness of defeat and discouragement? Did He fear that a continuous victory would dishonor Him, and bring reproach on His name? When all those declarations were made concerning His coming, and the work He was to accomplish, did they mean only this that you have experienced? Was there a hidden reserve in each promise that was meant to deprive it of its complete fulfilment? Did "delivering us out of the hand of our enemies" mean that they should still have dominion over us? Did "enabling us always to triumph" mean that we were only to triumph sometimes? Did being made "more than conquerors through Him that loved us" mean constant defeat and failure? Does being "saved to the uttermost" mean the meager salvation we see manifested among us now? Can we dream that the Saviour, who was wounded for our transgressions and bruised for our iniquities, could possibly see of the travail of His soul and be satisfied in such Christian lives as fill the Church today? The Bible tells us that "for this purpose the Son of God was manifested, that he might destroy the works of the devil"; and can we imagine for a moment that this is beyond His power, and that He finds Himself unable to accomplish the thing He was manifested to do?

In the very outset, then, settle down on this one thing, that Jesus came to save you now, in this life, from the power and dominion of sin, and to make you more than conquerors through His power. If you doubt this, search your Bible, and collect together every announcement or declaration concerning the purposes and object of His death on the cross. You will be astonished to find how full they are. Everywhere and always, His work is said to be to deliver us from our sins, from our bondage, from our defilement; and not a hint is given, anywhere, that this deliverance was to be only the limited and partial one with which Christians so continually try to be satisfied.

Let me give you the teaching of Scripture on this subject. When the angel of the Lord appeared unto Joseph in a dream, and announced the coming birth of the Saviour, he said, "And thou shalt call his name Jesus, for he shall save his people from their sins."

When Zacharias was "filled with the Holy Ghost" at the birth of his son, and "prophesied," he declared that God had visited His people in order to fulfil the promise and the oath He had made them; which promise was, "that he would grant unto us, that we, being delivered out of the hand of our enemies, might serve him without fear, in holiness and righteousness before him, all the days of our life."

When Peter was preaching in the porch of the temple to the wondering Jews, he said, "Unto you first, God, having raised up his Son Jesus, sent him to bless you in turning away every one of you from his iniquities."

When Paul was telling to the Ephesian Church the wondrous truth that Christ had so loved them as to give Himself for them, he went on to declare that His purpose in thus doing was "that he might sanctify and cleanse it by the washing of water by the word, that he might present it to himself a glorious church, not having spot or wrinkle, or any such thing; but that it should be holy and without blemish."

When Paul was seeking to instruct Titus, his own son after the common faith, concerning the grace of God, he declared that the object of that grace was to teach us "that,

denying ungodliness and worldly lusts, we should live so-
berly, righteously, and godly in this present world"; and
adds, as the reason of this, that Christ "gave himself for
us that he might redeem us from all iniquity, and purify
us unto himself a peculiar people, zealous of good works."

When Peter was urging upon the Christians to whom
he was writing a holy and Christlike walk, he tells them
that "even hereunto were ye called: because Christ also
suffered for us, leaving us an example that ye should
follow his steps: who did no sin, neither was guile found
in his mouth"; and adds, "Who his own self bare our sins
in his own body on the tree, that we, being dead to sins,
should live unto righteousness: by whose stripes ye were
healed."

When Paul was contrasting in the Ephesians the walk
suitable for a Christian with the walk of an unbe-
liever, he sets before them the truth in Jesus as being this,
"that ye put off concerning the former conversation the
old man, which is corrupt according to the deceitful lusts;
and be renewed in the spirit of your mind; and that ye put
new man, which after God is created in righteousness and
true holiness."

And when, in Romans 6, he was answering forever the
question as to a child of God continuing in sin, and showing how utterly foreign it was to the whole spirit and
aim of the salvation of Jesus, he brings up the fact of our
judicial death and resurrection with Christ as an unanswerable argument for our practical deliverance from it,
and says, "God forbid. How shall we, that are dead to
sin, live any longer therein? Know ye not, that so many of
us as were baptized into Jesus Christ were baptized into
his death? Therefore we are buried with him by baptism
into death: that like as Christ was raised up from the
dead by the glory of the Father, even so we also should
walk in newness of life"; and adds, "Knowing this, that
our old man is crucified with him, that the body of sin
might be destroyed, that henceforth we should not serve
sin."

It is a fact sometimes overlooked that, in the declarations concerning the object of the death of Christ, far
more mention is made of a present salvation from sin,
than of a future salvation in a heaven beyond, showing
plainly God's estimate of the relative importance of these
two things.

Dear Christians, will you receive the testimony of the

Scripture on this matter? The same crucial questions, that troubled the Church in Paul's day are troubling it now: first, "Shall we continue in sin that grace may abound?" and second, "Do we then make void the law through faith?" Shall our answer to these be Paul's emphatic "God forbid," and his triumphant assertions that, instead of making it void, "we establish the law"; and that "what the law could not do, in that it was weak through the flesh, God sending his own Son in the likeness of sinful flesh, and for sin, condemned sin in the flesh: that the righteousness of the law might be fulfilled in us, who walk not after the flesh, but after the Spirit?"

Can we, for a moment, suppose that the holy God, who hates sin in the sinner, is willing to tolerate it in the Christian, and that He has even arranged the plan of salvation in such a way as to make it impossible for those who are saved from the guilt of sin to find deliverance from its power?

As Dr. Chalmers well says, "Sin is that scandal which must be rooted out from the great spiritual household over which the Divinity rejoices. . . . Strange administration, indeed, for sin to be so hateful to God as to lay all who had incurred it under death, and yet, when readmitted into life, that sin should be permitted; and that what was before the object of destroying vengeance should now become the object of an upheld and protected toleration. Now that the penalty is taken off, think you it is possible that the unchangeable God has so given up His antipathy to sin as that man, ruined and redeemed man, may now perseveringly indulge, under the new arrangement, in that which under the old destroyed him? Does not the God who loved righteousness and hated iniquity six thousand years ago bear the same love to righteousness and hatred to iniquity still? . . . I now breathe the air of loving-kindness from heaven, and can walk before God in peace and graciousness; shall I again attempt the incompatible alliance of two principles so adverse as that of an approving God and a persevering sinner? How shall we, recovered from so awful a catastrophe, continue that which first involved us in it? The cross of Christ, by the same mighty and decisive stroke wherewith it moved the curse of sin away from us, also surely moves away the power and the love of it from over us."

And not Dr. Chalmers only, but many other holy men of his generation, and of our own, as well as of generations long past, have united in declaring that the redemption accomplished for us by our Lord Jesus Christ on the cross at Calvary is a redemption from the power of sin as well as from its guilt, and that He *is* able to save to the uttermost all who come unto God by Him.

A quaint old Quaker divine of the seventeenth century says: "There is nothing so contrary to God as sin, and God will not suffer sin always to rule His masterpiece, man. When we consider the infiniteness of God's power for destroying that which is contrary to Him, who can believe that the devil must always stand and prevail? I believe it is inconsistent and disagreeable with true faith for people to be Christians and yet to believe that Christ, the eternal Son of God, to whom all power in heaven and earth is given, will suffer sin and the devil to have dominion over them.

"But you will say no man by all the power he hath can redeem himself, and no man can live without sin. We will say Amen to it. But if men tell us that when God's power comes to help us and to redeem us out of sin, it cannot be effected, then this doctrine we cannot away with; nor I hope you neither.

"Would you approve of it if I should tell you that God puts forth His power to do such a thing, but the devil hinders Him? That it is impossible for God to do it, because the devil does not like it? That it is impossible that any one should be free from sin, because the devil hath got such a power in them that God cannot cast him out? This is lamentable doctrine, yet hath not this been preached? It doth in plain terms say, though God doth interpose His power, it is impossible, because the devil hath so rooted sin in the nature of man. Is not man God's creature, and cannot He new make him, and cast sin out of him? If you say sin is deeply rooted in man, I say so, too; yet not so deeply rooted but Christ Jesus hath entered so deeply into the root of the nature of man, that He hath received power to destroy the devil and his works, and to recover and redeem man into righteousness and holiness. Or else it is false that 'He is able to save to the uttermost all that come unto God by Him.' We must throw away the Bible if we say that it is impossible for God to deliver man out of sin.

"We know," he continues, "when our friends are in captivity, as in Turkey or elsewhere, we pay our money for their redemption; but we will not pay our money if they be kept in their fetters still. Would not any one think himself cheated to pay so much money for their redemption, and the bargain he made so that he shall be *said* to be redeemed, and be *called* a redeemed captive, but he must wear his fetters still? How long? As long as he hath a day to live. This is for bodies, but now I am speaking of souls. Christ must be made to me redemption, and rescue me from captivity. Am I a prisoner anywhere? Yes, verily, verily, he that committeth sin, saith Christ, he is a servant of sin, he is a slave of sin. If thou hast sinned, thou art a slave, a captive that must be redeemed out of captivity. Who will pay a price for me? I am poor; I have nothing; I cannot redeem myself: who will pay a price for me? There is One come who hath paid a price for me. That is well; that is good news; then I hope I shall come out of my captivity. What is His name? Is He called a Redeemer? So, then, I do expect the benefit of my redemption, and that I shall go out of my captivity. No, say they, you must abide in sin as long as you live. What! must we never be delivered? Must this crooked heart and perverse will always remain? Must I be a believer, and yet have no faith that reacheth to sanctification and holy living? Is there no mastery to be had, no getting victory over sin? Must it prevail over me as long as I live? What sort of a Redeemer, then, is this, or what benefit have I in this life, of my redemption?"

Similar extracts might be quoted from Marshall and Romaine, and many others, to show that this doctrine is no new one in the Church, however much it may have been lost sight of by the present generation of believers. It is the same old story that has filled with songs of triumph the daily lives of many saints of God, both Catholic and Protestant, throughout all ages; and it is now being sounded forth afresh to the unspeakable joy of weary and burdened souls.

Do not reject it, then, dear reader, until you have prayerfully searched the Scriptures to see whether these things be indeed so. Ask God to open the eyes of your understanding by His Spirit, that you may know "what is the exceeding greatness of his power to us-ward who believe, according to the working of his mighty power, which he wrought in Christ, when he raised him from the dead, and set him at his own right hand in the heavenly places." And when you have begun to have some faint glimpses of this power, learn to look away utterly from your own weakness, and, putting your case into His hands, trust Him to deliver you.

"When thou goest out to battle against thine enemies, and seest horses, and chariots, and a people more than thou, be not afraid of them: for the Lord thy God is with thee, which brought thee up out of the land of Egypt. And it shall be, when ye are come nigh unto the battle, that the priest shall approach and speak unto the people, and shall say unto them, Hear, O Israel, ye approach this day unto battle against your enemies: let not your hearts faint, fear not, and do not tremble, neither be ye terrified because of them; for the Lord your God is he that goeth with you, to fight for you against your enemies to save you."

Chapter Two

God's Side and Man's Side

MUCH MISUNDERSTANDING ARISES, IN REFERENCE TO THIS subject of the life and walk of faith, from the fact that its two sides are not clearly seen. People are apt to think that there is only one side to it, and, dwelling exclusively upon the one they happen to see the most clearly, without even a thought of any other, it is no wonder that distorted views of the whole matter are the legitimate consequence.

Now, there are two very decided and distinct sides to this subject, and, like all other subjects, it cannot be fully understood unless both of these sides are kept constantly in view. I refer of course to God's side and man's side; or, in other words, to God's part in the work of sanctification, and man's part. These are very distinct and even contrasting, but, although to a cursory observer they may sometimes so appear, they are not really contradictory.

At one time this was very strikingly illustrated to me. There were two teachers of this interior life holding meetings in the same place, at alternate hours. One spoke only of God's part in the work, and the other dwelt exclusively upon man's part. They were both in perfect sympathy with each other, and realized fully that they were each teaching different sides of the same great truth; and this also was understood by a large proportion of their hearers. But with some of the hearers it was different, and one lady said to me in the greatest perplexity, "I cannot understand it at all. Here are two preachers undertaking to teach just the same truth, and yet to me they seem flatly to contradict each other." And I felt at the time that she expressed a puzzle that, very often, causes great difficulty in the minds of many honest inquirers after this truth.

Suppose two friends go to see some celebrated building, and return home to describe it. One has seen only the north side, and the other only the south. The first says: "The building was built in such a manner, and has such and such stories and ornaments." "Oh, no," says the other, interrupting him, "you are altogether mistaken; I saw the building, and it was built in quite a different manner, and its ornaments and stories were so and so." A lively dispute might follow upon the truth of the respective descriptions, until the two friends should discover that they had been describing different *sides* of the building, and then all would be reconciled at once.

I would like to state, as clearly as I can, what I judge to be the two distinct sides in this matter; and to show how looking at one, without seeing the other, will be sure to create wrong impressions and views of the truth.

To state it in brief, I would say, that man's part is to trust, and God's part is to work; and it can be seen at a glance how these two parts contrast with each other, and yet are not necessarily contradictory. I mean this: there is a certain *work* to be accomplished. We are to be delivered from the power of sin, and are to be made perfect in every good work to do the will of God. "Beholding as in a glass the glory of the Lord," we are to be actually "changed into the same image from glory to glory, even as by the Spirit of the Lord." We are to be transformed by the renewing of our minds, that we may prove what is that good, and acceptable, and perfect will of God. A real work is to be wrought in us and upon us. Besetting sins are to be conquered; evil habits are to be overcome; wrong dispositions and feelings are to be rooted out, and holy tempers and emotions are to be begotten. A positive transformation is to take place. So at least the Bible teaches. Now, somebody must do this. Either we must do it for ourselves, or another must do it for us. We have most of us tried to do it for ourselves at first, and have grievously failed; then we discover, from the Scriptures and from our own experience, that it is something we are unable to do, but that the Lord Jesus Christ has come on purpose to do it, and that He will do it for all who put themselves wholly into His hands and trust Him without reserve. Now, under these circumstances, what is the part of the believer, and what is the part of the Lord? Plainly the believer can do nothing but trust; while the Lord, in whom he trusts, actually does the work entrusted to Him. *Trusting* and *doing* are certainly contrasted things, often indeed contradictory; but are they contradictory in this case? Manifestly not, because it is two different parties that are concerned. If we should say of one party in a transaction that he trusted his case to another, and yet attended to it himself, we should state a contradiction and an impossibility, but, when we say of two parties in a transaction that one trusts the other to do something, and that the other goes to work and does it, we are stating something that is perfectly simple and harmonious. When we say, therefore, that, in this higher life, man's part is to trust, and God's part is to do the thing entrusted to Him, we do not surely present any very difficult or puzzling problem.

The preacher who is speaking on man's part in the matter cannot speak of anything but surrender and trust, because this is positively all the man can do. We all agree about this. And yet such preachers are constantly criticised as though, in saying this, they had meant to imply there *was* no other part, and that therefore nothing but trusting is to be done. And the cry goes out that this doctrine of faith does away with all realities, that souls are just told to trust, and there is the end of it, and that they sit down thenceforward in a sort of religious easy-chair, dreaming away a life fruitless of any actual result. All this misapprehension arises, of course, from the fact that either the preacher has neglected to state, or the hearer has failed to hear the other side of the matter, which is that when we trust, the Lord works, and that a great deal is done, not by us, but by Him. Actual results are reached by our trusting, because our Lord undertakes the thing entrusted to Him, and accomplishes it. *We* do not do anything, but *He* does it, and it is all the more effec-

tually done because of this. As soon as this is clearly seen,
the difficulty as to the preaching of faith disappears entirely.

On the other hand, the preacher who dwells on God's
part in the matter is criticised on a totally different
ground. He does not speak of trust, for the Lord's part
is not to trust, but to work. The Lord's part is to *do* the
thing entrusted to Him. He disciplines and trains by
inward exercises and outward providences. He brings to
bear upon us all the refining and purifying resources of
His wisdom and His love. He makes everything in our
lives and circumstances subservient to the one great purpose of causing us to grow in grace, and of conforming us,
day by day and hour by hour, to the image of Christ. He
carries us through a process of transformation, longer or
shorter as our peculiar case may require, making actual
and experimental the results for which we have trusted.
We have dared, for instance, according to the command
in Rom. 6:11, by faith to reckon ourselves dead unto
sin. The Lord makes this a reality, and puts us to death by
a thousand little mortifications and crosses to the
natural man. Our reckoning is available only because God
thus makes it real. And yet the preacher who dwells upon
this practical side of the matter, and tells of God's processes for making faith's reckonings experimental realities, may be accused of contradicting the preaching of
faith altogether, and of declaring only a process of gradual
sanctification by works, and of setting before the soul an
impossible and hopeless task.

Now, sanctification is both a step of faith, and a process
of works. It is a step of surrender and trust on our part,
and it is a process of development on God's part. By a
step of faith we get into Christ; by a process we are made
to "grow up into him in all things." By a step of faith we
put ourselves into the hands of the Divine Potter; by a
gradual process He makes us into a vessel unto His own
honor, meet for His use, and prepared to every good
work.

To illustrate this, suppose I were to describe to a person who was entirely ignorant of the subject the way in
which a lump of clay is made into a beautiful vessel. I
tell him first the part of the clay in the matter; and all I
can say about this is that the clay is put into the potter's
hands, and then lies passive there, submitting itself to all
the turnings and overturnings of the potter's hands upon

it. There is really nothing else to be said about the clay's part. But could my hearer argue from this that nothing else is done because I say that this is all the clay can do? If he is an intelligent hearer he will not dream of doing so, but will say, "I understand; this is what the clay must do. But what must the potter do?" "Ah," I answer, "now we come to the important part. The potter takes the clay thus abandoned to his working, and begins to mold and fashion it according to his own will. He kneads and works it; he tears it apart and presses it together again; he wets it and then suffers it to dry. Sometimes he works at it for hours together; sometimes he lays it aside for days, and does not touch it. And then, when by all these processes he has made it perfectly pliable in his hands, he proceeds to make it up into the vessel he has proposed. He turns it upon the wheel, planes it and smooths it, and dries it in the sun, bakes it in the oven, and finally turns it out of his workshop, a vessel to his honor and fit for his use."

Will my reader be likely now to say that I am contradicting myself, that a little while ago I had said the clay had nothing to do but to lie passive in the potter's hands, and that now I am putting upon it a great work, which it is not able to perform, and that to make itself into such a vessel is an impossible and hopeless undertaking? Surely not. For he will see that while before I was speaking of the clay's part in the matter, I am now speaking of the potter's part, and that these two are necessarily contrasted, but not in the least contradictory, and that the clay is not expected to do the potter's work, but only to yield itself up to his working.

Nothing, it seems to me, could be clearer than the perfect harmony between these two *apparently* contradictory sorts of teaching.

What *can* be said about man's part in this great work but that he must continually surrender himself and continually trust? But when we come to God's side of the question, what is there that may not be said as to the manifold and wonderful ways, in which He accomplishes the work entrusted to Him? It is here that the growing comes in. The lump of clay could never grow into a beautiful vessel if it stayed in the clay pit for thousands of years; but when it is put into the hands of a skilful potter it grows rapidly, under his fashioning, into the vessel he intends it to be. And in the same way the soul, abandoned to the working of the Heavenly Potter, is made into a vessel unto honor, sanctified, and meet for the Master's use.

Having, therefore, taken the step of faith by which you have put yourself wholly and absolutely into His hands, you must now expect Him to begin to work. His way of accomplishing that which you have entrusted to Him may be different from your way; but He knows, and you must be satisfied.

I knew a lady who had entered into this life of faith with a great outpouring of the Spirit, and a wonderful flood of light and joy. She supposed, of course, this was a preparation for some great service, and expected to be put forth immediately into the Lord's harvest field. Instead of this, almost at once her husband lost all his money, and she was shut up in her own house to attend to all sorts of domestic duties, with no time or strength left for any Gospel work at all. She accepted the discipline, and yielded herself up as heartily to sweep, and dust, and bake, and sew, as she would have done to preach, or pray, or write for the Lord. And the result was that, through this very training, He made her into a vessel "meet for the master's use, and prepared unto every good work."

Another lady, who had entered this life of faith under similar circumstances of wondrous blessing, and who also expected to be sent out to do some great work, was shut up with two peevish invalid children to nurse, and humor, and amuse all day long. Unlike the first one, this lady did not accept the training, but chafed and fretted, and finally rebelled, lost all her blessing, and went back into a state of sad coldness and misery. She had understood her part of trusting to begin with, but, not understanding the Divine process of accomplishing that for which she had trusted, she took herself out of the hands of the Heavenly Potter, and the vessel was marred on the wheel.

I believe many a vessel has been similarly marred by a want of understanding these things. The maturity of a Christian experience cannot be reached in a moment, but is the result of the work of God's Holy Spirit, who, by His energizing and transforming power, causes us to grow up into Christ in all things. And we cannot hope to reach this maturity in any way other than by yielding ourselves up, utterly and willingly, to His mighty working. But the sanctification the Scriptures urge, as a present experience upon all believers, does not consist in maturity of growth, but in purity of heart; and this may be as complete in the early as in our later experiences.

The lump of clay, from the moment it comes under the transforming hand of the potter, is, during each day and each hour of the process, just what the potter wants it to be at that hour or on that day, and therefore pleases him; but it is very far from being matured into the vessel he intends in the future to make it.

The little babe may be all that a babe could be, or ought to be, and may therefore perfectly please its mother; and yet it is very far from being what that mother would wish it to be when the years of maturity shall come.

The apple in June is a perfect apple for June; it is the best apple that June can produce: but it is very different from the apple in October, which is a perfected apple.

God's works are perfect in every stage of their growth. Man's works are never perfect until they are in every respect complete.

All that we claim, then, in this life of sanctification is that by an act of faith we put ourselves into the hands of the Lord, for Him to work in us all the good pleasure of His will, and then, by a continuous exercise of faith, keep ourselves there. This is our part in the matter. And when we do it, and while we do it, we are, in the Scripture sense, truly pleasing to God, although it may require years of training and discipline to mature us into a vessel that shall be in all respects to His honor, and fitted to every good work.

Our part is the trusting; it is His to accomplish the results. And when we do our part, He never fails to do His, for no one ever trusted in the Lord and was confounded. Do not be afraid, then, that, if you trust, or tell others to trust, the matter will end there. Trust is the beginning and the continuing foundation; but when we trust, the Lord works, and His work is the important part of the whole matter. And this explains that apparent paradox which puzzles so many. They say, "In one breath you tell us to do nothing but trust, and in the next you tell us to do impossible things. How can you reconcile such contradictory statements?" They are to be reconciled, just as we reconcile the statements concerning a saw in a carpenter's shop when we say, at one moment, that the saw has sawn asunder a log, and the next moment declare that the carpenter has done it. The saw is the instrument used; the power that uses it is the carpenter's.

And so we, yielding ourselves unto God, and our members as instruments of righteousness unto Him, find that He works in us to will and to do of His good pleasure, and we can say with Paul, "I labored; yet not I, but the grace of God which was with me."

In the divine order, God's working depends upon our co-operation. Of our Lord it was declared that at a certain place He could do there no mighty work because of their unbelief. It was not that He would not, but He could not. I believe we often think of God that He will not, when the real truth is that He cannot. Just as the potter, however skilful, cannot make a beautiful vessel out of a lump of clay that is never put into his hands, so neither can God make out of me a vessel unto His honor unless I put myself into His hands. My part is the essential correlation of God's part in the matter of my salvation; and as God is *sure* to do His part all right, the vital thing for me is to find out what my part is, and then do it.

In this book, therefore, I shall of course dwell mostly upon man's side, as I am writing for human beings and in the hope of making it plain how we are to fulfil our part of this great work. But I wish it to be distinctly understood all through that, unless I believed with all my heart in God's effectual working on His side, not one word of this book would ever have been written.

Chapter Three

The Life Defined

IN THE FIRST CHAPTER I HAVE TRIED TO SETTLE THE question as to the scripturalness of the experience sometimes called the Higher Christian Life but which is the only true Christian life, and which to my own mind is best described in the words, the "life hid with Christ in God." In the second, I have sought to reconcile the two distinct sides of this life; that is, the part to be done by the Lord, and the part necessarily to be done by ourselves. I shall now, therefore, consider it as a settled point that the Scriptures do set before the believer in the Lord Jesus

a life of abiding rest and of continual victory, which is
very far beyond the ordinary run of Christian experience;
and that in the Bible we have presented to us a Saviour
able to save us from the power of our sins as really as He
saves us from their guilt.

The point to be next considered is as to what are the
chief characteristics of this life hid with Christ in God,
and how it differs from much in the ordinary Christian
experience.

Its chief characteristics are an entire surrender to the
Lord, and a perfect trust in Him, resulting in victory
over sin and inward rest of soul; and it differs from the
lower range of Christian experience in that it causes us
to let the Lord carry our burdens and manage our affairs
for us instead of trying to do it ourselves.

Most Christians are like a man who was toiling along
the road, bending under a heavy burden, when a wagon
overtook him, and the driver kindly offered to help him
on his journey. He joyfully accepted the offer but when
seated in the wagon, continued to bend beneath his burden, which he still kept on his shoulders. "Why do you
not lay down your burden?" asked the kind-hearted
driver. "Oh!" replied the man, "I feel that it is almost too
much to ask you to carry me, and I could not think of
letting you carry my burden too." And so Christians, who
have given themselves into the care and keeping of the
Lord Jesus still continue to bend beneath the weight of
their burdens, and often go weary and heavy-laden
throughout the whole length of their journey.

When I speak of burdens, I mean everything that
troubles us, whether spiritual or temporal.

I mean, first of all, ourselves. The greatest burden we
have to carry in life is self; the most difficult thing we have
to manage is self. Our own daily living, our frames and
feelings, our especial weaknesses and temptations, our peculiar temperaments, our inward affairs of every kind,—
these are the things that perplex and worry us more than
anything else, and that bring us most frequently into
bondage and darkness. In laying off your burdens, therefore, the first one you must get rid of is yourself. You
must hand yourself, with your temptations, your temperament, your frames and feelings, and all your inward
and outward experiences, over into the care and keeping
of your God, and leave it all there. He made you, and
therefore He understands you, and knows how to man-

age you; and you must trust Him to do it. Say to Him, "Here, Lord, I abandon myself to thee. I have tried in every way I could think of to manage myself, and to make myself what I know I ought to be, but have always failed. Now I give it up to thee. Do thou take entire possession of me. Work in me all the good pleasure of thy will. Mold and fashion me into such a vessel as seemeth good to thee. I leave myself in thy hands, and I believe thou wilt, according to thy promise, make me into a vessel unto thy own honor, 'sanctified, and meet for the master's use, and prepared unto every good work.' " And here you must rest, trusting yourself thus to Him, continually and absolutely.

Next, you must lay off every other burden,—your health, your reputation, your Christian work, your houses, your children, your business, your servants; everything, in short, that concerns you, whether inward or outward.

It is generally much less difficult for us to commit the keeping of our future to the Lord than it is to commit our present. We know we are helpless as regards the future, but we feel as if the present was in our own hands, and must be carried on our own shoulders; and most of us have an unconfessed idea that it is a great deal to ask the Lord to carry ourselves, and that we cannot think of asking Him to carry our burdens too.

I knew a Christian lady who had a very heavy temporal burden. It took away her sleep and her appetite, and there was danger of her health breaking down under it. One day, when it seemed especially heavy, she noticed lying on the table near her a little tract called "Hannah's Faith." Attracted by the title, she picked it up and began to read it, little knowing, however, that it was to create a revolution in her whole experience. The story was of a poor woman who had been carried triumphantly through a life of unusual sorrow. She was giving the history of her life to a kind visitor on one occasion, and at the close the visitor said feelingly, "Oh, Hannah, I do not see how you could bear so much sorrow!" "I did not bear it," was the quick reply; "the Lord bore it for me." "Yes," said the visitor, "that is the right way. We must take our troubles to the Lord." "Yes," replied Hannah, "but we must do more than that: we must *leave* them there. Most people," she continued, "take their burdens to Him, but they bring them away with them again, and are just as worried and unhappy as ever. But I take mine, and I

leave them with Him, and come away and forget them.
If the worry comes back, I take it to Him again; and I do
this over and over, until at last I just forget I have
any worries, and am at perfect rest."

My friend was very much struck with this plan, and
resolved to try it. The circumstances of her life she could
not alter, but she took them to the Lord, and handed
them over into His management; and then she believed
that He took it, and she left all the responsibility and the
worry and anxiety with Him. As often as the anxieties
returned, she took them back, and the result was that,
although the circumstances remained unchanged, her
soul was kept in perfect peace in the midst of them. She
felt that she had found out a practical secret; and from
that time she sought never to carry her own burdens, nor
to manage her own affairs, but to hand them over, as fast
as they arose, to the Divine Burden-bearer.

This same secret, also, which she had found to be so
effectual in her outward life, proved to be still more effectual in her inward life, which was in truth evermore
utterly unmanageable. She abandoned her whole self to
the Lord, with all that she was and all that she had, and,
believing that He took that which she had committed to
Him, she ceased to fret and worry, and her life became
all sunshine in the gladness of belonging to Him. It was
a very simple secret she found out: only this, that it was
possible to obey God's commandment contained in those
words, "Be careful for nothing; but in everything by
prayer and supplication, with thanksgiving, let your requests be made known unto God"; and that, in obeying it,
the result would inevitably be, according to the promise,
that the "peace of God which passeth all understanding
shall keep your hearts and minds through Christ Jesus."

There are many other things to be said about this
life hid with Christ in God, many details as to what the
Lord Jesus does for those who thus abandon themselves
to Him. But the gist of the whole matter is here stated;
and the soul that has discovered this secret of simple
faith has found the key that will unlock the whole trea-
sure-house of God.

I am sure these pages will fall into the hands of some
child of God who is hungering for just such a life as I
have been describing. You long unspeakably to get rid of
your weary burdens. You would be delighted to hand over
the management of your unmanageable self into the

hands of one who is able to manage you. You are tired and weary, and the rest I speak of looks unutterably sweet to you.

Do you recollect the delicious sense of rest with which you have sometimes gone to bed at night after a day of great exertion and weariness? How delightful was the sensation of relaxing every muscle, and letting your body go in a perfect abandonment of ease and comfort. The strain of the day had ceased, for a few hours at least, and the work of the day had been laid off. You no longer had to hold up an aching head or a weary back. You trusted yourself to the bed in an absolute confidence, and it held you up, without effort, or strain, or even thought, on your part. You rested!

But suppose you had doubted the strength or the stability of your bed, and had dreaded each moment to find it giving way beneath you and landing you on the floor; could you have rested then? Would not every muscle have been strained in a fruitless effort to hold yourself up, and would not the weariness have been greater than if you had not gone to bed at all?

Let this analogy teach you what it means to rest in the Lord. Let your souls lie down upon the couch of His sweet will, as your bodies lie down in their beds at night. Relax every strain, and lay off every burden. Let yourself go in a perfect abandonment of ease and comfort, sure that, since He holds you up, you are perfectly safe. Your part is simply to rest. His part is to sustain you; and He cannot fail.

Or take another analogy, which our Lord Himself has abundantly sanctioned,—that of the child-life. For "Jesus called a little child unto him, and set him in the midst of them, and said, Except ye be converted and become as little children, ye shall not enter into the kingdom of heaven."

Now, what are the characteristics of a little child, and how does it live? It lives by faith, and its chief characteristic is freedom from care. Its life is one long trust from year's end to year's end. It trusts its parents, it trusts its caretakers, it trusts its teachers; it even trusts people sometimes who are utterly unworthy of trust, out of the abounding trustfulness of its nature. And this trust is abundantly answered. The child provides nothing for itself, and yet everything is provided. It takes no thought for the morrow, and forms no plans, and yet all

its life is planned out for it, and it finds its paths made
ready, opening out as it comes to them day by day and
hour by hour. It goes in and out of its father's house with
an unspeakable ease and abandonment, enjoying all the
good things therein, without having spent a penny in
procuring them. Pestilence may walk through the streets
of its city, but the child regards it not. Famine and fire
and war may rage around it, but under its father's tender
care the child abides in utter unconcern and perfect rest.
It lives in the present moment, and receives its life un-
questioningly as it comes to it day by day from its father's
hands.

I was visiting once in a wealthy home, where there
was a little adopted child, upon whom was lavished all
the love and tenderness and care that human hearts
could bestow, or human means procure. And as I watched
that child running in and out day by day, free and light-
hearted, with the happy carelessness of childhood, I
thought what a picture it was of our wonderful position
as children in the house of our Heavenly Father. And I
said to myself, If nothing would so grieve and wound the
loving hearts around her as to see this little child beginning to be worried or anxious about herself in any way,—
about whether her food and clothes would be provided,
or how she was to get her education or her future support,
—how much more must the great, loving heart of our
God and Father be grieved and wounded at seeing His
children taking so much anxious care and thought! And I
understood why it was that our Lord had said to us so
emphatically, "Take no thought for yourselves."

Who is the best cared for in every household? Is it not
the little children? And does not the least of all, the helpless baby, receive the largest share? We all know that the
baby toils not, neither does it spin; and yet it is fed, and
clothed, and loved, and rejoiced in more tenderly than the
hardest worker of them all.

This life of faith, then, about which I am writing, con-
sists in just this,—being a child in the Father's house. And
when this is said, enough is said to transform every
weary, burdened life into one of blessedness and rest.

Let the ways of childish confidence and freedom from
care, which so please you and win your hearts in your
own little ones, teach you what should be your ways with
God; and, leaving yourselves in His hands, learn to be
literally "careful for nothing"; and you shall find it to be

a fact that the peace of God, which passeth all understanding, shall keep (as with a garrison) your hearts and
minds through Christ Jesus.

"Thou wilt keep him in perfect peace, whose mind is
stayed on thee: because he trusteth in thee." This is the
Divine description of the life of faith about which I am
writing. It is no speculative theory, neither is it a dream
of romance. There *is* such a thing as having one's soul
kept in perfect peace, now and here in this life; and childlike trust in God is the key to its attainment.

Chapter Four
_____

How to Enter In

HAVING SOUGHT TO SETTLE THE QUESTION AS TO THE
scripturalness of an actual living of this life hid with
Christ in God, and having also shown a little of what it
is, the next point is as to how it is to be reached and
realized.

I would say, first of all, that this blessed life must not be
looked upon in any sense as an attainment, but as an ob-
tainment. We cannot earn it, we cannot climb up to it,
we cannot win it; we can do nothing but ask for it and
receive it. It is the gift of God in Christ Jesus. And where
a thing is a gift, the only course left for the receiver is to
take it and thank the giver. We never say of a gift, "See
to what I have attained," and boast of our skill and wisdom in having attained it; but we say, "See what has
been given me," and boast of love and wealth and gener-
osity of the giver. And everything in our salvation is a
gift. From beginning to end, God is the giver and we are
the receivers; and it is not to those who do great things,
but to those who "receive abundance of grace and of the
gift of righteousness," that the richest promises are
made.

In order, therefore, to enter into a practical experience
of this interior life, the soul must be in a receptive attitude, fully recognizing the fact that it is God's gift in
Christ Jesus, and that it cannot be gained by any efforts

or works of our own. This will simplify the matter exceedingly; and the only thing left to be considered then will be to discover upon whom God bestows this gift, and how they are to receive it. To this I would answer, in short, that He can bestow it only upon the fully consecrated soul, and that it is to be received by faith.

Consecration is the first thing,—not in any legal sense, not in order to purchase or deserve the blessing, but to remove the difficulties out of the way and make it possible for God to bestow it. In order for a lump of clay to be made into a beautiful vessel, it must be entirely abandoned to the potter, and must lie passive in his hands. And similarly, in order for a soul to be made into a vessel unto God's honor, "sanctified and meet for the master's use, and prepared unto every good work," it must be utterly abandoned to Him, and must lie passive in His hands. This is manifest at the first glance.

I was once trying to explain to a physician who had charge of a large hospital the necessity and meaning of consecration, but he seemed unable to understand. At last I said to him, "Suppose, in going your rounds among your patients, you should meet with one man who entreated you earnestly to take his case under your especial care in order to cure him, but who should at the same time refuse to tell you all his symptoms or to take all your prescribed remedies, and should say to you, 'I am quite willing to follow your directions as to certain things, because they commend themselves to my mind as good, but in other matters I prefer judging for myself, and following my own directions.' What would you do in such a case?" I asked. "Do!" he replied with indignation,—"Do! I would soon leave such a man as that to his own care. For, of course," he added, "I could do nothing for him unless he would put his whole case into my hands without reserves, and would obey my directions implicitly." "It is necessary, then," I said, "for doctors to be obeyed if they are to have any chance to cure their patient?" "*Implicitly obeyed!*" was his emphatic reply. "And that is consecration," I continued. "God must have the whole case put into His hands without any reserves, and His directions must be implicitly followed." "I see it," he exclaimed, "I see it! And I will do it. God shall have His own way with me from henceforth."

To some minds perhaps the word "abandonment" might express this idea better than the word "consecration." But whatever word we use, we mean an entire surrender of the whole being to God,—spirit, soul, and body placed under His absolute control, for Him to do with us just what He pleases. We mean that the language of our hearts, under all circumstances and in view of every act, is to be "Thy will be done." We mean the giving up of all liberty of choice. We mean a life of inevitable obedience.

To a soul ignorant of God, this may look hard; but to those who know Him it is the happiest and most restful of lives. He is our Father, and He loves us, and He knows just what is best, and therefore, of course, His will is the very most blessed thing that can come to us under any circumstances. I do not understand how it is that the eyes of so many Christians have been blinded to this fact. But it really would seem as if God's own children were more afraid of His will than of anything else in life,—His lovely, lovable will, which only means loving-kindnesses and tender mercies, and blessings unspeakable to their souls! I wish only I could show to every one the unfathomable sweetness of the will of God. Heaven is a place of infinite bliss because His will is perfectly done there, and our lives share in this bliss just in proportion as His will is perfectly done in them. He loves us,—*loves us*, I say,—and the will of love is always blessing for its loved one. Some of us know what it is to love, and we know that could we only have our way, our beloved ones would be overwhelmed with blessings. All that is good and sweet and lovely in life would be poured out upon them from our lavish hands, had we but the power to carry out our will for them. And if this is the way of love with us, how much more must it be so with our God, who is love itself! Could we but for one moment get a glimpse into the mighty depths of His love, our hearts would spring out to meet His will and embrace it as our richest treasure; and we would abandon ourselves to it with an enthusiasm of gratitude and joy that such a wondrous privilege could be ours.

A great many Christians seem practically to think that all their Father in heaven wants is a chance to make them miserable and to take away all their blessings; and they imagine, poor souls, that if they hold on to things in their own will they can hinder Him from doing this. I am ashamed to write the words, yet we must face a fact which is making wretched hundreds of lives.

A Christian who was in a great deal of trouble was recounting to another Christian the various efforts he had made to find deliverance, and concluded by saying, "But it has all been in vain, and there is literally nothing left for me to do now but to trust the Lord."

"Alas!" exclaimed his friend in a tone of the deepest commiseration, as though no greater risk were possible,—"Alas! has it come to *that?*"

A Christian lady who had this feeling was once expressing to a friend how impossible she found it to say, "Thy will be done," and how afraid she should be to do it. She was the mother of an only little boy, who was the heir to a great fortune, and the idol of her heart. After she had stated her difficulties fully, her friend said, "Suppose your little Charley should come running to you to-morrow and say, 'Mother, I have made up my mind to let you have your own way with me from this time forward. I am always going to obey you, and I want you to do just whatever you think best with me. I will trust your love.' How would you feel towards him? Would you say to yourself, 'Ah, now I shall have a chance to make Charley miserable. I will take away all his pleasures, and fill his life with every hard and disagreeable thing that I can find. I will compel him to do just the things that are the most difficult for him to do, and will give him all sorts of impossible commands.' " "Oh, no, no, no!" exclaimed the indignant mother. "You know I would not. You know I would hug him to my heart and cover him with kisses, and would hasten to fill his life with all that was sweetest and best." "And are you more tender and more loving than God?" asked her friend. "Ah, no!" was the reply; "I see my mistake. Of course I must not be any more afraid of saying, 'Thy will be done,' to my Heavenly Father than I would want my Charley to be of saying it to me."

Better and sweeter than health, or friends, or money, or fame, or ease, or prosperity, is the adorable will of our God. It gilds the darkest hours with a divine halo, and sheds brightest sunshine on the gloomiest paths. He always reigns who has made it his kingdom, and nothing can go amiss to him. Surely, then, it is only a glorious privilege that is opening before you when I tell you that the first step you must take in order to enter into the life hid with Christ in God is that of entire consecration. I beg of you not to look at it as a hard and stern demand.

You must do it gladly, thankfully, enthusiastically. You must go in on what I call the privilege side of consecration; and I can assure you, from the universal testimony of all who have tried it, that you will find it the happiest place you have ever entered yet.

Faith is the next thing after surrender. Faith is an absolutely necessary element in the reception of any gift, for let our friends give a thing to us ever so fully, it is not really ours until we believe it has been given, and claim it as our own. Above all, this is true in gifts which are purely mental or spiritual. Love may be lavished upon us by another without stint or measure, but until we believe that we are loved, it never really becomes ours.

I suppose most Christians understand this principle in reference to the matter of their forgiveness. They know that the forgiveness of sins through Jesus might have been preached to them forever, but it would never really have become theirs until they believed this preaching, and claimed the forgiveness as their own. But when it comes to living the Christian life, they lose sight of this principle, and think that, having been saved by faith, they are now to live by works and efforts; and instead of continuing to *receive* they are now to begin to *do*. This makes our declaration, that the life hid with Christ in God is to be entered by faith, seem perfectly unintelligible to them. And yet it is plainly declared, that, "*as* we have received Christ Jesus the Lord, *so* we are to walk in him." We received Him by faith, and by faith alone; therefore we are to walk in Him by faith, and by faith alone. And the faith by which we enter into this hidden life is just the same as the faith by which we were translated out of the kingdom of darkness into the kingdom of God's dear Son, only it lays hold of a different thing. *Then* we believed that Jesus was our Saviour from the guilt of sin, and according to our faith it was unto us; *now* we must believe that He is our Saviour from the power of sin, and according to our faith it shall be unto us. *Then* we trusted Him for forgiveness, and it became ours; *now* we must trust Him for righteousness, and it shall become ours also. *Then* we took Him as a Saviour in the future from the penalties of our sins; *now* we must take Him as a Saviour in the present from the bondage of our sins. *Then* He was our Redeemer; *now* He is to be our Life. *Then* He lifted us out of the pit; *now* He is to seat us in heavenly places with Himself.

I mean all this, of course, experimentally and practically. Theologically and judicially I know that every believer has everything as soon as he is converted; but experimentally nothing is his until by faith he claims it. "Every place that the sole of your foot shall tread upon, that have I given unto you." God "hath blessed us with all spiritual blessings in heavenly places in Christ"; but until we set the foot of faith upon them, they do not practically become ours. "According to our faith," is always the limit and the rule.

But this faith of which I am speaking must be a present faith. No faith that is exercised in the future tense amounts to anything. A man may believe forever that his sins will be forgiven at some future time, and he will never find peace. He has to come to the *now* belief, and say by a present appropriating faith, "My sins are now forgiven," before his soul can be at rest. And, similarly, no faith that looks for a future deliverance from the power of sin will ever lead a soul into the life we are describing. The enemy delights in this future faith, for he knows it is powerless to accomplish any practical results. But he trembles and flees when the soul of the believer dares to claim a present deliverance, and to reckon itself *now* to be free from his power.

Perhaps no four words in the language have more meaning in them than the following, which I would have you repeat over and over with your voice and with your soul, emphasizing each time a different word:—

Jesus saves me now.—It is He.
Jesus *saves* me now.—It is His work to save.
Jesus saves *me* now.—I am the one to be saved.
Jesus saves me *now*.—He is doing it every moment.

To sum up, then, in order to enter into this blessed interior life of rest and triumph, you have two steps to take, —first, entire abandonment; and second, absolute faith. No matter what may be the complications of your peculiar experience, no matter what your difficulties, or your surroundings, or your "peculiar temperament," these two steps, definitely taken and unwaveringly persevered in, will certainly bring you out sooner or later into the green pastures and still waters of this life hid with Christ in God. You may be perfectly sure of this. And if you will let every other consideration go, and simply devote your attention to these two points, and be very clear and definite about them, your progress will be rapid, and your soul will reach its desired haven far sooner than you can now think possible.

Shall I repeat the steps, that there may be no mistake? You are a child of God, and long to please Him. You love your divine Master, and are sick and weary of the sin that grieves Him. You long to be delivered from its power. Everything you have hitherto tried has failed to deliver you: and now, in your despair, you are asking if it can indeed be, as these happy people say, that Jesus is able and willing to deliver you. Surely you must know in your very soul that He is,—that to save you out of the hand of all your enemies is, in fact, just the very thing He came to do. Then trust Him. Commit your case to Him in an absolute unreserve, and believe that He undertakes it; and at once, knowing what He is and what He has said, claim that He does even now save you. Just as you believed at first that He delivered you from the guilt of sin because He said it, so now believe that He delivers you from the power of sin because He says it. Let your faith now lay hold of a new power in Christ. You have trusted Him as your dying Saviour; now trust Him as your living Saviour. Just as much as He came to deliver you from future punishment did He also come to deliver you from present bondage. Just as truly as He came to bear your stripes for you has He come to live your life for you. You are as utterly powerless in the one case as in the other. You could as easily have got yourself rid of your own sins, as you could now accomplish for yourself practical righteousness. Christ, and Christ only, must do both for you; and your part in both cases is simply to give the thing to Him to do, and then believe that He does it.

A lady, now very eminent in this life of trust, when she was seeking in great darkness and perplexity to enter in, said to the friend who was trying to help her, "You all say, 'Abandon yourself and trust, abandon yourself and trust.' But I do not know how. I wish you would just do it out loud, so that I may see how you do it."

Shall I do it out loud for you?

"Lord Jesus, I believe that thou art able and willing to deliver me from all the care and unrest and bondage of my Christian life. I believe thou didst die to set me free, not only in the future, but now and here. I believe thou art stronger than sin, and that thou canst keep me,

even me, in my extreme of weakness, from falling into
its snares or yielding obedience to its commands. And,
Lord, I am going to trust thee to keep me. I have tried
keeping myself, and have failed, and failed, most grievously. I am absolutely helpless. So now I will trust thee.
I give myself to thee. I keep back no reserves. Body, soul,
and spirit, I present myself to thee as a piece of clay, to be
fashioned into anything thy love and thy wisdom shall
choose. And now I *am* thine. I believe thou dost accept
that which I present to thee; I believe that this poor, weak,
foolish heart has been taken possession of by thee, and
that thou hast even at this very moment begun to work in
me to will and to do of thy good pleasure. I trust thee
utterly, and I trust thee *now.*"

A man was obliged to descend into a deep well by sliding down a fixed rope which was supposed to be of ample
length. But to his dismay he came to the end of it before
his feet had touched the bottom. He had not the strength
to climb up again, and to let go and drop seemed to him
but to be dashed to pieces in the depths below. He held on
until his strength was utterly exhausted, and then
dropped, as he thought, to his death. He fell—just three
inches—and found himself safe on the rock bottom.

Are you afraid to take this step? Does it seem too sudden, too much like a leap in the dark? Do you not know
that the step of faith always "falls on the seeming void,
but finds the rock beneath"? If ever you are to enter this
glorious land, flowing with milk and honey, you must
sooner or later step into the brimming waters, for there is
no other path; and to do it now may save you months
and even years of disappointment and grief. Hear the
word of the Lord,—

"Have not I commanded thee? Be strong and of a good
courage; be not afraid, neither be thou dismayed: for the
Lord thy God is with thee, whithersoever thou goest."

PART II

Difficulties

Difficulties Concerning Consecration

IT IS VERY IMPORTANT THAT CHRISTIANS SHOULD NOT be ignorant of the temptations that seem to stand ready to oppose every onward step of their progress heavenward, and that are especially active when the soul is awakened to a hunger and thirst after righteousness, and begins to reach out after the fulness that is ours in Christ.

One of the greatest of these temptations is a difficulty concerning consecration. The seeker after holiness is told that he must consecrate himself, and he endeavors to do so. But at once he meets with a difficulty. He has done it as he thinks, and yet he finds no difference in his experience; nothing seems changed, as he has been led to expect it would be, and he is completely baffled, and asks the question almost despairingly, "How am I to know when I am consecrated?"

The one chief temptation that meets the soul at this juncture is the same that assaults it all along the pathway, at every step of its progress; namely, the question as to *feelings*. We cannot believe we are consecrated until we *feel* that we are: and because we do not feel that God has taken us in hand, we cannot believe that He has. As usual, we put feeling first, and faith second, and the fact last of all. No, God's invariable rule in everything is, fact first, faith second, and feeling last of all; and it is striving against the inevitable when we seek to change this order.

The way, then, to meet this temptation in reference to consecration, is simply to take God's side in the matter, and to adopt His order, by putting faith before feeling. Give yourself to the Lord definitely and fully, according to your present light, asking the Holy Spirit to show you all that is contrary to Him, either in your heart or life. If He shows you anything, give it to the Lord immediately, and say in reference to it, "Thy will be done." If he shows you nothing, then you must believe that there is nothing and must conclude that you have given Him all. Then recognize that it must be the fact, that, when you give yourself to God He accepts you; and at once let your faith take hold of this fact. Begin to believe, and hold on to it steadfastly, that He has taken that which you have surrendered to Him. You positively must not wait to feel either that you have given yourself, or that God has taken you. You must simply believe it, and reckon it to be the case. And if you are steadfast in this reckoning, sooner or later the feeling will come, and you will realize that it is indeed a blessed fact that you are wholly the Lord's.

If you were to give an estate to a friend, you would have to give it, and he would have to receive it, by faith. An estate is not a thing that can be picked up and handed over to another; the gift of it and its reception are altogether a transaction by word and on paper, and therefore one of faith. Now, if you should give an estate one day to a friend, and then should go away and wonder whether you really had given it, and whether he actually had taken it and considered it his own, and should feel it necessary to go the next day and renew the gift; and if on the third day you should still feel a similar uncertainty about it, and should again go and renew the gift; and on the fourth day go through a like process, and so on, day after day, for months and years,—what would your friend think, and what at last would be the condition of your own mind in reference to it? Your friend would certainly begin to doubt whether you ever had intended to give it to him at all, and you yourself would be in such hopeless perplexity about it, that you would not know whether the estate was yours or his, or whose it was.

Now, is not this very much the way in which you have been acting toward God in this matter of consecration? You have given yourself to Him over and over daily, perhaps for months, but you have invariably come away from your seasons of consecration wondering whether you really have given yourself after all, and whether He has taken you; and because you have not *felt* any change, you have concluded at last, after many painful tossings, that the thing has not been done. Do you know, dear believer, that this sort of perplexity will last forever, unless you cut it short by faith? You must come to the point of reckoning the matter to be an accomplished and settled thing, and must leave it there before you can possibly expect any change of feeling whatever.

The Levitical law of offerings to the Lord settles this as a primary fact, that everything which is given to Him becomes, by that very act, something holy, set apart from all other things, something that cannot without sacrilege be put to any other uses. "Notwithstanding, no devoted thing that a man shall devote unto the Lord of all that he hath, both of man and beast, and of the field of his possession, shall be sold or redeemed; every devoted thing is most holy unto the Lord." Having once given it to the Lord, the devoted thing henceforth was reckoned by all Israel as being the Lord's, and no one dared to stretch forth a hand to retake it. The giver might have made his offering very grudgingly and halfheartedly, but, having made it, the matter was taken out of his hands altogether, and the devoted thing, by God's own law, became "most holy unto the Lord." It was not made holy by the state of mind of the giver, but by the holiness of the Divine receiver. "The altar sanctifies the gift"; and an offering, once laid upon the altar, from that moment belonged to the Lord. I can imagine an offerer, after he had deposited a gift, beginning to search his heart as to his sincerity and honesty in doing it, and coming back to the priest to say that he was afraid, after all, he had not given it rightly, or had not been perfectly sincere in giving it. I feel sure the priest would have silenced him at once, saying, "As to how you gave your offering, or what were your motives in giving it, I do not know. The facts are that you did give it, and that it is the Lord's, for every devoted thing is most holy unto Him. It is too late to recall the transaction now." And not only the priest, but all Israel, would have been aghast at the man, who, having once given his offering, should have reached out his hand to take it back. Yet, day after day, earnest-hearted Christians, with no thought of the sacrilege they are committing, are guilty in their own experience of a similar act by giving themselves to the Lord in solemn consecration, and then, through unbelief, taking back that which they have given.

Because God is not visibly present to the eye, it is difficult to feel that a transaction with Him is real. I suppose that if, when we made our acts of consecration, we could actually see Him present with us, we should feel it to be a very real thing, and would realize that we had given our word to Him, and could not dare to take it back, no matter how much we might wish to do so. Such a transaction would have to us the binding power that a spoken promise to an earthly friend always has to a man of honor. What we need, therefore, is to see that God's presence is a certain fact always, and that every act of our soul is done before Him, and that a word spoken in prayer is as really spoken to Him as if our eyes could see Him and our hands could touch Him. Then we shall cease to have such vague conceptions of our relations with Him, and shall feel the binding force of every word we say in His presence.

I know some will say here, "Ah, yes; but if He would only speak to me, and say that He took me when I gave myself to Him, I would have no trouble then in believing it." No, of course you would not; but then where would be the room for faith? Sight is not faith, and hearing is not faith, neither is feeling faith; but believing when we can neither see, hear, nor feel, *is* faith; and everywhere the Bible tells us our salvation is to be by faith. Therefore we must believe before we feel, and often against our feelings, if we would honor God by our faith. It is always he that believeth who has the witness, not he that doubteth. But how can we doubt, since, by His very command to us to present ourselves to Him a living sacrifice, He has pledged Himself to receive us? I cannot conceive of an honorable man asking another to give him a thing which, after all, he was doubtful about taking; still less can I conceive of a loving parent acting so toward a beloved child. "My son, give me thy heart," is a sure warrant for knowing that the moment the heart is given, it will be taken by the One who has commanded the gift. We may, nay, we must, feel the utmost confidence, then, that when we surrender ourselves to the Lord, according to His own command, He does then and there receive us, and from that moment we are His. A real transaction has taken place, which cannot be violated without dishonor on our part, and which we know will not be violated by Him.

In Deuteronomy 26: 17–19, we see God's way of working under these circumstances: "Thou hast avouched the Lord this day to be thy God, and to walk in his ways, and to keep his statutes, and his commandments, and his judgments, and to hearken unto his voice; and the Lord hath avouched thee this day to be his peculiar people, as he hath promised thee, and that thou shouldst keep all his commandments; . . . and that thou mayest be an holy people unto the Lord thy God, as he hath spoken."

When we avouch the Lord to be our God, and that we

will walk in His ways and keep His commandments, He avouches us to be His, and that we *shall* keep all His commandments. And from that moment He takes possession of us. This has always been His principle of working, and it continues to be so. "Every devoted thing is most holy to the Lord." This is so plain as not to admit of a question.

But if the soul still feels in doubt or difficulty, let me refer you to a New Testament declaration which approaches the subject from a different side, but which settles it, I think, quite as definitely. It is in I John 5: 14, 15, and reads, "And this is the confidence that we have in him, that, if we ask anything according to his will, he heareth us; and if we know that he heareth us, whatsoever we ask, we know that we *have* the petitions that we desired of him." Is it according to His will that you should be entirely surrendered to Him? There can be, of course, but one answer to this, for He has *commanded* it. Is it not also according to His will that He should work in you to will and to do of His good pleasure? This question also can have but one answer, for He has declared it to be His purpose. You know, then, that these things are according to His will; therefore, on God's own word, you are obliged to know that He hears you. And knowing this much, you are compelled to go farther, and know that you have the petitions that you have desired of Him. That you *have*, I say,—not will have, or may have, but have now in actual possession. It is thus that we "obtain promises" by faith. It is thus that we have "access by faith" into the grace that is given us in our Lord Jesus Christ. It is thus, and thus only, that we come to know our hearts "purified by faith," and are enabled to live by faith, to stand by faith, to walk by faith.

I desire to make this subject so plain and practical that no one need have any further difficulty about it, and therefore I will repeat again just what must be the acts of your soul, in order to bring you out of this difficulty about consecration.

I suppose that you have trusted the Lord Jesus for the forgiveness of your sins, and know something of what it is to belong to the family of God, and to be made an heir of God through faith in Christ. And now you feel springing up in your heart the longing to be conformed to the image of your Lord. In order for this, you know there must be an entire surrender to yourself to Him, that He may

work in you all the good pleasure of His will; and you
have tried over and over to do it, but hitherto without any
apparent success. At this point it is that I desire to help
you. What you must do now is to come once more to Him,
in a surrender of your whole self to His will, as complete
as you know how to make it. You must ask Him to reveal to you, by His Spirit, any hidden rebellion; and if He
reveals nothing, then you must believe that there is nothing, and that the surrender is complete. This must,
then, be considered a settled matter; you have wholly
yielded yourself to the Lord, and from henceforth you
do not in any sense belong to yourself; you must never
even so much as listen to a suggestion to the contrary. If
the temptation comes to wonder whether you really have
completely surrendered yourself, meet it with an assertion that you have. Do not even argue the matter. Repel
any such idea instantly, and with decision. You meant it
then, you mean it now, you have really done it. Your
emotions may clamor against the surrender, but your will
must hold firm. It is your purpose God looks at, not your
feelings about that purpose; and your purpose, or will, is
therefore the only thing you need to attend to.

The surrender, then, having been made, never to be
questioned or recalled, the next point is to believe that
God takes that which you have surrendered, and to reckon
that it is His. Not that it will be His at some future time,
but that it is now; and that He has begun to work in
you to will and to do of His good pleasure. And here you
must rest. There is nothing more for you to do, except to
be henceforth an obedient child; for you are the Lord's
now, absolutely and entirely in His hands, and He has
undertaken the whole care and management and form-
ing of you, and will, according to His word, "work in you
that which is well-pleasing in His sight through Jesus
Christ." But you must hold steadily here. If you begin to
question your surrender, or God's acceptance of it, then
your wavering faith will produce a wavering experience,
and He cannot work in you to do His will. But while you
trust, He works; and the result of His working always is
to change you into the image of Christ, from glory to
glory, by His mighty Spirit.

Do you, then, now at this moment, surrender yourself
wholly to Him? You answer, Yes. Then, my dear friend,
begin at once to reckon that you are His, that He has
taken you, and that He is working in you to will and to do

of His good pleasure. And keep on reckoning this. You will find it a great help to put your reckoning into words, and say over and over to yourself and to your God, "Lord, I am thine; I do yield myself up entirely to thee, and I believe that thou dost take me. I leave myself with thee. Work in me all the good pleasure of thy will, and I will only lie still in thy hands and trust thee."

Make this a daily, definite act of your will, and many times a day recur to it, as being your continual attitude before the Lord. Confess it to yourself. Confess it to your God. Confess it to your friends. Avouch the Lord to be your God, continually and unwaveringly, and declare your purpose of walking in His ways and keeping His statutes; and sooner or later, you will find in practical experience that He has avouched you to be one of His peculiar people, and will enable you to keep all His commandments, and that you are being made into "an holy people unto the Lord, as he hath spoken."

'For Thou art making me, I thank Thee Sire.
What Thou hast done and doest, Thou knowest well;
And I will help Thee: gently in Thy fire
I will lie burning; on Thy potter's wheel
I will whirl patient, though my brain should reel;
Thy grace shall be enough my grief to quell,
And growing strength perfect through weakness dire."

Chapter Six

Difficulties Concerning Faith

THE NEXT STEP AFTER CONSECRATION, IN THE SOUL'S progress out of the wilderness of a failing Christian experience into the land that floweth with milk and honey is that of faith. And here, as in the first step, the soul encounters at once certain forms of difficulty and hindrance.

The child of God, whose eyes have been opened to see the fulness there is in Jesus for him, and whose heart has been made hungry to appropriate that fulness, is met with the assertion, on the part of every teacher to whom he applies, that this fulness is only to be received by faith. But the subject of faith is involved in such a hopeless mystery to his mind that this assertion, instead of throwing light upon the way of entrance, seems only to make it more difficult and involved than ever.

"Of course it is to be by faith," he says, "for I know that everything in the Christian life is by faith. But that is just what makes it so hard, for I have no faith, and I do not even know what it is, nor how to get it." And, thus, baffled at the very outset by this insuperable difficulty, he is plunged into darkness, and almost despair.

This trouble arises from the fact that the subject of faith is very generally misunderstood; for, in reality, faith is the simplest and plainest thing in the world, and the most easy of exercise.

Your idea of faith, I suppose, has been something like this. You have looked upon it as in some way a sort of *thing*,—either a religious exercise of soul, or an inward, gracious disposition of heart; something tangible, in fact, which, when you have secured it, you can look at and rejoice over, and use as a passport to God's favor, or a coin with which to purchase His gifts. And you have been praying for faith, expecting all the while to get something like this; and never having received any such thing, you are insisting upon it that you have no faith. Now, faith, in fact, is not in the least like this. It is nothing at all tangible. It is simply believing God; and, like sight, it is nothing apart from its object. You might as well shut your eyes and look inside, and see whether you have sight, as to look inside to discover whether you have faith. You see something, and thus know that you have sight; you believe something, and thus know that you have faith. For as sight is only seeing, so faith is only believing. And as the only necessary thing about sight is that you see the thing as it is, so the only necessary thing about belief is that you believe the thing as it is. The virtue does not lie in your believing, but in the thing you believe. If you believe the truth, you are saved; if you believe a lie, you are lost. The act of believing in both cases is the same; the things believed are exactly opposite, and this it is which makes the mighty difference. Your salvation comes, not because your faith saves you, but because it links you to the Saviour who saves; and your believing is really nothing but the link.

I do beg of you to recognize, then, the extreme simplicity of faith; namely, that it is nothing more nor less than just believing God when He says He either has done something for us, or will do it; and then trusting Him to keep His word. It is so simple that it is hard to explain. If anyone asks me what it means to trust another to do a piece of work for me, I can answer only that it means committing the work to that other, and leaving it without anxiety in his hands. All of us have many times trusted very important affairs to others in this way, and have felt perfect rest in thus trusting because of the confidence we have had in those who have undertaken them. How constantly do mothers trust their most precious infants to the care of nurses, and feel no shadow of anxiety! How continually we are all of us trusting our health and our lives, without a thought of fear, to cooks and coachmen, engine-drivers, railway-conductors, and all sorts of paid servants, who have us completely at their mercy, and who could, if they chose to do so, or even if they failed in the necessary carefulness, plunge us into misery or death in a moment. All this we do, and make no demur about it. Upon the slightest acquaintance, often, we thus put our trust in people, requiring only the general knowledge of human nature and the common rules of human intercourse as the foundation of our trust, and we never feel as if we were doing anything in the least remarkable.

You have done this yourself, dear reader, and are doing it continually. You could not live among your fellow men and go through the customary routine of life a single day if you were unable to trust your fellow men, and it never enters into your head to say you cannot. But yet you do not hesitate to say, continually, that you cannot trust your God! And you excuse yourself by the plea that you are "a poor weak creature" and "have no faith."

I wish you would try to imagine yourself acting in your human relations as you do in your spiritual relations. Suppose you should begin to-morrow with the notion in your head that you could not trust anybody because you had no faith. When you sat down to breakfast you would say, "I cannot eat anything on this table, for I have no faith, and I cannot believe the cook has not put poison in the coffee, or that the butcher has not sent home diseased or unhealthy meat"; so you would go away starving. When you went out to your daily avocations, you would say, "I cannot ride in the railway train, for I have no faith, and therefore I cannot trust the engineer, nor the conductor, nor the builders of the carriages, nor the managers of the road." And you would be compelled to walk everywhere, and would grow unutterably weary in the effort, besides being actually unable to reach the places you could have reached in the train. When your friends met you with any statements, or your business agent with any accounts, you would say, "I am very sorry that I cannot believe you, but I have no faith, and never can believe anybody." If you opened a newspaper, you would be forced to lay it down again, saying, "I really cannot believe a word this paper says, for I have no faith; I do not believe there is any such person as the Queen, for I never saw her; nor any such country as Ireland, for I was never there. I have no faith, so of course I cannot believe anything that I have not actually felt and touched myself. It is a great trial, but I cannot help it, for I have no faith."

Just picture such a day as this, and see how disastrous it would be to yourself, and what utter folly it would appear to anyone who should watch you through the whole of it. Realize how your friends would feel insulted, and how your servants would refuse to serve you another day. And then ask yourself the question, if this want of faith in your fellow men would be so dreadful, and such utter folly, what must it be when you tell God that you have no power to trust Him, nor to believe His word; that it is a great trial, but you cannot help it, "for you have no faith."

Is it possible that you can trust your fellow men, and cannot trust your God; that you can receive the "witness of men," and cannot receive the "witness of God"; that you can believe man's records, and cannot believe God's record; that you can commit your dearest earthly interests to your weak, failing fellow creatures without a fear, and are afraid to commit your spiritual interests to the Saviour who laid down His life for you, and of whom it is declared that He is "able to save to the uttermost all who came unto God by him"?

Surely, surely, dear believer, you, whose very name of believer implies that you can believe, you will never again dare to excuse yourself on the plea of having no faith. For when you say this, you mean of course that you have no faith in God, since you are not asked to have faith in yourself, and would be in a very wrong condition of soul if you had. Let me beg of you, then, when you think or say these things, always to complete the sentence, and say, "I have no faith in—God! I cannot believe—God!" and this I am sure will soon become so dreadful to you that you will not dare to continue it.

But, you say, I cannot believe without the Holy Spirit. Very well; will you conclude, then, that your want of faith is because of the failure of the Holy Spirit to do His work? For if it is, then surely you are not to blame, and need feel no condemnation; and all exhortations to you to believe are useless.

But no! Do you not see, that, in taking up the position that you have no faith and cannot believe, you are not only "making God a liar," but you are also showing an utter want of confidence in the Holy Spirit.

For He is always ready to help our infirmities. We never have to wait for Him, He is always waiting for us. And I for my part have such absolute confidence in the Holy Ghost, and in His being always ready to do His work, that I dare to say to every one of you, that you *can* believe now, at this very moment; and that if you do not, it is not the Spirit's fault, but your own. Put your will, then, over on the believing side. Say, "Lord, I will believe, I do believe," and continue to say it. Insist upon believing, in the face of every suggestion of doubt that intrudes itself. Out of your very unbelief, throw yourself unreservedly on the word and promises of God, and dare to abandon yourself to the keeping and saving power of the Lord Jesus. If you have ever trusted a precious interest in the hands of an earthly friend, I entreat you, trust yourself and all your spiritual interests now, in the hands of your Heavenly Friend, and never, *never*, NEVER, allow yourself to doubt again.

Remember always that there are two things which are more utterly incompatible even than oil and water, and these two are trust and worry. Would you call it trust if you should give something into the hands of a friend to attend to for you, and then should spend your nights and days in anxious thought and worry as to whether it would be rightly and successfully done? And can you call it trust, when you have given the saving and keeping of your soul into the hands of the Lord, if day after day, and night after night, you are spending hours of anxious thought and questionings about the matter? When a believer really trusts anything, he ceases to worry about the thing he has trusted. And when he worries, it is a plain proof that he does not trust. Tested by this rule, how little real trust there is in the Church of Christ! No wonder our Lord asked the pathetic question, "When the Son of man cometh, shall he find faith on the earth?" He will find plenty of work, a great deal of earnestness, and doubtless many consecrated hearts; but shall He find faith, the one thing He values more than all the rest? Every child of God, in his own case, will know how to answer this question. Should the answer, for any of you, be a sorrowful No, let me entreat you to let this be the last time for such an answer; and if you have ever known anything of the trustworthiness of our Lord, may you henceforth set to your seal that He is true, by the generous recklessness of your trust in Him!

I remember, very early in my Christian life, having every tender and loyal impulse within me stirred to the depths of an appeal I met with in a volume of old sermons to all who loved the Lord Jesus, that they should show to others how worthy He was of being trusted by the steadfastness of their own faith in Him. As I read the inspiring words, there came to me a sudden glimpse of the privilege and the glory of being called to walk in paths so dark that only an utter recklessness of trust would be possible!

"Ye have not passed this way heretofore," it may be; but to-day it is your happy privilege to prove, as never before, your loyal confidence in Jesus by starting out with Him on a life and walk of faith, lived, moment by moment, in absolute and childlike trust in Him.

You have trusted Him in a few things, and He has not failed you. Trust Him now for everything, and see if He does not do for you exceeding abundantly, above all that you could ever have asked or even thought, not according to your power or capacity, but according to His own mighty power, working in you all the good pleasure of His most blessed will.

It is not hard, you find, to trust the management of the universe, and of all the outward creation, to the Lord. Can your case then be so much more complex and difficult than these, that you need to be anxious or troubled about His management of you? Away with such unworthy doubtings! Take your stand on the power and trustworthiness of your God, and see how quickly all difficulties will vanish before a steadfast determination to believe. Trust in the dark, trust in the light, trust at night and trust in the morning, and you will find that the faith that many begin perhaps by a mighty effort will end, sooner or later, by becoming the easy and natural habit of the soul. It is a law of the spiritual life that every act of trust makes the next act less difficult, until at length, if these acts are persisted in, trusting becomes, like breathing, the natural unconscious action of the redeemed soul.

You must therefore put your will into your believing. Your faith must not be a passive imbecility, but an active energy. You may have to believe against every seeming; but no matter. Set your face like a flint to say, "I will believe, and I know I shall not be confounded." We are made "partakers of Christ if we hold the beginning of our faith steadfast unto the end." Hundreds fail just here. They have a little beginning of faith, but discouragements come, the "seemings" are all against it, their doubts clamor louder and louder, and at last they let them in; and when doubt comes in at the door, trust always flies out of the window.

We are told that all things are possible to God, and that all things are possible also to him that believeth. Faith has in times past "subdued kingdoms, wrought righteousness, obtained promises, stopped the mouths of lions, quenched the violence of fire, escaped the edge of the sword, waxed valiant in fight, turned to flight the armies of the aliens"; and faith can do it again. For our Lord Himself says unto us, "If ye have faith as a grain of mustard seed, ye shall say unto this mountain, remove hence to yonder place; and it shall remove; and nothing shall be impossible unto you."

If you are a child of God at all, you must have at least as much faith as a grain of mustard seed, and therefore you dare not say again that you "cannot trust because you have no faith." Say rather, "I can trust my Lord, and I will trust Him; and not all the powers of earth or hell shall be able to make me doubt my wonderful, glorious, faithful Redeemer!"

"Faith is sweetest of worships to Him, who so loves
His unbearable splendors in darkness to hide;
And to trust to Thy word, dearest Lord! is true love,
For those prayers are most granted which seem most denied.

"Our faith throws her arms around all Thou hast told her,
    And, able to hold as much more, can but grieve.
She could hold Thy grand self, Lord! if Thou wouldst re-
    veal it,
    And love makes her long to have more to believe."

Let your faith, then, "throw its arms around all God
has told you," and in every dark hour remember that
"though now for a season, if need be, ye are in heaviness
through manifold temptations," it is only like going
through a tunnel. The sun has not ceased shining because
the traveler through the tunnel has ceased to see it; and
the Sun of righteousness is still shining, although you in
your dark tunnel do not see Him. Be patient and trustful,
and wait. This time of darkness is only permitted that
"the trial of your faith, being much more precious than
of gold that perisheth, though it be tried with fire, might
be found unto praise and honor and glory at the appearing
of Jesus Christ."

Chapter Seven

Difficulties Concerning the Will

WHEN THE CHILD OF GOD HAS, BY ENTIRE ABANDON-
ment and absolute trust, stepped out of himself into
Christ, and has begun to know something of the blessedness of the life hid with Christ in God, there is one form of
difficulty which is especially likely to start up in his path.
After the first emotions of peace and rest have somewhat
subsided, or if, as is sometimes the case, they have never
seemed to come at all, he begins to feel such an utter unreality in the things he has been passing through that he
seems to himself like a hypocrite when he says or even
thinks they are real. It seems to him that his belief does
not go below the surface; that it is a mere lip-belief,
and therefore of no account, and that his surrender is not
a surrender of the heart, and therefore cannot be acceptable to God. He is afraid to say he is altogether the
Lord's, for fear he will be telling an untruth; and yet he

cannot bring himself to say he is not, because he longs for it so intensely. The difficulty is real and very disheartening.

But there is nothing here which will not be very easily overcome when the Christian once thoroughly understands the principles of the new life, and has learned *how* to live it. The common thought is that this life hid with Christ in God is to be lived in the emotions, and consequently all the attention of the soul is directed toward them, and as they are satisfactory or otherwise, the soul rests or is troubled. Now, the truth is, that this life is not to be lived in the emotions at all, but in the will; and therefore, if only the will is kept steadfastly abiding in its center, God's will, the varying states of emotion do not in the least disturb or affect the reality of the life.

To make this plain, I must enlarge a little. Fenelon says, somewhere, that "pure religion resides in the will alone." By this he means that, as the will is the governing power in the man's nature, if the will is set right, all the rest of the nature must come into harmony. By the will, I do not mean the wish of the man, or even his purpose, but the deliberate choice, the deciding power, the king, to which all that is in the man must yield obedience. It is the man, in short, the *"Ego,"* that which we feel to be ourselves.

It is sometimes thought that the emotions are the governing power in our nature. But I think we all of us know, as a matter of practical experience, that there is something within us, behind our emotions and behind our wishes, an independent self, that, after all, decides everything and controls everything. Our emotions belong to us, and are suffered and enjoyed by us, but they are not ourselves; and if God is to take possession of us, it must be into this central will or personality that He enters. If, then, He is reigning there by the power of His Spirit, all the rest of our nature must come under His sway; and as the will is, so is the man.

The practical bearing of this truth upon the difficulty I am considering is very great. For the decisions of our will are often so directly opposed to the decisions of our emotions, that, if we are in the habit of considering our emotions as the test, we shall be very apt to feel like hypocrites in declaring those things to be real which our will alone has decided. But the moment we see that the will is king, we shall utterly disregard anything that clamors against it, and shall claim as real its decisions, let the emotions rebel as they may.

I am aware that this is a difficult subject to deal with; but it is so exceedingly practical in its bearing upon the life of faith, that I beg of you, dear reader, not to turn from it until you have mastered it.

Perhaps an illustration will help you. A young man of great intelligence, seeking to enter into this new life, was utterly discouraged at finding himself the slave to an inveterate habit of doubting. To his emotions nothing seemed real; and the more he struggled, the more unreal did it all become. He was told this secret concerning the will, that if he would only put his will over on the believing side, if he would choose to believe, if, in short, he would in this Ego of his nature say, "I will believe! I do believe!" he need not then trouble about his emotions, for they would find themselves compelled, sooner or later, to come into harmony. "What!" he said. "Do you mean to tell me that I can *choose* to believe in that bald way, when nothing seems true to me? And will that kind of believing be real?" "Yes," was the answer; "it will. Fenelon says that true religion resides in the will alone; and he means that, since a man's will is really the man's self, of course, what his will does, he does. Your part then is simply to put your will, in this matter of believing, over on God's side, making up your mind that you will believe what He says because He says it, and that you will not pay any regard to the feelings that make it seem so unreal. God will not fail to respond, sooner or later, with His revelation to such a faith."

The young man paused a moment, and then said solemnly, "I understand, and will do what you say. I cannot control my emotions, but I can control my will; and the new life begins to look possible to me if it is only my will that needs to be set straight in the matter. I can give my will to God, and I do."

From that moment, disregarding all the pitiful clamoring of his emotions, which continually accused him of being a wretched hypocrite, this young man held on steadily to the decision of his will, answering every accusation with the continued assertion that he chose to believe, he meant to believe, he did believe; until at the end of a few days he found himself triumphant, with every emotion and every thought brought into captivity to the power of the Spirit of God, who had taken possession of the will thus put into His hands. He had held fast the *profession* of his faith without wavering, although it had seemed to him that, as to real faith itself, he had none to hold fast. At times it had drained all the will power he possessed to his lips to say that he believed, so contrary was it to all the evidence of his senses or of his emotions. But he had caught the idea that his will was, after all, himself, and that if he kept that on God's side, he was doing all he could do, and that God alone could change his emotions or control his being. The result has been one of the grandest Christian lives I know of, in its marvelous simplicity, directness, and power over sin.

The secret lies just here,—that our will, which is the spring of all our actions, has been in the past under the control of sin and self, and these have worked in us all their own good pleasure. But now God calls upon us to yield our wills up unto Him, that He may take the control of them, and may work in us to will and to do of His good pleasure. If we will obey this call, and present ourselves to Him as a living sacrifice, He will take possession of our surrendered wills, and will begin at once to work in us "that which is well pleasing in His sight, through Jesus Christ," giving us the mind that was in Christ, and transforming us into His image (see Rom. 12: 1, 2).

Let us take another illustration. A lady who had entered into this life hid with Christ was confronted by a great prospective trial. Every emotion she had within her rose up in rebellion against it; and had she considered her emotions to be her king, she would have been in utter despair. But she had learned this secret of the will, and knowing that, at the bottom, she herself did really choose the will of God for her portion, she did not pay the slightest attention to her emotions, but persisted in meeting every thought concerning the trial with the words, repeated over and over, "Thy will be done! Thy will be done!" asserting, in the face of all her rebelling feelings, that she did submit her will to God's, that she chose to submit it, and that His will should be and was her delight! The result was that in an incredibly short space of time every thought was brought into captivity, and she began to find even her very emotions rejoicing in the will of God.

Again, there was a lady who had a besetting sin, which

in her emotions she dearly loved, but which in her will she hated. Believing herself to be necessarily under control of her emotions, she had fully supposed she was unable to conquer it, unless her emotions should first be changed. But she learned this secret concerning the will, and going to her closet she said, "Lord, thou seest that with my emotions I love this sin, but in my real central self I hate it. Until now my emotions have had the mastery; but now I put my will into thy hands, and give it up to thy working. I will never again consent in my will to yield to this sin. Take possession of my will, and work in me to will and to do of thy good pleasure."

Immediately she began to find deliverance. The Lord took possession of the will thus surrendered to Himself, and began to work in her by His own power, so that His will in the matter gained the mastery over her emotions, and she found herself delivered, not by the power of an outward commandment, but by the inward power of the Spirit of God, "working in her that which was well pleasing in his sight."

And now, dear Christian, let me show you how to apply this principle to your difficulties. Cease to consider your emotions, for they are only the servants; and regard simply your will, which is the real king in your being. Is that given up to God? Is that put into His hands? Does your will decide to believe? Does your will choose to obey? If this is the case, then *you* are in the Lord's hands, and you decide to believe, and you choose to obey; for your will is yourself. And the thing is done. The transaction with God is as real, when only your will acts, as where every emotion coincides. It does not seem as real to you; but in God's sight it is as real. And when you have got hold of this secret, and have discovered that you need not attend to your emotions but simply to the state of your will, all the Scripture commands to yield yourself to God, to present yourself a living sacrifice to Him, to abide in Christ, to walk in the light, to die to self, become possible to you; for you are conscious that in all these your will can act, and can take God's side; whereas, if it had been your emotions that must do it, you would, knowing them to be utterly uncontrollable, sink down in helpless despair.

When, then, this feeling of unreality or hypocrisy comes, do not be troubled by it. It is only in your emotions, and is not worth a moment's thought. Only see to it that your will is in God's hands, that your inward self is abandoned to His working, that your choice, your decision, is on His side; and there leave it. Your surging emotions, like a tossing vessel at anchor, which by degrees yields to the steady pull of the cable, finding themselves attached to the mighty power of God by the choice of your will, must inevitably come into captivity, and give in their allegiance to Him; and you will sooner or later verify the truth of the saying that "if any man will do his will, he shall know of the doctrine."

The will is like a wise mother in a nursery; the feelings are like a set of clamoring, crying children. The mother makes up her mind to a certain course of action which she believes to be right and best. The children clamor against it and declare it shall not be. But the mother, knowing that she is mistress and not they, pursues her course lovingly and calmly in spite of all their clamors; and the result is that the children are sooner or later won over to the mother's course of action, and fall in with her decisions, and all is harmonious and happy. But if that mother should for a moment let in the thought that the children were the masters instead of herself, confusion would reign unchecked. And in how many souls at this very moment is there nothing but confusion, simply because the feelings are allowed to govern, instead of the will.

Remember, then, that the real thing in your experience is what your will decides, and not the verdict of your emotions; and that you are far more in danger of hypocrisy and untruth in yielding to the assertions of your feelings than in holding fast to the decision of your will. So that, if your will is on God's side, you are no hypocrite at this moment in claiming as your own the blessed reality of belonging altogether to Him, even though your emotions may all declare the contrary.

I am convinced that throughout the Bible the expressions concerning the "heart" do not mean the emotions, that which we now understand by the word "heart," but they mean the will, the personality of the man, the man's own central self; and that the object of God's dealings with man is that this "I" may be yielded up to Him, and this central life abandoned to His entire control. It is not the feelings of the man God wants, but the man himself.

But do not let us make a mistake here. I say we must "give up" our wills, but I do not mean we are to be left will-less. We are not so to give up our wills as to be left like limp nerveless creatures, without any will at all. We are simply to substitute for our foolish, misdirected wills of ignorance and immaturity the higher, divine, mature will of God. If we lay the emphasis on the word "our," we shall understand it better. The will we are to give up is our will, as it is misdirected, and so parted off from God's will, not our will when it is one with God's will; for when our will is in harmony with His will, when it has the stamp of oneness with Him, it would be wrong for us to give it up.

The child is required to give up the misdirected will that belongs to it *as a child,* and we cannot let it say, "I will" or "I will not"; but when its will is in harmony with ours, we want it to say, "I will" or "I will not," with all the force of which it is capable.

When God is "working in us to will," we must set our faces like a flint to carry out his will, and must respond with an emphatic "I will" to every "Thou shalt" of His. For God can only carry out His own will with us as we consent to it, and will in harmony with Him.

Have you thus consented, dear reader, and is your face set as a flint to will what God wills? He wills that you should be entirely surrendered to Him, and that you should trust Him perfectly. Do you will the same?

Again I repeat, it is all in the will. Fenelon says, "The will to love God is the whole of religion." If, therefore, you have in your will taken the steps of surrender and faith, it is your right to believe even now, no matter how much your feelings may clamor against it, that you *are* all the Lord's, and that He *has* begun to "work in you to will and to do of His good pleasure."

After this chapter was first written some years ago, the following remarkable practical illustration of its teaching was handed to me by Pastor Theodore Monod, of Paris. It is the experience of a Presbyterian minister, which this pastor had carefully kept for many years:—

NEWBURGH, Sept. 26, 1842

DEAR BROTHER,—I take a few moments of that time which I have devoted to the Lord, in writing a short epistle to you, His servant. It is sweet to feel we are wholly the

Lord's, that He has received us and called us His. This is religion, a relinquishment of the principle of self-ownership, and the adoption in full of the abiding sentiment, "I am not my own, I am bought with a price." Since I last saw you I have been pressing forward, and yet there has been nothing remarkable in my experience, of which I can speak; indeed, I do not know that it is best to look for remarkable things; but strive to be holy, as God is holy, pressing right on toward the mark of the prize.

I do not feel myself qualified to instruct you: I can only tell you the way in which I was led. The Lord deals differently with different souls, and we ought not to attempt to copy the experience of others; yet there are certain things which must be attended to by every one who is seeking after a clean heart.

There must be a personal consecration of all to God; a covenant made with God that we will be wholly and forever His. This I made intellectually, without any change in my feelings, with a heart full of hardness and darkness, unbelief and sin and insensibility.

I covenanted to be the Lord's, and laid all upon the altar, a living sacrifice, to the best of my ability. And after I rose from my knees I was conscious of no change in my feelings. I was painfully conscious that there was no change. But yet I was sure that I did, with all the sincerity and honesty of purpose of which I was capable, make an entire and eternal consecration of myself to God. I did not then consider the work as done by any means, but I engaged to abide in a state of entire devotion to God, a living perpetual sacrifice. And now came the effort to do this.

I knew also that I must believe that God did accept me, and did come to dwell in my heart. I was conscious I did not believe this and yet I desired to do so. I read with much prayer John's first epistle, and endeavored to assure my heart of God's love to me as an individual. I was sensible that my heart was full of evil. I seemed to have no power to overcome pride, or to repel evil thoughts which I abhorred. But Christ was manifested to destroy the works of the devil, and it was clear that the sin in my heart was the work of the devil. I was enabled, therefore, to believe that God was working *in* me to will and to do, while I was working *out* my own salvation with fear and trembling.

I was convinced of unbelief, that it made the faithful God a liar. The Lord brought before me my besetting sins which had dominion over me, especially preaching myself instead of Christ, and indulging in self-complacent thoughts after preaching. I was enabled to make myself of no reputation, and to seek the honor which cometh from God only. Satan struggled hard to beat me back from the Rock of Ages; but thanks to God, I finally hit upon the method of living by the moment, and then I found rest.

*   *   *

I felt shut up to a momentary dependence upon the grace of Christ. I would not permit the adversary to trouble me about the past or future, for I each moment looked for the supply for that moment. I agreed that I would be a child of Abraham, and walk by naked faith in the word of God, and not by inward feelings and emotions; I would seek to be a Bible Christian. *Since that time the Lord has given me a steady victory over sins which before enslaved me.* I delight in the Lord and in His word. I delight in my work as a minister; my fellowship is with the Father and with His Son Jesus Christ. I am a babe in Christ; I know my progress has been small, compared with that made by many. My feelings vary; but when I have feelings I praise God and trust in His word; and when I am empty and my feelings are gone, I do the same. I have covenanted to walk by faith, and not by feelings.

The Lord, I think, is beginning to revive His work among my people. "Praise the Lord!" May the Lord fill you with all His fulness, and give you all the mind of Christ. Oh, be faithful! Walk before God and be perfect. Preach the Word. Be instant in season and out of season. The Lord loves you. He works with you. Rest your soul fully upon that promise, "Lo, I am with you always, even unto the end of the world."

Your fellow-soldier,

WILLIAM HILL

Chapter Eight

Difficulties Concerning Guidance

YOU HAVE NOW BEGUN, DEAR READER, THE LIFE OF faith. You have given yourself to the Lord to be His wholly and altogether, and you are now entirely in His hands to be molded and fashioned according to His own divine purpose into a vessel unto His honor. Your one most earnest desire is to follow Him whithersoever He may lead you, and to be very pliable in His hands; and you are trusting Him to "work in you to will and to do of his good pleasure." But you find a great difficulty here. You have not learned yet to know the voice of the Good Shepherd, and are therefore in great doubt and perplexity as to what really is His will concerning you.

Perhaps there are certain paths into which God seems to be calling you, of which your friends disapprove. And these friends, it may be, are older than yourself in the Christian life, and seem to you also to be much farther advanced. You can scarcely bear to differ from them or to distress them; and you feel also very diffident of yielding to any seeming impressions of duty of which they do not approve. And yet you cannot get rid of these impressions, and you find yourself therefore plunged into great doubt and uneasiness.

There is a way out of all these difficulties to the fully surrendered soul. I would repeat *fully* surrendered, because, if there is any reserve of will upon any point, it becomes almost impossible to find out the mind of God in reference to that point; and therefore the first thing is to be sure that you really do *purpose* to obey the Lord in every respect. If however this is your purpose, and your soul only needs to know the will of God in order to consent to it, then you surely cannot doubt His willingness to make His will known, and to guide you in the right paths. There are many very clear promises in reference to this. Take, for instance, John 10: 3, 4, "He calleth his own sheep by name, and leadeth them out. And when he putteth forth his own sheep he goeth before them, and the sheep follow him, for they know his voice." Or John 14: 26: "But the Comforter, which is the Holy Ghost, whom the Father will send in my name, he shall teach you all things and bring all things to your remembrance, whatsoever I have said unto you." Or James 1: 5, 6: "If any of you lack wisdom, let him ask of God, that giveth to all men liberally, and upbraideth not; and it shall be given him."

With such declarations as these, and many more like them, we must believe that Divine guidance is promised to us, and our faith must therefore confidently look for and expect it. This is essential, for in James 1: 6, 7, we are told, "Let him ask in faith, nothing wavering. For he that wavereth is like a wave of the sea, driven with the wind and tossed. For let not that man think that he shall receive anything of the Lord."

Settle this point then, first of all, and let no suggestion of doubt turn you from a steadfast faith in regard to it, that Divine guidance has been promised, and that, if you seek it, you are sure to receive it.

Next, you must remember that our God has all knowledge and all wisdom, and that therefore it is very possible He may guide you into paths wherein *He* knows great blessings are awaiting you, but which, to the short-sighted human eyes around you, seem sure to result in confusion and loss. You must recognize the fact that God's thoughts are not as man's thoughts, nor His ways as man's ways; and that He alone, who knows the end of things from the beginning, can judge of what the results of any course of action may be. You must therefore realize that His very love for you may perhaps lead you to run counter to the loving wishes of even your dearest friends. You must learn, from Luke 14: 26–33, and similar passages, that in order to be a disciple and follower of your Lord, you may perhaps be called upon to forsake inwardly all that you have, even father or mother, or brother or sister, or husband or wife, or it may be your own life also. Unless the possibility of this is clearly recognized, you will be very likely to get into difficulty, because it often happens that the child of God who enters upon this life of obedience is sooner or later led into paths which meet with the disapproval of those he best loves; and unless he is prepared for this, and can trust the Lord through it all, he will scarcely know what to do.

But, these points having all been settled, we come now

to the question as to how God's guidance is to come to us, and how we shall be able to know His voice. There are four ways in which He reveals His will to us,—through the Scriptures, through providential circumstances, through the convictions of our own higher judgment, and through the inward impressions of the Holy Spirit on our minds. Where these four harmonize, it is safe to say that God speaks. For I lay it down as a foundation principle, which no one can gainsay, that of course His voice will always be in harmony with itself, no matter in how many different ways He may speak. The voices may be many, the message can be but one. If God tells me in one voice to do or to leave undone anything, He cannot possibly tell me the opposite in another voice. If there is a contradiction in the voices, the speakers cannot be the same. Therefore my rule for distinguishing the voice of God would be to bring it to the test of this harmony.

The Scriptures come first. If you are in doubt upon any subject, you must, first of all, consult the Bible about it, and see whether there is any law there to direct you. Until you have found and obeyed God's will as it is there revealed, you must not ask nor expect a separate, direct, personal revelation. A great many fatal mistakes are made in the matter of guidance by the overlooking of this simple rule. Where our Father has written out for us a plain direction about anything, He will not of course make an especial revelation to us about that thing. And if we fail to search out and obey the Scripture rule, where there is one, and look instead for an inward voice, we shall open ourselves to delusions, and shall almost inevitably get into error. No man, for instance, needs or could expect any direct personal revelation to tell him not to steal, because God has already in the Scriptures plainly declared His will about stealing. This seems such an obvious thing that I would not speak of it, but that I have frequently met with Christians who have altogether overlooked it, and who have, as the result, gone off into fanaticism. I knew one earnest Christian who had the text "All things are yours" so strongly impressed upon her mind in reference to some money belonging to a friend, that she felt it was a direct command to her to steal that money; and after a great struggle she obeyed this apparent guidance, with of course most grievous after-results. Had she submitted her "leading" to the plain teaching of Scripture in reference to stealing, she would have been saved.

The Bible, it is true, does not always give a rule for every particular course of action, and in these cases we need and must expect guidance in other ways. But the Scriptures are far more explicit, even about details, than most people think, and there are not many important affairs in life for which a clear direction may not be found in God's book. Take the matter of dress and we have I Peter 3: 3, 4, and I Timothy 2: 9. Take the matter of conversation, and we have Ephesians 4: 29, and 5: 4. Take the matter of avenging injuries and standing up for our rights, and we have Romans 12: 19–21, and Matthew 5: 38–48, and I Peter 2: 19–21. Take the matter of forgiving one another, and we have Ephesians 4: 32, and Mark 11: 25, 26. Take the matter of conformity to the world, and we have Romans 12: 2, and I John 2: 15–17, and James 4: 4. Take the matter of anxieties of every kind, and we have Matthew 6: 25–34, and Philippians 4: 6, 7.

I only give these as examples to show how very full and practical the Bible guidance is. If, therefore, you find yourself in perplexity, first of all search and see whether the Bible speaks on the point in question, asking God to make plain to you, by the power of His Spirit, through the Scriptures, what is His mind. And whatever shall seem to you to be plainly taught here, that you must obey. No especial guidance will ever be given about a point on which the Scriptures are explicit, nor could any guidance ever be contrary to the Scriptures.

It is essential, however, in this connection to remember that the Bible is a book of principles, and not a book of disjointed aphorisms. Isolated texts may often be made to sanction things to which the principles of Scripture are totally opposed. I believe all fanaticism comes in this way. An isolated text is so impressed upon the mind that it seems a necessity to obey it, no matter into what wrong thing it may lead; and thus the principles of Scripture are violated, under the very plea of obedience to the Scriptures. In Luke 4 the enemy is represented as using isolated texts to endorse his temptations, while Christ repelled him by announcing principles.

If, however, upon searching the Bible you do not find any principles that will settle your especial point of difficulty, you must then seek guidance in the other ways mentioned; and God will surely voice Himself to you, either by a conviction of your judgment, or by providential circumstances, or by a clear inward impression. In all true guidance these four voices will, as I have said, necessarily harmonize, for God cannot say in one voice that which He contradicts in another. Therefore, if you have an impression of duty, you must see whether it is in accordance with Scripture, and whether it commends itself to your own higher judgment, and also whether, as we Quakers say, the "way opens" for its carrying out. If any one of these tests fails, it is not safe to proceed, but you must wait in quiet trust until the Lord shows you the point of harmony, which He surely will, sooner or later, if it is His voice that is speaking. Anything which is out of this divine harmony must be rejected, therefore, as not coming from God. For we must never forget that "impressions" can come from other sources as well as from the Holy Spirit. The strong personalities of those around us are the source of a great many of our impressions. Impressions also arise often from our wrong physical conditions, which color things far more than we dream. And finally, impressions come from those spiritual enemies which seem to lie in wait for every traveler who seeks to enter the higher regions of the spiritual life. In the same epistle which tells us that we are seated in "heavenly places in Christ" (Eph. 2: 6), we are also told that we shall have to fight there with spiritual enemies (Eph. 6: 12). These spiritual enemies, whoever or whatever they may be, must necessarily communicate with us by means of our spiritual faculties; and their voices therefore will be, as the voice of God is, an inward impression made upon our spirits. Consequently, just as the Holy Spirit may tell us by impressions what is the will of God concerning us, so also will these spiritual enemies tell us by impressions what is their will concerning us, disguising themselves, of course, as "angels of light" who have come to lead us closer to God.

Many earnest and honest-hearted children of God have been thus deluded into paths of extreme fanaticism, while all the while thinking they were closely following the Lord. God, who sees the sincerity of their hearts, can and does, I am sure, pity and forgive; but the consequences as to this life are often very sad. It is not enough to have a "leading"; we must find out the source of that leading before we give ourselves up to follow it. It is not enough, either, for the leading to be very "remarkable," or the coincidences to be very striking, to stamp it as being surely from God. In all ages of the world evil and deceiving agencies have been able to work miracles, foretell events, reveal secrets, and give "signs"; and God's people have always been emphatically warned about being deceived thereby.

It is essential, therefore, that our "leadings" should all be tested by the teachings of Scripture. But this alone is not enough. They must be tested as well by our own spiritually enlightened judgment, or what is familiarly called "common sense."

So far as I can see, the Scriptures everywhere make it an essential thing for the children of God, in their journey through this world, to use all the faculties that have been given them. They are to use their outward faculties for their outward walk, and their inward faculties for their inward walk; and they might as well expect to be "kept" from dashing their feet against a stone in the outward, if they walk blindfold, as to be "kept" from spiritual stumbling if they put aside their judgment and common sense in their interior life.

Some, however, may say here, "But I thought we were not to depend on our human understanding in Divine things." I answer to this that we are not to depend on our unenlightened human understanding, but upon our human judgment and common sense enlightened by the Spirit of God. That is, God will speak to us through the faculties He has Himself given us, and not independently of them; so that just as we are to use our outward eyes in our outward walk, no matter how full of faith we may be, so also we are to use the interior "eyes of our understanding" in our interior walk with God.

The third test to which our impressions must be brought is that of providential circumstances. If a "leading" is of God, the way will always open for it. Our Lord assures us of this when He says, in John 10: 4, "And when he putteth forth his own sheep, *he goeth before them,* and the sheep *follow* him; for they know his voice." Notice here the expressions "goeth before," and "follow." He goes before to open a way, and we are to follow in the way thus opened. It is never a sign of a Divine leading when the Christian insists on opening his own way, and riding roughshod over all opposing things. If the Lord "goes before" us, He will open the door for us, and we shall not need to batter down doors for ourselves.

The fourth point I would make is this,—that, just as our

impressions must be tested, as I have shown, by the other three voices, so must these other voices be tested by our inward impressions; and if we feel a "stop in our minds" about anything, we must wait until that is removed before acting. A Christian who had advanced with unusual rapidity in the Divine life gave me, as her secret, this simple receipt: "I always mind the checks." We must not ignore the voice of our inward impressions, nor ride roughshod over them, any more than we must the other three voices of which I have spoken.

Every peculiarly precious spiritual gift is always necessarily linked with some peculiar danger. When the spiritual world is opened to a soul, both the good and the evil there will meet it. But we must not be discouraged by this. Who would not rather take manhood with all its risks and dangers than remain forever in the ignorance and innocence of childhood; and who would not rather grow up into the stature of Christ, even if it shall involve new and more subtle forms of temptation?

Therefore we must not be deterred from embracing the blessed privilege of Divine guidance by a dread of the dangers that environ it. With the four tests I have mentioned, and a divine sense of "oughtness," derived from the harmony of all of God's voices, there need be nothing to fear. And to me it seems that the blessedness and joy of this direct communication of God's will to us is one of our grandest privileges. That God *cares* enough about us to desire to regulate the details of our lives is the strongest proof of love He could give; and that He should condescend to tell us all about it, and to let us know just how to live and walk so as perfectly to please Him seems almost too good to be true. We never care about the little details of people's lives unless we love them. It is a matter of indifference to us what the majority of people we meet do, or how they spend their time. But as soon as we begin to love any one we begin at once to care. God's law, therefore, is only another name for God's love; and the more minutely that law descends into the details of our lives, the more sure we are made of the depth and reality of the love. We can never know the full joy and privileges of the life hid with Christ in God until we have learned the lesson of a daily and hourly guidance.

God's promise is that He will work in us to *will* as well as to do of His good pleasure. This means, of course, that He will take possession of our will, and work it for us; and that His suggestions will come to us, not so much commands from the outside as desires springing up within. They will originate in our will; we shall feel as though we *desired* to do so and so, not as though we *must*. And this makes it a service of perfect liberty; for it is always easy to do what we desire to do, let the accompanying circumstances be as difficult as they may. Every mother knows that she could secure perfect and easy obedience in her child if she could only get into that child's will and work it for him, making him want himself to do the things she willed he should. And this is what our Father, in the new dispensation, does for His children; He "writes his laws on our hearts and on our minds," so that our affection and our understanding embrace them, and we are *drawn* to obey instead of being *driven* to it.

The way in which the Holy Spirit, therefore, usually works, in a fully obedient soul, in regard to this direct guidance, is to impress upon the mind a wish or desire to do or to leave undone certain things.

The child of God when engaged in prayer feels, perhaps, a sudden suggestion made to his inmost consciousness in reference to a certain point of duty. "I would like to do this or the other," he thinks; "I wish I could." At once this matter should be committed to the Lord, with an instant consent of the will to obey Him, should the suggestion prove to be really from Him. And then the tests I have mentioned should be intelligently applied, namely, as to whether the suggestion is in accordance with the teaching of Scripture, with a sanctified judgment, and with providential circumstances. Often no distinct consciousness of this process is necessary, as our spiritual intelligence can see at a glance the right or wrong of the matter. But, however it may come, when the divine harmony is reached, and the divine sense of "oughtness" settles down on the heart, then an immediate obedience is the safest and easiest course. The first moment that we clearly see a thing to be right is always the moment when it is easy to do it. If we "let in the reasoner," as the Quakers express it, the golden opportunity is lost, and obedience becomes more and more difficult with every moment's delay. The old self-will wakens into life; and the energies that should have been occupied with obeying are absorbed instead in the struggle with doubts and reasonings.

It sometimes happens, however, that, in spite of all our efforts to discover the truth, the divine sense of "oughtness" does not seem to come, and our doubts and perplexities continue unenlightened. In addition to this our friends differ from us, and would, we know, oppose our course. In such a case there is nothing to do but to wait until the light comes. But we must wait in faith, and in an attitude of entire surrender, saying a continual "Yes" to the will of our Lord, let it be what it may. If the suggestion is from Him, it will continue and strengthen; if it is not from Him, it will disappear, and we shall almost forget we ever had it. If it continues, if every time we are brought into near communion with the Lord it seems to return, if it troubles us in our moments of prayer, and disturbs all our peace, and if finally it conforms to the test of the divine harmony of which I have spoken, we may then feel sure it is from God, and we must yield to it, or suffer an unspeakable loss.

The Apostle gives us a rule in reference to doubtful things which seems to me very explicit. He is speaking about certain kinds of meat-eating which were ceremonially unclean, and after declaring his own liberty says, "I know, and am persuaded by the Lord Jesus, that there is nothing unclean of itself; but to him that esteemeth anything to be unclean, to him it is unclean." And in summing up the whole subject he writes: "Hast thou faith? Have it to thyself before God. Happy is he that condemneth not himself in that thing which he alloweth. And he that doubteth is damned [condemned] if he eat, because he eateth not of faith: for whatsoever is not of faith is sin." In all doubtful things you must stand still and refrain from action until God gives you light to know more clearly His mind concerning them. Very often you will find that the doubt has been His voice calling upon you to come into more perfect conformity to His will; but sometimes these doubtful things are only temptations, or morbid feelings, to which it would be most unwise for you to yield, and the only safe way is to wait until you can act in faith, for "whatsoever is not of faith is sin."

Take all your present perplexities, then, to the Lord. Tell Him you only want to know and obey His voice, and ask Him to make it plain to you. Promise Him that you will obey, whatever it may be. Believe implicitly that He is guiding you, according to His word. In all doubtful things,

wait for clear light. Look and listen for His voice continually; and the moment you are sure of it, then, but not until then, yield an immediate obedience. Trust Him to
make you forget the impression if it is not His will; and
if it continues, and is in harmony with all His other
voices, do not be afraid to obey.

Above everything else, trust Him. Nowhere is faith more
needed than here. He has promised to guide. You have
asked Him to do it. And now you must believe that He
does, and must take what comes as being His guidance.
No earthly parent or master could guide his children or
servants if they should refuse to take his commands as
being really the expression of his will; and God *cannot*
guide those souls who never trust Him enough to believe
that He is doing it.

Above all, do not be afraid of this blessed life, lived
hour by hour and day by day under the guidance of thy
Lord! If He seeks to bring thee out of the world and into
very close conformity to Himself, do not shrink from it.
It is thy most blessed privilege. Rejoice in it. Embrace it
eagerly. Let everything go that it may be thine.

"God only is the creature's home,
    Though rough and strait the road;
Yet nothing else can satisfy
    The love that longs for God.

"How little of that road, my soul!
    How little hast thou gone!
Take heart, and let the thought of God
    Allure thee further on.

"Dole not thy duties out to God,
    But let thy hand be free;
Look long at Jesus,—His sweet love
    How was it dealt to thee?

"The perfect way is hard to flesh,
    It is not hard to love;
If thou wert sick for want of God,
    How swiftly wouldst thou move!

"And only this perfection needs
    A heart kept calm all day,
To catch the words the Spirit there
    From hour to hour may say.

"Then keep thy conscience sensitive,
   No inward token miss;
And go where grace entices thee,—
   Perfection lies in this.

"Be docile to thine unseen Guide,
   Love Him as He loves thee;
Time and obedience are enough,
   And thou a saint shall be."

Chapter Nine

Difficulties Concerning Doubts

A GREAT MANY CHRISTIANS ARE SLAVES TO AN IN-
veterate habit of doubting. I do not mean doubts as
to the existence of God or the truths of the Bible, but
doubts as to their own personal relations with the God in
whom they profess to believe, doubts as to the forgiveness of their sins, doubts as to their hopes of heaven, and
doubts about their own inward experience. No drunkard
was ever more in bondage to his habit of drink than they
are to their habit of doubting. Every step of their spiritual progress is taken against the fearful odds of an
army of doubts that are forever lying in wait to assail
them at each favorable moment. Their lives are made
wretched, their usefulness is effectually hindered, and
their communion with God is continually broken, by
their doubts. And although the entrance of the soul upon
the life of faith does, in many cases, take it altogether
out of the region where these doubts live and flourish, yet
even here it sometimes happens that the old tyrant will
rise up and reassert his sway, and will cause the feet to
stumble and the heart to fail, even when he cannot
succeed in utterly turning the believer back into the
dreary wilderness again.

We all of us remember, doubtless, our childish fascination, and yet horror, in the story of Christian's imprisonment in Doubting Castle by the wicked giant Despair,

and our exultant sympathy in his escape through those massive gates and from that cruel tyrant. Little did we suspect then that we should ever find ourselves taken prisoner by the same giant, and imprisoned in the same castle. But I fear that each one of us, if we were perfectly honest, would have to confess to at least one such experience, and some of us perhaps to a great many.

It seems strange that people whose very name of Believers implies that their one chiefest characteristic is that they believe, should have to confess that they have doubts. And yet it is such a universal habit, that I feel, if the name were to be given over again, the only fitting and descriptive name that could be given to many of God's children would have to be that of Doubters. In fact, most Christians have settled down under their doubts, as to a sort of inevitable malady, from which they suffer acutely, but to which they must try to be resigned as a part of the necessary discipline of this earthly life; and they lament over their doubts as a man might lament over his rheumatism, making themselves out as "interesting cases" of especial and peculiar trial which require the tenderest sympathy and the utmost consideration.

This is too often true even of believers who are earnestly longing to enter upon the life and walk of faith, and who have made, perhaps, many steps towards it. They have got rid, it may be, of the old doubts that once tormented them, as to whether their sins are really forgiven, and whether they shall, after all, get safe to heaven; but they have not got rid of doubting. They have simply shifted the habit to a higher platform. They are saying, perhaps, "Yes, I believe my sins are forgiven, and I am a child of God through faith in Jesus Christ. I dare not doubt this any more. But then—" and this "but then" includes an interminable array of doubts concerning most of the declarations and promises our Father has made to His children. One after another they fight with these promises, and refuse to believe them until they can have some more reliable proof of their being true than the simple word of their God; and then they wonder why they are permitted to walk in such darkness, and look upon themselves almost in the light of martyrs, and groan under the peculiar spiritual conflicts they are compelled to endure.

Spiritual conflicts! Far better would they be named

did we call them spiritual rebellions! Our fight is to be a fight of faith; and the moment we let in doubts, our fight ceases, and our rebellion begins.

I desire to put forth, if possible, a vigorous protest against this whole thing.

Just as well might I join in with the laments of a drunkard, and unite with him in prayer for grace to endure the discipline of his fatal appetite, as to give way for one instant to the weak complaints of these enslaved souls, and try to console them under their slavery. To one and to the other I would dare to do nothing else but proclaim the perfect deliverance which the Lord Jesus Christ has in store for them, and beseech, entreat, and importune them, with all the power at my command, to avail themselves of it and be free. Not for one moment would I listen to their despairing excuses. You ought to be free, you can be free, you must be free!

Will you undertake to tell me that it is an inevitable necessity for God to be doubted by His children? Is it an inevitable necessity for your children to doubt you? Would you tolerate their doubts a single hour? Would you pity your son, and condole with him, and feel that he was an "interesting case" if he should come to you and say, "Father, I am such a doubter that I cannot believe I am your child, or that you really love me"? And yet how often we hear a child of God excuse himself for his doubts by saying, "Oh, but I am such a doubter that I cannot believe in God's love and forgiveness"; and no one seems shocked at it. You might just as well say, with a like complacency, "Oh, but I am such a liar that I cannot help telling lies," and expect people to consider it a sufficient excuse. In the sight of God, I verily believe doubting is in some cases as displeasing as lying. It certainly is more dishonoring to Him, for it impugns His truthfulness and defames His character. John says that "he that believeth not God hath made him a liar," and it seems to me that hardly anything could be worse than thus to fasten on God the character of being a liar! Have you ever thought of *this* as the result of your doubting?

I remember seeing once the indignation and sorrow of a mother's heart deeply stirred by a little doubting on the part of one of her children. She had brought two little girls to my house, to leave them while she did some errands. One of them, with the happy confidence of childhood, abandoned herself to all the pleasures she could find in my nursery, and sang and played until her mother's return. The other one, with the wretched caution and mistrust of maturity, sat down alone in a corner, to wonder, first whether her mother would remember to come back for her, and to fear she would be forgotten, and then to imagine her mother would be glad of the chance to get rid of her anyhow, because she was such a naughty girl; and ended with working herself up into a perfect frenzy of despair. The look on that mother's face, when upon her return the weeping little girl told what was the matter with her, I shall not easily forget. Grief, wounded love, indignation, and pity all strove together for mastery; and the mother hardly knew who was most at fault, herself or the child, that such doubts should be possible.

Perhaps such doubts might be possible with an earthly mother, but never, never with God; and a hundred times in my life since, has that scene come up before me with deepest teaching, and has compelled me, peremptorily, to refuse admittance to the doubts about my Heavenly Father's love and care and remembrance of me that have clamored at the door of my heart for entrance.

Doubting is, I am convinced, to many people a real luxury, and to deny themselves this luxury would be the hardest piece of self-denial they have ever known. It is a luxury which, like the indulgence in some other luxuries, brings very sorrowful results; and perhaps, looking at the sadness and misery it has brought into your own Christian experience, you may be inclined to say, "Alas! it is no luxury to me, but only a fearful trial." But pause for a moment. Try giving it up, and you will soon find out whether it is a luxury or not. Do not your doubts come trooping to your door like a company of sympathizing friends who appreciate your hard case and have come to condole with you? And is it no luxury to sit down with them, and entertain them, and listen to their arguments, and join in with their condolences? Would it be no self-denial to turn resolutely from them, and refuse to hear a word they have to say? If you do not know, try it and see.

Have you never tasted the luxury of indulging in hard thoughts against those who have, as you think, injured you? Have you never known what a positive fascination it is to brood over their unkindnesses, and to pry into their malice, and to imagine all sorts of wrong and uncomfortable things about them? It has made you wretched, of course; but it has been a fascinating sort of wretchedness, that you could not easily give up.

Just like this is the luxury of doubting. Things have gone wrong with you in your experience. Dispensations have been mysterious, temptations have been peculiar, your "case" has seemed different from others. What more natural than to conclude that for some reason God has forsaken you, and does not love you, and is indifferent to your welfare? How irresistible is the conviction that you are too wicked for Him to care for, or too difficult for Him to manage!

You do not mean to blame Him, or accuse Him of injustice, for you feel that His indifference and rejection of you are, because of your unworthiness, fully deserved; and this very subterfuge leaves you at liberty, under the guise of a just and true appreciation of your own shortcomings, to indulge in your dishonoring doubts. Although you think it is yourself you are doubting, you are really doubting the Lord, and are indulging in as hard and wrong thoughts of Him as ever you did of a human enemy. For He declares that He came to save, not the righteous, but sinners; and your very sinfulness and unworthiness, instead of being a reason why He should not love you and care for you, are really your chiefest claim upon His love and His care.

As well might the poor little lamb that has wandered from the flock and got lost in the wilderness say, "I am lost, and therefore the Shepherd cannot love me, nor care for me, nor remember me; he only loves and cares for the lambs that never wander." As well might the ill man say, "I am ill, and therefore the doctor will not come to see me, nor give me any medicine; he only cares for and visits well people." Jesus says, "They that are whole need not a physician, but they that are sick." And again He says, "What man of you, having an hundred sheep, if he lose one of them, doth not leave the ninety and nine in the wilderness, and go after that which is lost until he find it?" Any thoughts of Him, therefore, that are different from this which He Himself has said, are hard thoughts; and to indulge in them is far worse than to indulge in hard thoughts of any earthly friend or foe. From beginning to end of your Christian life it is always sinful to indulge in doubts. Doubts and discouragements are all from an evil source, and are always untrue. A direct and emphatic denial is the only way to meet them.

This brings me to the practical part of the whole subject, as to how to get deliverance from this fatal habit. My answer would be that the deliverance from this must be by the same means as the deliverance from any other sin. It is to be found in Christ, and in Him only. You must hand your doubting over to Him as you have learned to hand your other temptations. You must do with it just what you do with your temper or your pride; that is, you must give it up to the Lord. I believe myself the only effectual remedy is to take a pledge against it as you would urge a drunkard to do against drink, trusting in the Lord alone to keep you steadfast.

Like any other sin, the stronghold is in the will, and the will or purpose to doubt must be surrendered exactly as you surrender the will or purpose to yield to any other temptation. God always take possession of a surrendered will; and if we come to the point of saying that we will not doubt, and surrender this central fortress of our nature to Him, His blessed Spirit will begin at once to "work in us all the good pleasure of his will," and we shall find ourselves kept from doubting by His mighty and overcoming power.

The trouble is, that in this matter of doubting the Christian does not always make a full surrender, but is apt to reserve a little secret liberty to doubt, looking upon it as being sometimes a necessity.

"I do not want to doubt any more," we will say, or, "I hope I shall not"; but it is hard to come to the point of saying, "I *will* not doubt again," and no surrender is effectual until it reaches the point of saying, "I will not." The liberty to doubt must be given up forever; and we must consent to a continuous life of inevitable trust. It is often necessary, I think, to make a definite transaction of this surrender of doubting, and come to a point about it. I believe it is quite as necessary in the case of a doubter as in the case of a drunkard. It will not do to give it up by degrees. The total-abstinence principle is the only effectual one here.

Then, the surrender once made, we must rest absolutely upon the Lord for deliverance in each time of temptation. The moment the assault comes, we must lift up the shield of faith against it. We must hand the very first suggestion of doubt over to the Lord, and must let Him manage it. We must refuse to entertain the doubt a single moment. Let it come ever so plausibly, or under whatever guise of humility, we must simply say, "I dare not doubt; I must trust. God *is* my Father, and He does love me. Jesus saves me; He saves me now." Those three little words, repeated over and over, "Jesus saves me, Jesus saves me," will put to flight the greatest army of doubts that ever assaulted any soul. I have tried it times without number, and have never known it to fail. Do not stop to argue out the matter with yourself or with your doubts. Pay no attention to them whatever, but treat them with the utmost contempt. Shut your door in their very face, and emphatically deny every word they say to you. Bring up some "It is written," and hurl it after them. Look right at Jesus, and tell Him that you do trust Him, and that you intend to go on trusting Him. Then let the doubts clamor as they may, they cannot hurt you if you will not let them in.

I know it will look to you sometimes as though you were shutting your door against your best friends, and your hearts will long after your doubts more than ever the Israelites longed after the flesh-pots of Egypt. But deny yourself; take up your cross in this matter, and quietly but firmly refuse ever to listen to a single word.

Often has it happened to me to find, on awaking in the morning, a perfect army of doubts clamoring at my door for admittance. Nothing has seemed real, nothing has seemed true; and least of all has it seemed possible that I—miserable, wretched I—could be the object of the Lord's love, or care, or notice. If I only had been at liberty to let these doubts in, and invite them to take seats and make themselves at home, what a luxury I should many times have felt it to be! But years ago I made a pledge against doubting, and I would as soon think of violating my pledge against intoxicating liquor as of violating this one. I have never dared to admit the first doubt. At such times, therefore, I have been compelled to lift up the "shield of faith" the moment I have become conscious of these suggestions of doubt; and handing the whole army over to the Lord to conquer, I have begun to assert, over and over, my faith in Him, in the simple words, "God *is* my Father; I *am* His forgiven child; He *does* love me; Jesus saves me; Jesus saves me now!" The victory has always been complete. The enemy has come in like a flood, but the "Spirit of the Lord has lifted up a standard against him," and my doubts have been put to flight. And I have been able to join in the song of Moses and the children of Israel, saying, "I will sing unto the Lord, for he hath triumphed gloriously: the horse and his rider hath he thrown into the sea. The Lord is my strength and song, and he is become my salvation."

Dear doubting souls, go and do likewise, and a similar victory shall be yours. You may think, perhaps, that doubts are a necessity in your case, owing to the peculiarity of your temperament; but I assure you most emphatically that this is not so. You are no more under a necessity to be doubtful as to your relationships to your Heavenly Father than you are to be doubtful as to your relationships to your earthly father. In both cases the thing you must depend on is their word, not your feelings; and no earthly father has ever declared or manifested his fatherhood one thousandth part as unmistakably or as lovingly as your Heavenly Father has declared and manifested His. If you would not "make God a liar," therefore, you must make your believing as inevitable and necessary a thing as your obedience. You would obey God, I believe, even though you should die in the act. Believe Him, also, even though the effort to believe should cost you your life. The conflict may be very severe; it may seem at times unendurable. But let your unchanging declaration be from henceforth, "Though he slay me, yet will I trust in him." When doubts come, meet them, not with arguments, but with assertions of faith. All doubts are an attack of the enemy; the Holy Spirit never suggests them, never. He is the Comforter, not the Accuser; and He never shows us our need without at the same time revealing the Divine supply.

Do not give heed to your doubts, therefore, for a moment. Turn from them with horror, as you would from blasphemy; for they *are* blasphemy. You cannot perhaps hinder the suggestions of doubt from coming to you any more than you can hinder the boys in the street from swearing as you go by; and consequently you are not sinning in the one case any more than in the other. But just as you can refuse to listen to the boys or join in their oaths, so can you also refuse to listen to the doubts or join in with them. They are not *your* doubts until you consent to them and adopt them as true. When they come you must at once turn from them as you would from swearing. Often a very good practical way of getting rid of them is to go at once and confess your faith, in the strongest language possible, somewhere or to someone. If you can-

not do this by word of mouth, write it in a letter, or repeat it over and over in your heart to the Lord.

As you lay down this book, therefore, take up your pen
and write out your determination never to doubt again.
Make it a real transaction between your soul and the
Lord. Give up your liberty to doubt forever. Put your will
in this matter over on the Lord's side, and trust Him to
keep you from falling. Tell Him all about your utter
weakness and your long-encouraged habits of doubt, and
how helpless you are before it, and commit the whole
battle to Him. Tell Him you *will* not doubt again, putting
forth all your will power on His side, and against
His enemy and yours; and then, henceforward, keep your
face steadfastly "looking unto Jesus," away from yourself
and away from your doubts, holding fast the profession
of your faith without wavering, because "he is faithful
who hath promised." Rely on *His* faithfulness, not on
your own. You have committed the keeping of your soul
to Him as unto a "faithful Creator," and you must never
again admit the possibility of His being unfaithful. Believe He is faithful, not because you feel it, or see it, but
because He says He is. Believe it, whether you feel it or not.
Believe it, even when it seems to you that you are believing something that is absolutely untrue. Believe it actively, and believe it persistently. Cultivate a continuous
habit of believing, and never let your faith waver for any
"seeming," however plausible it may be. The result will
be that sooner or later you will come to *know* that it is
true, and all doubts will vanish in the blaze of the glory of
the absolute faithfulness of God!

It is an inexorable rule in the spiritual life that according to our faith it is to be unto us; and of course this rule
must work both ways, and therefore we may fairly expect
that it will be also unto us according to our doubts.

Doubts and discouragements are, I believe, inlets by
which evil enters, while faith is an impregnable wall
against all evil.

Dear doubting souls, my heart yearns over you with a
tender sympathy! I know your sincerity and your earnestness, and your struggles after an abiding experience
of peace with God, through the Lord Jesus Christ: and I
know also how effectually your fatal habit of doubting has
held you back. I would that my words might open your
eyes to see the deliverance that lies at your very door.
Try my plan, I beseech of you, and see if it will not be

true, that "according to your faith" it shall inevitably be unto you.

Chapter Ten

Difficulties Concerning Temptation

CERTAIN VERY GREAT MISTAKES ARE MADE CONCERNING this matter of temptation in the practical working out of the life of faith.

First of all, people seem to expect, that, after the soul has entered into rest in the Lord, temptations will cease; and they think that the promised deliverance is to be not only from yielding to temptation, but even also from being tempted. Consequently, when they find the "Canaanite still in the land," and see the "cities great and walled up to heaven," they are utterly discouraged, and think they must have gone wrong in some way, and that this cannot be the true land, after all.

Then, next, they make the mistake of looking upon temptation as sin, and of blaming themselves for suggestions of evil, even while they abhor them. This brings them into condemnation and discouragement; and discouragement, if continued in, always ends at last in actual sin. Sin makes an easy prey of a discouraged soul; so that we fall often from the very fear of having fallen.

To meet the first of these difficulties, it is only necessary to refer to the Scripture declarations which state that the Christian life is to be throughout a warfare; and that it is to be especially so when we are "seated in heavenly places in Christ Jesus," and are called to wrestle against spiritual enemies, whose power and skill to tempt us must doubtless be far superior to any we have heretofore encountered. As a fact, temptations generally increase in strength tenfold, after we have entered into the interior life, rather than decrease; and no amount or sort of them must ever for a moment lead us to suppose we have not really found the true abiding place. Strong temptations are often more a sign of great grace than of little grace. When the children of Israel had first left Egypt, the

Lord did not lead them through the country of the Philistines, although that was the nearest way; "for God said, Lest peradventure the people repent when they see war, and they return to Egypt." But afterwards, when they had learned how to trust Him better, He permitted their enemies to attack them. Moreover, even in their wilderness journey they met with but few enemies, and fought but few battles, compared to those they encountered in the land of Canaan, where they found seven great nations and thirty-one kings to be conquered, besides walled cities to be taken, and giants to be overcome.

They could not have fought with the "Canaanites, and the Hittites, and the Amorites, and the Perizzites, and the Hivites, and the Jebusites," until they had gone into the land where these enemies were. The very power of your temptations, dear Christian, therefore, may perhaps be one of the strongest proofs that you really are in the land of promise you have been seeking to enter, because they are temptations peculiar to that land; consequently you must never allow them to cause you to question the fact of your having entered it.

The second mistake is not quite so easy to deal with. It seems hardly worth while to say that temptation is not sin, and yet much distress arises from not understanding this fact. The very suggestion of wrong seems to bring pollution with it; and the poor tempted soul begins to feel as if it must be very bad indeed, and very far off from God, to have had such thoughts and suggestions. It is as though a burglar should break into a man's house to steal, and, when the master of the house begins to resist him and drive him out, should turn round and accuse the owner of being himself the thief. It is the enemy's grand ruse for entrapping us. He comes and whispers suggestions of evil to us,—doubts, blasphemies, jealousies, envyings, and pride,—and then turns round and says, "Oh, how wicked you must be to think such things! It is very plain that you are not trusting the Lord; for if you had been, it would be impossible for these things to have entered your heart." This reasoning sounds so very plausible that we often accept it as true, and so come under condemnation, and are filled with discouragement; and then it is easy for temptation to develop into actual sin. One of the most fatal things in the life of faith is discouragement; one of the most helpful is confidence. A very wise man once said that in overcoming temptations confidence was

the first thing, confidence the second, and confidence
the third. We must *expect* to conquer. That is why the
Lord said so often to Joshua, "Be strong and of a good
courage"; "Be not afraid, neither be thou dismayed";
"Only be thou strong and very courageous." And it is also
the reason He says to us, "Let not your heart be troubled,
neither let it be afraid." The power of temptation is in the
fainting of our own hearts. The enemy knows this well,
and he always begins his assaults by discouraging us, if
he can in any way accomplish it.

This discouragement arises sometimes from what we
think is a righteous grief and disgust at ourselves that
such things *could* be any temptation to us, but which is
really mortification coming from the fact that we have
been indulging in a secret self-congratulation that our
tastes were too pure, or our separation from the world
was too complete, for such things to tempt us. We are
discouraged because we have expected something from
ourselves, and have been sorely disappointed not to find
that something there. This mortification and discouragement, though they present an appearance of true humility, are really a far worse condition than the temptation
itself, for they are nothing but the results of wounded
self-love. True humility can bear to see its own utter
weakness and foolishness revealed, because it never expected anything from itself, and knows that its only hope
and expectation must be in God. Therefore, instead of
discouraging the humble soul from trusting, such revela-
tions drive it to a deeper and more utter trust. But the
counterfeit humility that self-love produces plunges the
soul into the depths of a faithless discouragement, and
drives it into the very sin with which it is so distressed.

There is an allegory that illustrates this to me wonderfully. Satan called together a council of his servants to
consult how they might make a good man sin. One evil
spirit started up and said, "I will make him sin." "How
will you do it?" asked Satan. "I will set before him the
pleasures of sin," was the reply; "I will tell him of its
delights, and the rich rewards it brings." "Ah," said Satan, "that will not do; he has tried it, and knows better
than that." Then another imp started up and said, "I
will make him sin." "What will you do?" asked Satan. "I
will tell him of the pains and sorrows of virtue. I will
show him that virtue has no delights, and brings no rewards." "Ah, no!" exclaimed Satan, "that will not do at

all; for he has tried it, and knows that 'Wisdom's ways *are* ways of pleasantness, and all her paths are peace.' " "Well," said another imp, starting up, "I will undertake to make him sin." "And what will you do?" asked Satan, again. "I will discourage his soul," was the short reply. "Ah, that will do!" cried Satan; "that will do! We shall conquer him now."

An old writer says, "All discouragement is from the devil;" and I wish every Christian would take this as a motto, and would realize that he must fly from discouragement as he would from sin.

But if we fail to recognize the truth about temptation, this is impossible; for if the temptations are our own fault, we cannot help being discouraged. But they are not. The Bible says, "Blessed is the man that endureth temptation"; and we are exhorted to "count it all joy when we fall into divers temptations." Temptation, therefore, cannot be sin; and the truth is, it is no more a sin to hear these whispers and suggestions of evil in our souls than it is for us to hear the wicked talk of bad men as we pass along the street. The sin comes, in either case, only by our stopping and joining in with them. If, when the wicked suggestions come, we turn from them at once, as we would from wicked talk, and pay no more attention to them than we would to the talk, we do not sin. But if we carry them on in our minds, and roll them under our tongues, and dwell on them with a half consent of our will to them as true, then we sin. We may be enticed by temptations a thousand times a day without sin, and we cannot help these enticings, and are not to blame for them. But if we begin to think that these enticings are actual sin on our part, then the battle is half lost already, and the sin can hardly fail to gain a complete victory.

A dear lady once came to me under great darkness, simply from not understanding this. She had been living very happily in the life of faith for some time, and had been so free from temptations as almost to begin to think she would never be tempted again. But suddenly a very peculiar form of temptation had assailed her, which had horrified her. She found that the moment she began to pray, dreadful thoughts of all kinds would rush into her mind. She had lived a very sheltered, innocent life; and these thoughts seemed so awful to her that she felt she must be one of the most wicked of sinners to be capable of having them. She began by thinking that she could not possibly have entered into the rest of faith, and ended by concluding that she had never even been born again. Her soul was in an agony of distress. I told her that these dreadful thoughts were purely and simply temptations, and that she herself was not to blame for them at all; that she could not help them any more than she could help hearing if a wicked man should pour out his blasphemies in her presence. And I urged her to recognize and treat them as temptations only, and not to blame herself or be discouraged, but rather to turn at once to the Lord and commit them to Him. I showed her how great an advantage the enemy had gained by making her think these thoughts were originated by herself, and by plunging her into condemnation and discouragement on account of them. And I assured her she would find a speedy victory if she would pay no attention to them; but, ignoring their presence, would simply turn her back on them and look to the Lord.

She grasped the truth, and the next time these blasphemous thoughts came, she said inwardly to the enemy, "I have found you out now. It is you who are suggesting these dreadful thoughts to me, and I hate them, and will have nothing to do with them. The Lord is my helper; take them to Him, and settle them in His presence." Immediately the baffled enemy, finding himself discovered, fled in confusion, and her soul was perfectly delivered.

Another thing also. Our spiritual enemies know that if a Christian recognizes a suggestion of evil as coming from them, he will recoil from it far more quickly than if it seems to be the suggestion of his own mind. If the devil prefaced each temptation with the words "I am the devil, your relentless enemy; I have come to make you sin," I suppose we would hardly feel any desire at all to yield to his suggestions. He has to hide himself in order to make his baits attractive. And our victory will be far more easily gained if we are not ignorant of his devices, but recognize them at his very first approach.

We also make another great mistake about temptations in thinking that all time spent in combating them is lost. Hours pass, and we seem to have made no progress, because we have been so beset with temptations. But it often happens that we have been serving God far more truly during these hours than in our times of comparative freedom from temptation. For we are fighting our Lord's battles when we are fighting temptation, and hours are often worth days to us under these circumstances. We read, "Blessed is the man that *endureth* temptation," and I am sure this means enduring the continuance of it and its frequent recurrence. Nothing so cultivates the grace of patience as the endurance of temptation, and nothing so drives the soul to an utter dependence upon the Lord Jesus as its continuance. And finally, nothing brings more praise and honor and glory to our Lord Himself than the trial of our faith that comes through manifold temptations. We are told that it is "more precious than gold, though it be tried with fire," and that we, who patiently endure the trial, shall receive for our reward "the crown of life which the Lord hath promised to them that love him."

We cannot wonder, therefore, any longer at the exhortation with which the Holy Ghost opens the Book of James: "Count it all joy when ye fall into divers temptations; knowing this, that the trying of your faith worketh patience. But let patience have her perfect work, that ye may be perfect and entire, wanting nothing."

Temptation is plainly one of the instruments used by God to complete our perfection; and thus sin's own weapons are turned against itself, and we see how it is that all things, even temptations, can work together for good to them that love God.

As to the way of victory over temptation, it seems hardly necessary to say to those whom I am at this time especially addressing, that it is to be by faith; for this is, of course, the foundation upon which the whole interior life rests. Our one great motto is throughout, "We are nothing: Christ is all"; and always and everywhere we have started to stand, and walk, and overcome, and live by faith. We have discovered our own utter helplessness, and know that we cannot do anything for ourselves; and we have learned that our only way, therefore, is to hand the temptation over to our Lord, and trust Him to conquer it for us. But when we put it into His hands we must *leave* it there. The greatest difficulty of all is, I think, this *leaving*. It seems impossible to believe that the Lord can or will manage our temptations without our help, especially if they do not immediately disappear. To go on patiently "enduring" the continuance of a temptation without yielding to it, and also without snatching ourselves out of the Lord's hands in regard to it, is a wonderful victory for our impatient natures; but it is a victory we must gain, if we would do what will please God.

We must then commit ourselves as really to the Lord for victory over our temptations, as we committed ourselves at first for forgiveness; and we must leave ourselves just as utterly in His hands for one as for the other.

Thousands of God's children have done this, and can testify to-day that marvelous victories have been gained for them over numberless temptations, and that they have in very truth been made "more than conquerors" through Him who loves them.

But into this part of the subject I cannot go at present, as my object has been rather to present temptation in its true light than to develop the way of victory over it. I desire greatly that conscientious, faithful souls should be delivered from the bondage into which they are sure to be brought if they fail to understand the true nature and use of temptation, and confound it with sin. When temptation is recognized *as* temptation, we shall be able to say at once, "Get thee behind me," and shall walk even through the midst of the fiercest assaults with unclouded and triumphant peace; knowing that, "when the enemy shall come in like a flood, the Spirit of the Lord shall lift up a standard against him."

Chapter Eleven

Difficulties Concerning Failures

THE VERY TITLE OF THIS CHAPTER MAY PERHAPS STARTLE some. "Failures!" they will say; "we thought there were no failures in this life of faith."

To this I would answer that there ought not to be, and need not be; but, as a fact, there sometimes are, and we must deal with facts, and not with theories. No safe teacher of this interior life ever says that it becomes impossible to sin; they only insist that sin ceases to be a necessity, and that a possibility of continual victory is opened before us. And there are very few, if any, who do not confess that, as to their own actual experience, they have at times been overcome by at least a momentary temptation.

Of course, in speaking of sin here, I mean conscious, known sin. I do not touch on the subject of sins of ignorance, or what are called the inevitable sins of our nature, which are all met by the provisions of Christ, and do not disturb our fellowship with God. I have no desire or ability to treat of the doctrines concerning sin; these I will leave with the theologians to discuss and settle, while I speak only of the believer's experience in the matter.

There are many things which we do innocently enough until an increasing light shows them to be wrong, and these may all be classed under sins of ignorance; but because they are done in ignorance they do not bring us under condemnation, and do not come within the range of the present discussion.

An illustration of this occurred once in my presence. A little baby girl was playing about the library one warm summer afternoon, while her father was resting on the lounge. A pretty inkstand on the table took the child's fancy, and, unnoticed by any one, she climbed on a chair and secured it. Then, walking over to her father with an air of childish triumph, she turned it upside down on the white expanse of his shirt bosom, and laughed with glee as she saw the black streams trickling down on every side.

This was a very wrong thing for the child to do, but it could not be called sin, for she knew no better. Had she been older, and been made to understand that inkstands were not playthings, it would have been sin. "To him that knoweth to do good and doeth it not, to him it is sin"; and in all I shall say concerning sin in this chapter I desire it to be fully understood that I have reference simply to that which comes within the range of our consciousness.

Misunderstanding, then, on this point of known or conscious sin, opens the way for great dangers in the life of faith. When a believer who has, as he trusts, entered upon the highway of holiness, finds himself surprised into sin, he is tempted either to be utterly discouraged, and to give everything up as lost; or else in order to preserve the doctrines untouched, he feels it necessary to cover his sin up, calling it infirmity, and refusing to be candid and aboveboard about it. Either of these courses is equally fatal to any real growth and progress in the life of holiness.

The only way is to face the sad fact at once, call the thing by its right name, and discover, if possible, the reason and the remedy. This life of union with God requires the utmost honesty with Him and with ourselves. The blessing that the sin itself would only momentarily disturb, is sure to be lost by any dishonest dealing with it. A sudden failure is no reason for being discouraged and giving up all as lost. Neither is the integrity of our doctrine touched by it. We are not preaching a *state*, but a *walk*. The highway of holiness is not a *place*, but a *way*. Sanctification is not a thing to be picked up at a certain stage of our experience, and forever after possessed, but it is a life to be lived day by day, and hour by hour. We may for a moment turn aside from a path, but the path is not obliterated by our wandering, and can be instantly regained. And in this life and walk of faith, there may be momentary failures that, although very sad and greatly to be deplored, need not, if rightly met, disturb the attitude of the soul as to entire consecration and perfect trust, nor interrupt, for more than the passing moment, its happy communion with its Lord.

The great point is an instant return to God. Our sin is no reason for ceasing to trust, but only an unanswerable argument why we must trust more fully than ever. From whatever cause we have been betrayed into failure, it is very certain that there is no remedy to be found in discouragement. As well might a child who is learning to walk, lie down in despair when he has fallen, and refuse to take another step, as a believer, who is seeking to learn how to live and walk by faith, give up in despair because of having fallen into sin. The only way in both cases is to get right up and try again. When the children of Israel had met with that disastrous defeat, soon after their entrance into the land, before the little city of Ai, they were all so utterly discouraged that we read: "Wherefore the hearts of the people melted, and became as water. And Joshua rent his clothes, and fell to the earth upon his face before the ark of the Lord until the eventide, he and the elders of Israel, and put dust upon their heads. And Joshua said, Alas, O Lord God, wherefore hast thou at all brought this people over Jordan, to deliver us into the hand of the Amorites, to destroy us? Would to God we had been content, and dwelt on the other side Jordan! O Lord, what shall I say, when Israel turneth their backs before their enemies! For the Canaanites and all the inhabitants of the land shall hear of it, and shall environ us round, and cut off our name from the earth: and what wilt thou do unto thy great name?"

What a wail of despair this was! And how exactly it is repeated by many a child of God in the present day, whose heart, because of a defeat, melts and becomes as water, and who cries out, "Would to God we had been content and dwelt on the other side Jordan!" and predicts for itself further failures and even utter discomfiture before its enemies. No doubt Joshua thought then, as we are apt to think now, that discouragement and despair were the only proper and safe condition after such a failure. But God thought otherwise. "And the Lord said unto Joshua, Get thee up; wherefore liest thou upon thy face?" The proper thing to do, was not to abandon themselves thus to utter discouragement, humble as it might look, but at once to face the evil and get rid of it, and afresh and immediately to "sanctify themselves."

"Up, sanctify the people," is always God's command. "Lie down and be discouraged," is always our temptation. Our feeling is that it is presumptuous, and even almost impertinent, to go at once to the Lord, after having sinned against Him. It seems as if we ought to suffer the consequences of our sin first for a little while, and endure the accusings of our conscience; and we can hardly believe that the Lord *can* be willing at once to receive us back into loving fellowship with Himself.

A little girl once expressed this feeling to me, with a child's outspoken candor. She had asked whether the Lord Jesus always forgave us for our sins as soon as we asked Him, and I had said, "Yes, of course He does." "*Just* as soon?" she repeated doubtingly. "Yes," I replied, "the very minute we ask, He forgives us." "Well," she said deliberately, "I cannot believe that. I should think He would make us feel sorry for two or three days first. And then I should think He would make us ask Him a great many times, and in a very pretty way too, not just in common talk. And I believe that *is* the way He does, and you need not try to make me think He forgives me right at once, no matter what the Bible says." She only *said* what most Christians *think*, and what is worse, what most Christians act on, making their discouragement and their very remorse separate them infinitely further off from God than their sin would have done. Yet it is so totally contrary to the way we like our children to act to-

ward us, that I wonder how we ever could have conceived such an idea of God. How a mother grieves when
a naughty child goes off alone in despairing remorse, and
doubts her willingness to forgive; and how, on the other
hand, her whole heart goes out in welcoming love to the
repentant little one who runs to her at once and begs her
forgiveness! Surely our God felt this yearning love when
He said to us, "Return, ye backsliding children, and I
will heal your backslidings."

The fact is, that the same moment which brings the
consciousness of sin ought to bring also the confession
and the consciousness of forgiveness. This is especially
essential to an unwavering walk in the "life hid with
Christ in God," for no separation from Him can be toler-
ated here for an instant.

We can only walk this path by "looking continually
unto Jesus," moment by moment; and if our eyes are
turned away from Him to look upon our own sin and our
own weakness, we shall leave the path at once. The believer, therefore, who has, as he trusts, entered upon this
highway, if he finds himself overcome by sin, must flee
with it instantly to the Lord. He must act on I John 1: 9,
"If we confess our sins, He is faithful and just to forgive
us our sins, and to cleanse us from all unrighteousness."
He must not hide his sin, and seek to salve it over with
excuses, or to push it out of his memory by the lapse of
time. But he must do as the children of Israel did, rise
up *early* in the morning," and *"run"* to the place where
the evil thing is hidden, and take it out of its hiding-
place, and lay it "out before the Lord." He must confess his sin. And then he must stone it with stones, and
burn it with fire, and utterly put it away from him, and
raise over it a great heap of stones, that it may be forever
hidden from his sight. And he must believe, then and there,
that God *is,* according to His word, faithful and just
to forgive him his sin, and that He does do it; and
further, that He also cleanses him from all unrighteousness. He must claim by faith an immediate forgiveness
and an immediate cleansing, and must go on trusting
harder and more absolutely than ever.

As soon as Israel's sin had been brought to light and
put away, at once God's word came again in a message of
glorious encouragement: "Fear not, neither be thou dismayed. . . . See, I have given into thy hand the king of
Ai, and his people, and his city, and his land." Our

courage must rise higher than ever, and we must abandon ourselves more completely to the Lord, that His mighty power may the more perfectly "work in us all the good pleasure of His will." Moreover, we must forget our sin as soon as it is thus confessed and forgiven. We must not dwell on it, and examine it, and indulge in a luxury of distress and remorse. We must not put it on a pedestal, and then walk around it and view it on every side, and so magnify it into a mountain that hides God from our eyes. We must follow the example of Paul, and, "forgetting those things which are behind, and reaching forth unto those things which are before," we must "press toward the mark for the prize of the high calling of God in Christ Jesus."

Let me recall two contrasting illustrations of these things. One was an earnest Christian man, an active worker in the Church, who had been living for several months in an experience of great peace and joy. He was suddenly overcome by a temptation to treat a brother unkindly. Having supposed it to be an impossibility that he could ever so sin again, he was plunged at once into the deepest discouragement, and concluded he had been altogether mistaken, and had never entered into the life of full trust at all. Day by day his discouragement increased until it became despair, and he concluded at last that he had never even been born again, and gave himself up for lost. He spent three years of utter misery, going farther and farther away from God, and being gradually drawn off into one sin after another, until his life was a curse to himself and to all around him. His health failed under the terrible burden, and fears were entertained for his reason. At the end of three years he met a Christian lady, who understood this truth about sin that I have been trying to explain. In a few moments' conversation she found out his trouble, and at once said, "You sinned in that act, there is no doubt about it, and I do not want you to try to excuse it. But have you never confessed it to the Lord and asked Him to forgive you?" "Confessed it!" he exclaimed. "Why, it seems to me I have done nothing but confess it, and entreat God to forgive me, night and day, for all these three dreadful years." "And you have never believed He did forgive you?" asked the lady. "No," said the poor man, "how could I, for I never *felt* as if He did?" "But suppose He had said He forgave you, would not that have done as well as for you to feel it?" "Oh, yes,"

replied the man; "if God said it, of course I would believe
it." "Very well, He does say so," was the lady's answer;
and she turned to the verse we have taken above (I John
1: 9) and read it aloud. "Now," she continued, "you
have been all these three years confessing and confessing
your sin, and all the while God's record has been declaring that He was faithful and just to forgive it and to
cleanse you, and yet you have never once believed it. You
have been 'making God a liar' all this while by refusing to
believe His record."

The poor man saw the whole thing, and was dumb
with amazement and consternation; and when the lady
proposed that they should kneel down, and that he
should confess his past unbelief and sin, and should
claim, then and there, a present forgiveness and a present
cleansing, he obeyed like one in a maze. But the result
was glorious. The light broke in, his darkness vanished,
and he began aloud to praise God for the wonderful deliverance. In a few minutes his soul was enabled to traverse back by faith the whole long, weary journey that he
had been three years in making, and he found himself
once more resting in the Lord, and rejoicing in the fulness
of His Salvation.

The other illustration was the case of a Christian lady,
who had been living in the land of promise a few weeks,
and who had had a very bright and victorious experience.
Suddenly at the end of that time, she was overcome by a
violent burst of anger. For a moment a flood of discouragement swept over her soul. The temptation came, "There
now, that shows it was all a mistake. Of course you have
been deceived about the whole thing, and have never
entered into the life of faith at all. And now you may as
well give up altogether, for you never can consecrate yourself any more entirely nor trust any more fully than
you did this time; so it is very plain this life of holiness is
not for you!" These thoughts flashed through her mind
in a moment; but she was well taught in the ways of
God, and she said at once, "Yes, I have sinned, and it is
very sad. But the Bible says that, if we confess our sins,
God is faithful and just to forgive us our sins, and to
cleanse us from all unrighteousness; and I believe He will
do it." She did not delay a moment, but, while still boiling
over with anger, she ran (for she could not walk) into a
room where she could be alone, and kneeling down beside the bed she said, "Lord, I confess my sin. I have

sinned; I am even at this very moment sinning. I hate it, but I cannot get rid of it. I confess it with shame and confusion of face to thee. And now I believe that, according to thy word, thou dost forgive and thou dost cleanse." She said it out loud, for the inward turmoil was too great for it to be said inside. As the words, "Thou dost forgive and thou dost cleanse," passed her lips, the deliverance came. The Lord said, "Peace, be still!" and there was a great calm. A flood of light and joy burst on her soul, the enemy fled, and she was more than conquered through Him that loved her. The whole thing, the sin and the recovery from it, had occupied not five minutes, and her feet trod more firmly than ever in the blessed highway of holiness. Thus the "valley of Achor" became to her a "door of hope," and she sang afresh and with deeper meaning her song of deliverance, "I will sing unto the Lord, for he hath triumphed gloriously."

The truth is, the only remedy, after all, in every emergency is to trust in the Lord. And if this is all we ought to do, and all we can do, is it not better to do it at once? I have often been brought to a stand by the question, "Well, what *can* I do but trust?" And I have realized at once the folly of seeking for deliverance in any other way by saying to myself, "I shall have to come to simple trusting in the end, and why not come to it at once, now in the beginning." It is a life and walk of *faith* we have entered upon; and if we fail in it, our only recovery must lie in an increase of faith, not in a lessening of it.

Let every failure, then, if any occur, drive you instantly to the Lord, with a more complete abandonment and a more perfect trust; and if you do this, you will find that, sad as it is, your failure has not taken you out of the land of rest, nor broken for long your sweet communion with Him.

Where failure is thus met, a recurrence is far more likely to be prevented than where the soul allows itself to pass through a season of despair and remorse. If it should however sometimes recur, and is always similarly treated, it is sure to become less and less frequent, until finally it ceases altogether. There are some happy souls who learn the whole lesson at once; but the blessing is also upon those who take slower steps and gain a more gradual victory.

Having shown the way of deliverance from failure, I would now say a little as to the causes of failure in this life of full salvation. The causes do not lie in the strength of the temptation, nor in our own weakness, nor above all in any lack in the power or willingness of our Saviour to save us. The promise to Israel was positive: "There shall not any man be able to stand before thee all the days of thy life." And the promise to us is equally positive: "God is faithful, who will not suffer you to be tempted above that ye are able; but will with the temptation also make a way to escape, that ye may be able to bear it." The men of Ai were "but few," and yet the people who had conquered the mighty Jericho "fled before the men of Ai." It was not the strength of their enemy, neither had God failed them. The cause of their defeat lay somewhere else, and the Lord Himself declares it: "Israel hath sinned, and they have also transgressed my covenant which I commanded them: for they have even taken of the accursed thing, and have also stolen, and dissembled also, and they have put it even among their own stuff. Therefore the children of Israel could not stand before their enemies, but turned their backs before their enemies." It was a hidden evil that conquered them. Buried under the earth, in an obscure tent in that vast army, was hidden something against which God had a controversy; and this little hidden thing made the whole army helpless before their enemies. "There is an accursed thing in the midst of thee, O Israel: thou canst not stand before thine enemies until ye take away the accursed thing from among you."

The lesson here is simply this, that anything cherished in the heart which is contrary to the will of God, let it seem ever so insignificant, or be ever so deeply hidden, will cause us to fall before our enemies. Any conscious root of bitterness cherished toward another, any self-seeking, any harsh judgments, any slackness in obeying the voice of the Lord, any doubtful habits or surroundings,—these things or any one of them, consciously indulged, will effectually cripple and paralyze our spiritual life. We may have hidden the evil in the remote corner of our hearts, and may have covered it over from our sight, refusing even to recognize its existence, although we cannot help being all the time secretly aware that it is there. We may steadily ignore it, and persist in declarations of consecration and full trust; we may be more earnest than ever in our religious duties, and have the eyes of our understanding opened more and more to the truth and the beauty of the life and walk of faith. We may seem to our-selves and to others to have reached an almost impregnable position of victory, and yet we may find ourselves suffer-ing bitter defeats. We may wonder, and question, and despair, and pray. Nothing will do any good until the wrong thing is dug up from its hiding-place, brought out to the light, and laid before God.

The moment, therefore, that a believer who is walking in this interior life meets with a defeat, he must at once seek for the cause, not in the strength of that particular enemy, but in something behind,—some hidden want of consecration lying at the very center of his being. Just as a headache is not the disease itself, but only a symptom of a disease, situated in some other part of the body, so the failure in such a Christian is only the symptom of an evil, hidden in probably a very different part of his na-ture.

Sometimes the evil may be hidden even in what at a cursory glance would look like good. Beneath apparent zeal for the truth, may be hidden a judging spirit, or a subtle leaning to our own understanding. Beneath ap-parent Christian faithfulness may be hidden an absence of Christian love. Beneath an apparently rightful care for our affairs, may be hidden a great want of trust in God. I believe our blessed Guide, the indwelling Holy Spirit, is always secretly discovering these things to us by continual little checks and pangs of conscience, so that we are left without excuse. But it is very easy to disregard His gentle voice, and insist upon it to ourselves that all is right, while the fatal evil continues hidden in our midst, caus-ing defeat in most unexpected quarters.

A capital illustration of this occurred to me once in my housekeeping. We had moved into a new house, and in looking it over to see if it was all ready for occupancy, I noticed in the cellar a very clean-looking cider-cask headed up at both ends. I debated with myself whether I should have it taken out of the cellar and opened to see what was in it, but concluded, as it seemed empty and looked clean, to leave it undisturbed, especially as it would have been quite a piece of work to get it up the stairs. I did not feel quite easy, but reasoned away my scruples and left it. Every spring and fall, when housecleaning time came on, I would remember that cask with a little twinge of my housewifely conscience, feeling I could not quite rest in the thought of a perfectly clean house while

it remained unopened, as how did I know but under its
fair exterior it contained some hidden evil? Still I managed to quiet my scruples on the subject, thinking always
of the trouble it would involve to investigate it; and for
two or three years the innocent-looking cask stood quietly
in our cellar. Then, most unaccountably, moths began
to fill our house. I used every possible precaution against
them, and made every effort to eradicate them, but in
vain. They increased rapidly, and threatened to ruin everything we had. I suspected our carpets as being the
cause, and subjected them to a thorough cleaning. I suspected our furniture, and had it newly upholstered. I suspected all sorts of impossible things. At last the thought
of the cask flashed on me. At once I had it brought up out
of the cellar and the head knocked in, and I think it safe
to say that thousands of moths poured out. The previous
occupant of the house must have headed it up with something in it which bred moths, and this was the cause of
all my trouble.

Now, I believe that, in the same way, some innocent-
looking habit or indulgence, some apparently unimportant
and safe thing, about which, however, we have now and
then little twinges of conscience,—something which is not
brought out fairly into the light, and investigated under
the searching eye of God,—lies at the root of most of the
failure in this interior life. *All* is not given up. Some secret corner is kept locked against the entrance of the Lord.
Some evil thing is hidden in the recesses of our hearts,
and therefore we cannot stand before our enemies, but
find ourselves smitten down in their presence.

In order to prevent failure, or to discover its cause, if
we find we have failed, it is necessary to keep continually
before us this prayer: "Search me, O God, and know my
heart; try me and know my thoughts; and see if there be
any wicked way in me, and lead me in the way everlasting."

Let me beg of you, however, dear Christians, do not
think, because I have said all this about failure, that I believe in it. There is no necessity for it whatever. The Lord
Jesus *is* able, according to the declaration concerning
Him, to deliver us out of the hands of our enemies, that
we may "serve him without fear, in holiness and righteousness before him all the days of our life." Let us then
pray, every one of us, day and night, "Lord, keep us from
sinning, and make us living witnesses of Thy mighty

power to save to the uttermost"; and let us never be satisfied until we are so pliable in His hands, and have learned so to trust Him, that He will be able to "make us perfect in every good work to do his will, working in us that which is well pleasing in his sight, through Jesus Christ; to whom be glory for ever and ever. Amen!"

Chapter Twelve

Is God in Everything?

ONE OF THE GREATEST OBSTACLES TO AN UNWAVERing experience in the interior life is the difficulty of seeing God in everything. People say, "I can easily submit to things that come from God; but I cannot submit to man, and most of my trials and crosses come through human instrumentality." Or they say, "It is all well enough to talk of trusting; but when I commit a matter to God, man is sure to come in and disarrange it all; and while I have no difficulty in trusting God, I do see serious difficulties in the way of trusting men."

This is no imaginary trouble, but is of vital importance; and if it cannot be met, it does really make the life of faith an impossible and visionary theory. For nearly everything in life comes to us through human instrumentalities, and most of our trials are the result of somebody's failure, or ignorance, or carelessness, or sin. We know God cannot be the author of these things; and yet, unless He is the agent in the matter, how can we say to Him about it, "Thy will be done"?

Besides, what good is there in trusting our affairs to God, if, after all, man is to be allowed to come in and disarrange them; and how is it possible to live by faith, if human agencies, in which it would be wrong and foolish to trust, are to have a prevailing influence in moulding our lives?

Moreover, things in which we can see God's hand always have a sweetness in them that consoles while it wounds; but the trials inflicted by man are full of nothing but bitterness.

What is needed, then, is to see God in everything, and to receive everything directly from His hands, with no intervention of second causes; and it is to just this that we must be brought before we can know an abiding experience of entire abandonment and perfect trust. Our abandonment must be to God, not to man; and our trust must be in Him, not in any arm of flesh, or we shall fail at the first trial.

The question here confronts us at once, "But is God in everything, and have we any warrant from the Scripture for receiving everything from His hands without regarding the second causes that may have been instrumental in bringing them about?" I answer to this, unhesitatingly, Yes. To the children of God, everything comes directly from their Father's hand, no matter who or what may have been the apparent agents. There are no "second causes" for them.

The whole teaching of Scripture asserts and implies this. Not a sparrow falls to the ground without our Father. The very hairs of our head are all numbered. We are not to be careful about anything, because our Father cares for us. We are not to avenge ourselves, because our Father has charged Himself with our defense. We are not to fear, for the Lord is on our side. No one can be against us, because he is for us. We shall not want, for He is our Shepherd. When we pass through the rivers they shall not overflow us, and when we walk through the fire we shall not be burned, because He will be with us. He shuts the mouths of lions, that they cannot hurt us. "He delivereth and rescueth." "He changeth the times and the seasons; he removeth kings and setteth up kings." A man's heart is in His hand, and, "as the rivers of water, he turneth it whithersoever he will." He ruleth over all the kingdoms of the heathen; and in His hand there is power and might, "so that none is able to withstand" Him. "He ruleth the raging of the sea; when the waves thereof arise, he stilleth them." He "bringeth the counsel of the heathen to naught; he maketh the devices of the people of none effect." "Whatsoever the Lord pleaseth, that doeth he, in heaven and in earth, in the seas and all deep places." "Lo, these are parts of his ways: but how little a portion is heard of him? But the thunder of his power who can understand?" "Hast thou not known? hast thou not heard, that the everlasting God, the Lord, the Creator of the ends of the earth, fainteth not, neither is weary? There is no searching of his understanding."

And it is this very God who is declared to be "our refuge and strength, a very present help in trouble. Therefore will not we fear, though the earth be removed, and though the mountains be carried into the midst of the sea; though the waters thereof roar and be troubled, though the mountains shake with the swelling thereof." "I will say of the Lord, he is my refuge and my fortress: my God; in him will I trust. Surely he shall deliver thee from the snare of the fowler, and from the noisome pestilence. He shall cover thee with his feathers, and under his wings shalt thou trust: his truth shall be thy shield and buckler. Thou shalt not be afraid for the terror by night; nor for the arrow that flieth by day; nor for the pestilence that walketh in darkness; nor for the destruction that wasteth at noonday. A thousand shall fall at thy side, and ten thousand at thy right hand; but it shall not come nigh thee. . . . Because thou hast made the Lord, which is my refuge, even the most High, thy habitation; there shall no evil befall thee, neither shall any plague come nigh thy dwelling. For he shall give his angels charge over thee, to keep thee in all thy ways." "Be content, therefore, with such things as ye have: for he hath said, I will never leave thee nor forsake thee. So that we may boldly say, The Lord is my helper, and I will not fear what man shall do unto me."

To my own mind, these scriptures, and many others like them, settle forever the question as to the power of "second causes" in the life of the children of God. Second causes must all be under the control of our Father, and not one of them can touch us except with His knowledge and by His permission. It may be the sin of man that originates the action, and therefore the thing itself cannot be said to be the will of God; but by the time it reaches us it has become God's will for us, and must be accepted as directly from His hands. No man or company of men, no power in earth or heaven, can touch that soul which is abiding in Christ, without first passing through His encircling presence, and receiving the seal of His permission. If God be for us, it matters not who may be against us; nothing can disturb or harm us, except He shall see that it is best for us, and shall stand aside to let it pass.

An earthly parent's care for his helpless child is a fee-

ble illustration of this. If the child is in its father's
arms, nothing can touch it without that father's consent,
unless he is too weak to prevent it. And even if this
should be the case, he suffers the harm first in his own
person before he allows it to reach his child. If an earthly
parent would thus care for his little helpless one, how
much more will our Heavenly Father, whose love is infinitely greater, and whose strength and wisdom can never
be baffled, care for us! I am afraid there are some, even
of God's own children, who scarcely think that He is
equal to themselves in tenderness, and love, and thoughtful care; and who, in their secret thoughts, charge Him
with a neglect and indifference of which they would feel
themselves incapable. The truth really is that His care
is infinitely superior to any possibilities of human care;
and that He, who counts the very hairs of our heads,
and suffers not a sparrow to fall without Him, takes note
of the minutest matters that can affect the lives of His
children, and regulates them all according to His own perfect will, let their origin be what they may.

The instances of this are numberless. Take Joseph.
What could have seemed more apparently on the face of
it to be the result of sin, and utterly contrary to the will
of God, than the action of his brethren in selling him
into slavery? And yet Joseph, in speaking of it said, "As
for you, ye thought evil against me; but God meant it
unto good." "Now therefore be not grieved, nor angry
with yourselves, that ye sold me hither: for God did
send me before you to preserve life." It was undoubtedly
sin in Joseph's brethren, but by the time it had reached
Joseph it had become God's will for him, and was, in
truth, though he did not see it then, the greatest blessing
of his whole life. And thus we see how God can make
even "the wrath of man to praise Him," and how all
things, even the sins of others, "shall work together for
good to them that love him."

I learned this lesson practically and experimentally,
long years before I knew the scriptural truth concerning it.
I was attending a prayer-meeting held in the interests of
the life of faith, when a strange lady rose to speak, and I
looked at her, wondering who she could be, little thinking
she was to bring a message to my soul which would teach
me a grand practical lesson. She said she had great difficulty in living the life of faith, on account of the second
causes that seemed to her to control nearly everything

that concerned her. Her perplexity became so great that at last she began to ask God to teach her the truth about it, whether He really was in everything or not. After praying this for a few days, she had what she described as a vision. She thought she was in a perfectly dark place, and that there advanced toward her, from a distance, a body of light which gradually surrounded and enveloped her and everything around her. As it approached, a voice seemed to say, "This is the presence of God! This is the presence of God!" While surrounded with this presence, all the great and awful things in life seemed to pass before her,—fighting armies, wicked men, raging beasts, storms and pestilences, sin and suffering of every kind. She shrank back at first in terror; but she soon saw that the presence of God so surrounded and enveloped herself and each one of these things that not a lion could reach out its paw, nor a bullet fly through the air, except as the presence of God moved out of the way to permit it. And she saw that if there were ever so thin a film, as it were, of this glorious Presence between herself and the most terrible violence, not a hair of her head could be ruffled, nor anything touch her, except as the Presence divided to let the evil through. Then all the small and annoying things of life passed before her; and equally she saw that there also she was so enveloped in this presence of God that not a cross look, nor a harsh word, nor petty trial of any kind could affect her, unless God's encircling presence moved out of the way to let it.

Her difficulty vanished. Her question was answered forever. God *was* in everything; and to her henceforth there were no second causes. She saw that her life came to her, day by day and hour by hour, directly from the hand of God, let the agencies which should seem to control it be what they might. And never again had she found any difficulty in an abiding consent to His will and an unwavering trust in His care.

Would that it were only possible to make every Christian see this truth as plainly as I see it! For I am convinced it is the only clue to a completely restful life. Nothing else will enable a soul to live only in the present moment, as we are commanded to do, and to take no thought for the morrow. Nothing else will take all the risks and "supposes" out of a Christian's life, and enable him to say, "Surely goodness and mercy shall follow me all the days of my life." Under God's care we run no risks. I once heard of a poor colored woman who earned a precarious living by daily labor, but who was a joyous, triumphant Christian. "Ah, Nancy," said a gloomy Christian lady to her one day, who almost disapproved of her constant cheerfulness, and yet envied it,—"Ah, Nancy, it is all well enough to be happy now, but I should think the thoughts of your future would sober you. Only suppose, for instance, that you should have a spell of sickness, and be unable to work; or suppose your present employers should move away, and no one else should give you anything to do; or suppose—" "Stop!" cried Nancy, "I never supposes. De Lord is my Shepherd, and I knows I shall not want. And, honey," she added to her gloomy friend, "it's all dem *supposes* as is makin' you so mis-able. You'd better give dem all up, and just trust de Lord."

Nothing else but this seeing God in everything will make us loving and patient with those who annoy and trouble us. They will be to us then only the instruments for accomplishing His tender and wise purposes toward us, and we shall even find ourselves at last inwardly thanking them for the blessings they bring.

Nothing else will completely put an end to all murmuring or rebelling thoughts. Christians often feel at liberty to murmur against man, when they would not dare to murmur against God. Therefore this way of receiving things would make it impossible ever to murmur. If our Father permits a trial to come, it must be because the trial is the sweetest and best thing that could happen to us, and we must accept it with thanks from His dear hand. This does not mean, however, that we must like or enjoy the trial itself, but that we must like God's will in the trial; and it is not hard to do this when we have learned to know that His will is the will of love, and is therefore always lovely.

A very good illustration of this may be found in the familiar fact of a mother giving medicine to her dearly loved child. The bottle *holds* the medicine, but the mother *gives* it; and the bottle is not responsible, but the mother. No matter how full her closet may be of bottles of medicine, the mother will not allow one drop to be given to the child unless she believes it will be good for it; but when she does believe it will be good for her darling, the very depth of her love compels her to force it on the child, no matter how bitter may be its taste.

The human beings around us are often the bottles

that hold our medicine, but it is our Father's hand of love that pours out the medicine, and compels us to drink it. The human bottle is the "second cause" of our trial; but it has no real agency in it, for the medicine that these human "bottles" hold is prescribed for us and given to us by the Great Physician of our souls, who is seeking thereby to heal all our spiritual diseases.

For instance, I know no better medicine to cure the disease of irritability than to be compelled to live with a human "bottle" of sensitiveness whom we are bound to consider and yield to.

Shall we rebel against the human bottles then? Shall we not rather take thankfully from our Father's hand the medicine they contain, and, losing sight of the second cause, say joyfully, "Thy will be done," in everything that comes to us, no matter what its source may be?

This way of seeing our Father in everything makes life one long thanksgiving, and gives a rest of heart, and, more than that, a gayety of spirit that is unspeakable.

Faber says, in his wonderful hymn on the Will of God,—

"I know not what it is to doubt,
    My heart is always gay;
I run no risks, for, come what will,
    Thou always hast Thy way."

Since, therefore, God is sure to have His own way concerning those who abandon themselves to Him in perfect trust, into what wonderful green pastures of inward rest, and beside what blessedly still waters of inward refreshment, will He lead all such!

If the will of God is our will, and if He always has His way, then we always have our way also, and we reign in a perpetual kingdom. He who sides with God cannot fail to win in every encounter; and whether the result shall be joy or sorrow, failure or success, death or life, we may under all circumstances join in the Apostle's shout of victory, "Thanks be unto God, which always causeth us to triumph in Christ!"

THE WILL OF GOD.*

Thou sweet, beloved Will of God,
    My anchor ground, my fortress hill,

*From "Hymns of Consecration."

My spirit's silent, fair abode,
  In Thee I hide me, and am still.

O Will, that willest good alone,
  Lead Thou the way, Thou guidest best;
A little child I follow on,
  And trusting lean upon Thy breast.

Thy beautiful, sweet Will, my God,
  Holds fast in Its sublime embrace
My captive will, a gladsome bird,
  Prisoned in such a realm of grace.

Within this place of certain good,
  Love ever more expands her wings;
Or, nestling in Thy perfect choice,
  Abides content with what it brings.

Oh, sweetest burden, lightest yoke,
  It lifts, it bears my happy soul,
It giveth wings to this poor heart;
  My freedom is Thy grand control.

Upon God's Will I lay me down,
  As child upon its mother's breast;
No silken couch, nor softest bed,
  Could ever give me such sweet rest.

Thy wonderful, grand Will, my God,
  With triumph now I make It mine,
And Love shall cry a jealous *Yes*,
  To every dear command of Thine.

PART III
Results

Chapter Thirteen

Bondage or Liberty

IT IS A FACT BEYOND QUESTION THAT THERE ARE TWO
kinds of Christian experience, one of which is an experience of bondage, and the other an experience of liberty.

In the first case the soul is controlled by a stern sense
of duty, and obeys the law of God, either from fear of
punishment or from expectation of wages. In the other
case the controlling power is an inward life-principle that
works out, by the force of its own motions or instincts,
the will of the Divine Life-giver, without fear of punishment or hope of reward. In the first the Christian is a servant, and works for hire; in the second he is a son, and
works for love.

There ought not, it is true, to be this contrast in the
experience of Christians, for to "walk at liberty" is plainly
their only right and normal condition; but as we have to
deal with what is rather than with what ought to be we
cannot shut our eyes to the sad condition of bondage in
which so many of God's children pass a large part of their
Christian lives. The reason of this, and the remedy for it
are not difficult to find. The reason is legality, and the
remedy is Christ.

Nowhere do we find those two forms or stages of Christian life more fully developed and contrasted than in the
Epistle to the Galatians. The occasion of its being written
was that some Jewish brethren had come among the
churches in Galatia, and, by representing that certain
forms and ceremonies were necessary to their salvation,
had tried to draw them away from the liberty of the gospel. And with these teachers Peter had allowed himself to
unite. Therefore Paul reproves, not only the Galatians,
but also Peter himself.

Neither Peter nor the Galatians had committed any
moral sin; but they had committed a spiritual sin. They
had got into a wrong attitude of soul toward God,—a legal
attitude. They had begun, as Christians generally do, in
the right attitude; that is, they had entered by the

111

"hearing of faith" into the spiritual life. But when it came to a question of how they were to live in this life, they had changed their ground. They had sought to substitute works for faith. Having "begun in the Spirit," they were now seeking to be "made perfect by the flesh." They had, in short, descended, in their Christian living, from the plane of life to the plane of law.

An illustration will help us to understand this. Here are two men neither of whom steals. Outwardly their actions are equally honest; but inwardly there is a vital difference. One man has a dishonest nature that wants to steal, and is only deterred by the fear of a penalty; while the other possesses an honest nature that hates thieving, and could not be induced to steal, even by the hope of a reward. The one is honest in the spirit; the other is honest only in the flesh. No words are needed to say of which sort the Christian life is meant to be.

We are, however, continually tempted to forget that it is not what men *do* that is the vital matter, but rather what they *are*. In Christ Jesus neither legal observances nor the omission of legal observances avails anything, "but a new creature." God is a great deal more concerned about our really *being* "new creatures" than about anything else; because He knows that if we *are* right as to our inward being, we shall certainly *do* right as to our outward actions. We may, in fact, sometimes even *do* right without *being* right at all; and it is very evident that no doing of this kind has any vitality in it, nor is of any real account. The essential thing, therefore, is character; and *doing* is valuable only as it is an indication of *being*.

Paul was grieved with the Galatian Christians because they seemed to have lost sight of this vital truth, that the inward life, the "new creature," was the only thing that availed. They had begun on this plane, but they had "fallen from grace" to a lower plane, where the "oldness of the letter" was put in place of the "newness of the spirit." "Christ is become of no effect unto you, whosoever of you are justified by the law; ye are fallen from grace."

This passage is the only one in which the expression "fallen from grace" is used in the New Testament; and it means that the Galatians had made the mistake of thinking that something else besides Christ was necessary for their right Christian living. The Jewish brethren who had come among them had taught them that Christ alone was not enough, but that obedience to the ceremonial law must be added.

They had therefore imported, as being necessary for salvation, some ceremonies out of the Jewish ritual, and had tried to compel the "Gentiles to live as do the Jews." Modern Christians are greatly surprised at them, and wonder how they could have been so legal. But is there not the same temptation to legality, under a different form, among these same modern Christians? *They* added the ceremonial law; *we* add resolutions, or agonizings, or Christian work, or churchgoing, or religious ceremonies of one sort or another; and what is there, therefore, to choose between us and them? It does not make much difference what you add; the wrong thing is to add anything at all.

We are full of condemnation of the "Jew's religion," because it "frustrates the grace of God," and makes Christ to be "dead in vain" by depending upon outward deeds and outward ceremonies to bring salvation. But I fear there is a great deal of the "Jew's religion" mixed up with the Christian religion now, just as there was among these Galatian Christians, and that the grace of God is as much frustrated by our legality as it was by theirs; although ours may manifest itself in a slightly different form.

The following contrasts may help some to understand the difference between these two kinds of religion, and may also enable them to discover where the secret of their own experience of legal bondage lies:

The law says, This *do* and thou shalt live.

The gospel says, *Live,* and then thou shalt do.

The law says, *Pay* me that thou owest.

The gospel says, I frankly *forgive* thee all.

The law says, *Make* you a new heart and a new spirit.

The gospel says, A new heart will I *give* you, and a new spirit will I put within you.

The law says, Thou shalt love the Lord thy God with all thy heart, and with all thy soul, and with all thy mind.

The gospel says, Herein is love, not that we loved God, but that He loved us and sent His son to be the propitiation for our sins.

The law says, *Cursed* is every one who continueth not in all things written in the book of the law to do them.

The gospel says, *Blessed* is the man whose inquities are forgiven, and whose sins are covered.

The law says, The *wages* of sin is death.

The gospel says, The *gift* of God is eternal life through Jesus Christ our Lord.

The law *demands* holiness.

The gospel *gives* holiness.

The law says, *Do.*

The gospel says, *Done.*

The law *extorts* the unwilling service of a bondman.

The gospel *wins* the loving service of a son and freeman.

The law makes blessings the result of *obedience*.

The gospel makes obedience the result of *blessings*.

The law places the day of rest at the end of the week's work.

The gospel places it at its beginning.

The law says, *If.*

The gospel says, *Therefore.*

The law was given for the restraint of the old man.

The gospel was given to bring liberty to the new man.

Under the law, salvation was *wages*.

Under the gospel, salvation is a *gift*.

These two forms of the religious life began at exactly opposite ends. The religion of legality is as though a man should decide to have an apple orchard, and should try to make one by first getting some apples of the kind desired, and then getting a tree and fastening the apples on its branches, and then getting roots to fasten to the trunk, and finally purchasing a field in which to plant his manufactured tree. That is, first the fruit, second the branches, third the root, fourth the field. But the religion of grace follows a different order. It begins at the root, and grows up, and blossoms out into flowers and fruit.

Paul tells us that the law "is our schoolmaster," not our saviour; and he emphasizes the fact that it is our schoolmaster only for the purpose of bringing us to Christ, for, after faith in Christ is come, he declares, we are no longer to be under a schoolmaster. He uses the contrast between a servant and a son as an illustration of his meaning. "Wherefore," he says, "thou art no more a servant, but a son," and he entreats us, because of this, to "stand fast in the liberty wherewith Christ hath made us free, and be not entangled again with the yoke of bondage."

It is as if a woman had been a servant in a house, paid for her work in weekly wages, and under the law of her master, whom she had tried to please, but towards whom her service had been one of duty only. Finally, however, the master offers her his love, and lifts her up from the place of a servant to be his bride and to share his fortunes. At once the whole spirit of her service is changed. She may perhaps continue to do the same things that she did before, but she does them now altogether from a different motive. The old sense of duty is lost in the new sense of love. The cold word "master" is transformed into the loving word "husband." "And it shall be at that day, saith the Lord, that thou shalt call me Ishi (my husband), and shalt call me no more Baali (my lord)."

But imagine this bride beginning after a while to look back upon her low estate, and to be so overwhelmed by the retrospect as to feel unworthy of union with her husband, and to lose consequently the inward sense of this union. Who can doubt that very soon the old sense of working for wages would drive out the new sense of working for love, and in spirit the old name of "my master" would again take the place of the new name of "my husband"?

We exclaim at the folly of such a course. But is not this just what happens to many Christians now? The servitude of duty takes the place of the service of love; and God is looked upon as the stern taskmaster who demands our obedience, instead of the loving Father who wins it.

We all know that nothing so destroys the sweetness of any relation as the creeping in of this legal spirit. The moment a husband and wife cease to perform their services to each other out of a heart of love and union, and begin to perform them from a sense of duty alone, that moment the sweetness of the union is lost, and the marriage tie becomes a bondage, and things that were a joy before are turned into crosses. This lies at the bottom, I think, of the current idea of "taking up the cross" in the Christian Church. We think it means doing something we ought to do, but dislike to do. And such service is thought to be very meritorious toward God; although we all know very well that we would not endure it a moment as toward ourselves. What wife could endure it if her husband should use toward her the language that Christians are continually using toward the Lord; if he should say, for instance, every morning, as he went out to business, "I am going to work for you to-day, but I wish you to know that it is a very great cross, and I hardly know how to bear it." O what husband would like such language from his wife? No wonder Paul was alarmed when he found there was danger of a legal spirit such as this creeping into the Church of Christ.

Legal Christians do not deny Christ; they only seek to add something to Christ. Their idea is, Christ and—something besides. Perhaps it is Christ and good works, or Christ and earnest feelings, or Christ and clear doctrines, or Christ and certain religious performances. All these are good in themselves, and good as the results of fruits of salvation; but to add anything to Christ, no matter how good it may be, as the procuring cause of salvation, is to deny His completeness, and to exalt self. Men will undergo many painful self-sacrifices rather than take the place of utter helplessness and worthlessness. A man will gladly be a Saint Simeon Stylites or even a fakir, if only it is self that does it, so that self may share the glory. And a religion of bondage always exalts self. It is what *I* do,—*my* efforts, *my* wrestlings, *my* faithfulness. But a religion of liberty leaves self nothing to glory in; it is all Christ, and what He does, and what He is, and how wonderfully He saves. The child does not boast of itself, but of its father and mother; and our souls can "make their boast in the Lord," when, in this life of liberty, we have learned to know that He and He alone is the sufficient supply for our every need.

We are the children of God, and therefore of course His heirs; and our possessions come to us, not by working for them, but by inheritance from our Father. Ah, dear friends, how little some of you act like the "heirs of God"! How poverty-stricken you are, and how hard you work for the little you do possess!

You may perhaps point to the results of your legal working or your asceticism, which, it is true, do seem to have a "show of wisdom in will worship, and humility, and neglecting of the body," as being a proof of the rightness of your course. But I am convinced that whatever really good results there are, have come in spite of, and not because of, your legal working.

I had a friend once whose Christian life was a life of bondage. She worked for her salvation harder than any slave ever worked to purchase his freedom. Among other things, she never felt as if the day could go right for herself or any of her family unless she started it with a long season of wrestling, and agonizing, and conflict; "winding up her machine," I called it. One day we were talking about it together, and she was telling me of the hardness and bondage of her Christian life, and was wondering what the Bible *could* mean when it said Christ's yoke was easy and His burden light. I told her that I thought she must have got things wrong somehow, that the Bible always expressed the truth of our relationships with God by using figures that did not admit of any such wrestlings and agonizings as she described. "What would you think," I asked, "of children that had to wrestle and agonize with their parents every morning for their necessary food and clothing, or of sheep that had to wrestle with their shepherd before they could secure the necessary care?" "Of course I see that would be all wrong," she said; "but, then, why do I have such good times after I have gone through these conflicts?" This puzzled me for a moment, but then I asked, "what brings about those good times finally?" "Why, finally," she replied, "I come to the point of trusting the Lord." "Suppose you should come to that point to begin with?" I asked. "Oh," she replied, with a sudden illumination, "I never until this minute thought that I might!"

Christ says that except we "become as little children" we cannot enter into the kingdom of Heaven. But it is impossible to get the child-spirit until the servant-spirit has disappeared. Notice, I do not say the spirit of service, but the servant-spirit. Every good child is filled with the spirit of service, but ought not to have anything of the servant-spirit. The child serves from love; the servant works for wages.

If a child of loving parents should get the idea that its parents would not give it food and clothing unless it earned them in some way, all the sweetness of the relationship between parent and child would be destroyed. I knew a little girl who did get this idea, and who went around the neighborhood asking at the doors for work, that she might earn a little money to buy herself some clothes. It nearly broke the hearts of her parents when they discovered it. Legal Christians grieve the heart of their Heavenly Father far more than they dream by letting the servant-spirit creep into their relations with Him. As soon as we begin to "work for our living" in spiritual things, we have stepped out of the son's place into the servant's, and have "fallen from grace."

One servant, of whom we read in the Bible, thought his lord was a "hard master," and the spirit of bondage makes us think the same now. How many Christians there are who have bowed their necks to the yoke of Christ as to a "yoke of bondage," and have read His declaration that His yoke is easy as though it were a fairy tale, and gone on their way, never dreaming that it was meant to be actually realized as a fact! In truth, so deeply is the idea that the Christian life is a species of bondage ingrained in the Church that whenever any of the children of God find themselves "walking at liberty" they at once begin to think there must be something wrong in their experience, because they no longer find anything to be a "cross" to them. As well might the wife think there must be something wrong in her love for her husband when she finds all her services for him are a pleasure instead of a trial!

Sometimes I think that the whole secret of the Christian life that I have been trying to describe, is revealed in the child relationship. Nothing more is needed than just to believe that God is as good a Father as the best ideal earthly father, and that the relationship of a Christian to Him is just the same as that of a child to its parent in this world. Children do not need to carry about in their own pockets the money for their support. If the father has plenty, that satisfies them, and is a great deal better than if it were in the child's own possession, since in that case it might get lost. In the same way it is not necessary for Christians to have all their spiritual possessions in their own keeping. It is far better that their riches should be stored up for them in Christ, and that when they want anything they should receive is direct from His hands. He of God is "made unto us wisdom, and righteousness, and sanctification, and redemption," and apart from Him we have nothing.

When people are comparative strangers to one another they cannot with any comfort receive great gifts from each other. But when they are united in spirit, with a bond of true love between them, then, no matter how great the gifts may be that pass from one to the other, they can be accepted without any feeling of embarrassment or obligation on either side.

This principle holds good in the spiritual life. When Christians are living far off from God they cannot be brought to accept any great gifts from Him. They feel as if they were too unworthy, and did not deserve such gifts; and, even when He puts the blessing into their very laps, as it were, their false humility prevents them from seeing it, and they go on their way without it.

But when Christians get near enough to the Lord to feel the true spirit of adoption, they are ready to accept with delight all the blessings He has in store for them, and never think anything too much to receive. For then they discover that He is only eager, as parents are, to pour out every good gift upon His children, and that, in fact, all things are theirs, because they are Christ's, and Christ is God's.

Sometimes a great mystery is made out of the life hid with Christ in God, as though it were a strange mystical thing that ordinary people could not understand. But this contrast between bondage and liberty makes it very plain. It is only to find out that we really are "no more servants, but sons," and practically to enter into the blessed privileges of this relationship. All can understand what it is to be a little child; there is no mystery about that. God did not use the figure of Father and children without knowing all that this relationship implies; and those, therefore, who know Him as their Father know the whole secret. They are their Father's heirs, and may enter now into possession of all that is necessary for their present needs. They will therefore be very simple in their prayers. "Lord," they will say, "I am Thy child, and I need such and such things." "My child," He answers, "all things are thine in Christ; come and take just what thou needest."

Where the executors are honorable men, the heirs to an estate are not obliged to "wrestle" for their inheritance. The executors are appointed, not to keep them out of it, but to help them into possession of it. I sometimes think Christians look upon our Lord as someone appointed to keep them out of their possessions instead of the one who has come to bring them in. They little know how such an implication grieves and dishonors Him.

It is because legal Christians do not know the truth of their relationship to God, as children to a father, and do not recognize His fatherly heart toward them, that they are in bondage. When they do recognize it, the spirit of bondage becomes impossible to them.

Our liberty must come, therefore, from an understanding of the mind and thoughts of God towards us.

What are the facts of the case? If He has called us only to the servants' place, then the Christians whose lives are lives of weary bondage are right. But if He has called us to be children and heirs, if we are His friends, His brethren, His bride, how sadly and grievously wrong we are in being entangled under any yoke of bondage whatever, no matter how pious a yoke it may seem to be!

The thought of bondage is utterly abhorrent to any of earth's true relationships, and surely it must be more repugnant to heavenly relationship. It will not, of course, hinder the final entrance of the poor enslaved soul into its heavenly rest, but it will, I am sure, put it into the sad condition of those who are described in I Corinthians 3: 11–15. Their work shall be burned, and they shall suffer loss; yet they themselves shall be saved, but so as by fire.

"Against such there is no law," is the Divine sentence concerning all who live and walk in the Spirit; and you shall find it most blessedly true in your own experience if you will but lay aside all self-effort and self-dependence of every kind, and will consent to let Christ live in you, and work in you, and be your indwelling life.

The man who lives by the power of an inward righteous nature is not under bondage to the outward law of righteousness; but he who is restrained by the outward law alone, without the inward restraint of a righteous nature, is a slave to the law. The one fulfils the law in his soul, and is therefore free. The other rebels against the law in his soul, and is therefore bound.

I would that every child of God did but know the deliverance from bondage which I have tried to set forth!

Let me entreat of you, my readers, to abandon yourselves so utterly to the Lord Jesus Christ that He may be able to "work in you all the good pleasure of his will," and may, by the law of the Spirit of Life in Himself, deliver you from every other law that could possibly enslave you.

Chapter Fourteen

Growth

ONE GREAT OBJECTION MADE AGAINST THOSE WHO ADVO-cate this life of faith is that they do not teach a growth in grace. They are supposed to teach that the soul arrives in one moment at a state of perfection, beyond which there is no advance, and that all the exhortations in the Scriptures that point towards growth and development are rendered void by this teaching.

Since exactly the opposite of this is true, I will try, if possible, to answer these objections, and to show what seems to me the Scriptural way of growing, and in what place the soul must be in order to grow.

The text which is most frequently quoted, is II Peter 3: 18: "But grow in grace, and in the knowledge of our Lord and Saviour Jesus Christ." Now, this text ex-presses exactly what we who teach this life of faith believe to be God's will for us, and what we also believe He has made it possible for us to experience. We accept, in their very fullest meaning, all the commands and promises concerning our being no more children, and our growing up into Christ in all things, until we come unto a perfect man, unto the "measure of the stature of the fulness of Christ." We rejoice that we need not continue always to be babes, needing milk; but that we may, by reason of use and development, become such as have need of strong meat, skilful in the word of righteousness, and able to discern both good and evil. And none would grieve more than we ourselves at the thought of any finality in the Christian life beyond which there could be no advance.

But, then, we believe in a growing that does really pro-duce continually progressing maturity, and in a develop-ment that, as a fact, does bring forth ripe fruit. We expect to reach the aim set before us; and if we do not find our-selves on the way towards it we feel sure there must be some fault in our growing. No parent would be satisfied with the growth of his child if day after day, and year

121

after year, it remained the same helpless babe it was in the first months of its life. And no farmer would feel comfortable under such growing of his grain as should stop short at the blade, and never produce the ear, or the full corn in the ear. Growth, to be real, must be progressive, and the days and weeks and months should bring a development and increase of maturity in the thing growing. But is this the case with a large part of that which is called growth in grace? Does not the very Christian who is the most strenuous in his longings and his efforts after this growth too often find that, at the end of the year, he is not as far on in his Christian experience as at the beginning, and that his zeal, and his devotedness, and his separation from the world, are not as whole-souled or complete as when his Christian life first began?

I was once urging upon a company of Christians the duty and privilege of an immediate and definite step into the "land of promise," when a lady of great intelligence interrupted me with what she evidently felt to be a complete rebuttal of all I had been saying by exclaiming, "Ah! but, Mrs. Smith, I believe in *growing* in grace." "How long have *you* been growing?" I asked. "About twenty-five years," was her answer. "And how much more unworldly and devoted to the Lord are you now, than when your Christian life began?" I continued. "Alas!" was the answer, "I fear I am not nearly so much so." And with this answer her eyes were opened to see that at all events her way of growing had not been successful, but quite the reverse.

The trouble with her, and with every other such case, is simply this: they are trying to grow *into* grace instead of *in* it. They are like a rosebush planted by a gardener in the hard, stony path with a view to its growing *into* the flower-bed, and which has of course dwindled and withered in consequence instead of flourishing and maturing. The children of Israel, wandering in the wilderness, are a perfect picture of this sort of growing. They were traveling about for forty years, taking many weary steps, and finding but little rest from their wanderings; and yet, at the end of it all, were no nearer the promised land than they were at the beginning. When they started on their wanderings at Kadesh Barnea, they were at the borders of the land, and a few steps would have taken them into it. When they ended their wanderings in the plains of Moab, they were also at its borders; only with this difference,

that now there was a river to cross, which at first there
would not have been. All their wanderings and fightings
in the wilderness had not put them in possession of
one inch of the promised land. In order to get possession
of this land it was necessary first to be in it; and in order
to grow in grace it is necessary first to be planted in grace.
When once in the land, however, their conquest was
rapid; and when once planted in grace, the growth of the
spiritual life becomes vigorous and rapid beyond all con-
ceiving. For grace is a most fruitful soil, and the plants
that grow therein are plants of a marvelous growth. They
are tended by a Divine Husbandman, and are warmed by
the Sun of Righteousness, and watered by the dew from
Heaven. Surely it is no wonder that they bring forth fruit,
"some an hundred-fold, some sixty-fold, some thirty-
fold."

But, it will be asked, what is meant by growing in grace?
It is difficult to answer this question, because so few people
have any conception of what the grace of God really is.
To say that it is free unmerited favor only expresses a
little of its meaning. It is the unhindered, wondrous,
boundless love of God, poured out upon us in an infinite
variety of ways, without stint or measure, not according
to our deserving, but according to His measureless heart
of love, which passeth knowledge, so unfathomable are
its heights and depths. I sometimes think a totally different meaning is given to the word "love" when it is
associated with God from that which we so well understand in its human application. We seem to consider that
Divine love is hard and self-seeking and distant, concerned about its own glory, and indifferent to the fate
of others. But if ever human love was tender and self-
sacrificing and devoted, if ever it could bear and forbear,
if ever it could suffer gladly for its loved one, if ever
it was willing to pour itself out in a lavish abandonment for the comfort or pleasure of its objects, then
infinitely more is Divine love tender and self-sacrificing
and devoted, and glad to bear and forbear, and suffer,
and eager to lavish its best of gifts and blessings upon
the objects of its love. Put together all the tenderest
love you know of, dear reader, the deepest you have
ever felt, and the strongest that has ever been poured
out upon you, and heap upon it all the love of all the
loving human hearts in the world, and then multiply

it by infinity, and you will begin perhaps to have some faint glimpses of the love and grace of God!

In order to "grow in grace," therefore, the soul must be planted in the very heart of this Divine love, be enveloped by it, steeped in it. It must let itself out to the joy of it, and must refuse to know anything else. It must grow in the apprehension of it, day by day, it must entrust everything to its care, and must have no shadow of doubt but that it will surely order all things well.

To grow in grace is opposed to all growth in self-dependence or self-effort,—to all legality, in fact, of every kind. It is to put our growing, as well as everything else, into the hands of the Lord and leave it with him. It is to be so satisfied with our Husbandman, and with His skill and wisdom, that not a question will cross our minds as to His mode of treatment or His plan of cultivation. It is to grow as the lilies grow, or as the babies grow, without care and without anxiety; to grow by the power of an inward life-principle that cannot help but grow; to grow because we live, and therefore must grow; to grow because He who has planted us has planted a growing thing, and has made us on purpose to grow.

Surely this is what our Lord meant when He said, "Consider the lilies, how they grow: they toil not, neither do they spin: and yet I say unto you, that even Solomon in all his glory was not arrayed like one of these." Or, when He says again, "Which of you by taking thought can add one cubit unto his stature?" There is no effort in the growing of a babe or of a lily. The lily does not toil nor spin, it does not stretch nor strain, it does not make any effort of any kind to grow, it is not conscious even that it is growing; but by an inward life-principle, and through the nurturing care of God's providence and the fostering of care-taker or gardener, by the heat of the sun and the falling of the rain, it grows and buds and blossoms into the beautiful plant God meant it to be.

The result of this sort of growing in the Christian life is sure. Even Solomon in all his glory, our Lord says, was not arrayed like one of God's lilies. Solomon's array cost much toiling and spinning, and gold and silver in abundance: but the lily's array costs none of these. And though we may toil and spin to make for ourselves beautiful spiritual garments, and may strain and stretch in our efforts after spiritual growth, we shall accomplish nothing; for no man by taking thought *can* add one cubit to his stature, and no array of ours can ever equal the beautiful dress with which the great Husbandman clothes the plants that grow in His garden of grace and under His fostering care.

Could I but make each one of my readers realize how utterly helpless we are in this matter of growing, I am convinced a large part of the strain would be taken out of many lives at once.

Imagine a child possessed of the monomania that he would not grow unless he made some personal effort after it, and who should insist upon a combination of ropes and pulleys whereby to stretch himself up to the desired height. He might, it is true, spend his days and years in a weary strain, but after all there would be no change in the inexorable fiat, "No man by taking thought can add one cubit unto his stature," and his weary efforts would be only wasted, if they did not actually hinder the longed-for end.

Imagine a lily trying to clothe itself in beautiful colors and graceful lines, and drawing to its aid, as so many of God's children try to do, the wisdom and strength of all the lilies around it! I think such a lily would very soon become a chronic "case" of spiritual perplexities and difficulties, similar to some that are familiar to every Christian worker.

Neither child nor lily is ever found doing such a vain and foolish thing as *trying* to grow. But I fear many of God's children are doing exactly this foolish thing. They know that they ought to grow, and they feel within them an instinct that longs for growth; but, instead of letting the Divine Husbandman care for their growing, as it is surely His business to do, they think to accomplish it by their own toiling and spinning, and stretching and straining; and in consequence they pass their lives in a round of wearisome self-efforts that exhausts their energies, while all the time they find themselves, to their infinite grief, growing backward rather than forward.

> " 'Ye flowrets of the field,' Siddartha said,
>   'Who turn your tender faces to the sun,
>   What secret know ye, that ye grow content?' "

What we all need is to "consider the flowers of the field," and learn their secret. Grow, by all means, dear Christians; but grow, I beseech you, in God's way, which is the only effectual way. See to it that you are planted in grace, and then let the Divine Husbandman cultivate you in His own way and by His own means. Put yourselves out in the sunshine of His presence, and let the dew of heaven come down upon you, and see what will be the result. Leaves and flowers and fruit must surely come in their season; for your Husbandman is skilful, and He never fails in His harvesting. Only see to it that you oppose no hindrance to the shining of the Sun of Righteousness, or the falling of the dew from Heaven. The thinnest covering may serve to keep off the sunshine and the dew, and the plant may wither, even where these are most abundant. And so also the slightest barrier between your soul and Christ may cause you to dwindle and fade, as a plant in a cellar or under a bushel. Keep the sky clear. Open wide every avenue of your being to receive the blessed influences your Divine Husbandman may bring to bear upon you. Bask in the sunshine of His love. Drink of the waters of His goodness. Keep your face upturned to Him as the flowers do to the sun. Look, and your soul shall live and grow.

But it may be objected here that we are not inanimate flowers, but intelligent human beings, with personal powers and personal responsibilities. This is true; and it makes this important difference, that what the flower is by nature we must be by an intelligent and free surrender. To be one of God's lilies means an interior abandonment of the rarest kind. It means that we are to be infinitely passive, and yet infinitely active also: passive as regards self and its workings, active as regards attention and response to God. It is very hard to explain this so as to be understood. But it means that we must lay down all the activity of the creature as such, and must let only the activities of God work in us, and through us, and by us. Self must step aside to let God work.

You need make no efforts to grow, therefore; but let your efforts instead be all concentrated on this, that you abide in the Vine. The Divine Husbandman who has the care of the Vine, will care also for you who are His branches, and will so prune and purge and water and tend you that you will grow and bring forth fruit, and your fruit shall remain, and, like the lily, you shall find yourself arrayed in apparel so glorious, that the apparel of Solomon will be as nothing to it.

What if you seem to yourselves to be planted at this

moment in a desert soil, where nothing can grow. Put
yourselves absolutely into the hands of the good Husbandman, and He will at once begin to make that very desert
blossom as the rose, and will cause springs and fountains
of water to start up out of its sandy wastes. For the promise is sure, that the man who trusts in the Lord "shall be
as a tree planted by the waters, and that spreadeth out
her roots by the river, and shall not see when heat cometh, but her leaf shall be green; and shall not be careful
in the year of drought, neither shall cease from yielding
fruit."

It is the great prerogative of our Divine Husbandman
that He is able to turn any soil, whatever it may be like,
into the soil of grace the moment we put our growing into
His hands. He does not need to transplant us into a different field, but right where we are, with just the circumstances that surround us, He makes His sun to shine and
His dew to fall upon us, and transforms the very things
that were before our greatest hindrances into the chiefest
and most blessed means of our growth. I care not what
the circumstances may be, His wonder-working power
can accomplish this; and we must trust Him with it all.
Surely He is a Husbandman we *can* trust; and if He sends
storms, or winds, or rains, or sunshine, all must be accepted at His hands with the most unwavering confidence
that He who has undertaken to cultivate us, and to bring
us to maturity, knows the very best way of accomplishing
His end, and regulates the elements, which are all at His
disposal, expressly with a view to our most rapid growth.

Let me entreat of you, then, to give up all your efforts
after growing, and simply to *let* yourselves grow. Leave
it all to the Husbandman whose care it is, and who alone
is able to manage it. No difficulties in your case can baffle
Him. If you will only put yourselves absolutely into His
hands, and let Him have His own way with you, no dwarf-
ing of your growth in the years that are past, no apparent
dryness of your inward springs of life, no crookedness or
deformity in your development, can in the least mar the
perfect work that He will accomplish. His own gracious
promise to His backsliding children assures you of this. "I
will heal their backslidings," He says, "I will love them
freely: for mine anger is turned away from him. I will
be as the dew unto Israel; he shall grow as the lily, and
cast forth his roots as Lebanon. His branches shall spread
and his beauty shall be as the olive-tree, and his smell

as Lebanon. They that dwell under his shadow shall return; they shall revive as the corn, and grow as the vine: the scent thereof shall be as the wine of Lebanon." And again He says: "Be not afraid: for the pastures of the wilderness do spring, for the tree beareth her fruit, the fig-tree and the vine do yield their strength. . . . And the floors shall be full of wheat, and the vats shall overflow with wine and oil. And I will restore to you the years that the locust hath eaten. . . . And ye shall eat in plenty, and be satisfied, and praise the name of the Lord your God, that hath dealt wondrously with you: and my people shall never be ashamed."

Oh that you could but know just what your Lord meant when He said, "Consider the lilies of the field, *how they grow;* they toil not, neither do they spin!" Surely these words give us the picture of a life and growth far different from the ordinary life and growth of Christians,— a life of rest, and a growth without effort; and yet a life and a growth crowned with glorious results. And to every soul that will thus become a lily in the garden of the Lord, and will grow as the lilies grow, the same glorious array will be as surely given as was given to them; and they will know the fulfilment of that wonderful mystical passage concerning their Beloved, that "He feedeth among the lilies."

> "I feel as weak as a violet
>   Alone with the awful sky:
>   Winds wander, and dews drop earthward,
>   Rains fall, suns rise and set,
>   Earth whirls; and all but to prosper
>   A poor little violet!"

We may rest assured of this, that all the resources of God's infinite grace will be brought to bear on the growing of the tiniest flower in His spiritual garden, as certainly as they are in His earthly creation; and as the violet abides peacefully in its little place, content to receive its daily portion without concerning itself about the wandering of the winds, or the falling of the rain, so must we repose in the present moment as it comes to us from God, contented with our daily portion, and without anxious thought as to anything that may be whirling around us in God's glorious universe, sure that all things will be made to "prosper" for us.

This is the kind of "growth in grace" in which we who have entered into the life of full trust believe; a growth without care or anxiety on our part, but a growth which does actually grow, which blossoms out into flower and fruit, and becomes like a "tree planted by the rivers of water, that bringeth forth his fruit in his season"; whose leaf also does not wither, and who prospers in whatsoever he doeth. And we rejoice to know that there are growing up now in the Lord's heritage many such plants, who, as the lilies behold the face of the sun and grow thereby, are, by "beholding as in a glass the glory of the Lord," being changed into the same image from glory to glory, even as by the Spirit of the Lord.

Should you ask such how it is that they grow so rapidly and with such success, their answer would be that they are not concerned about their growing, and are hardly conscious that they do grow. That their Lord has told them to abide in Him, and has promised that, if they do thus abide, they shall certainly bring forth much fruit; and that they are concerned, therefore, only about the abiding, which is their part, and are content to leave the cultivating, and the growing, and the training, and the pruning, to their good Husbandman, who alone is able to manage these things or to bring them about. You will find that such souls are not engaged in watching self, but in "looking unto Jesus." They do not "toil and spin" for their spiritual garments, but leave themselves in the hands of the Lord, to be arrayed as it may please Him. Self-effort and self-dependence are at an end with them. Formerly they tried to be not only the garden but the gardener also as well, and undertook to fulfil the duties of both. Now they are content to *be* what they *are*,—willing to leave the gardener's duties to the Divine Husbandman, who alone is responsible for their rightful performance. Their interest in self is gone, transferred over into the hands of another; and self in consequence has become nothing to them more and more, and Christ alone is seen to be all in all. And the blessed result is that not even Solomon in all his glory was arrayed as these shall be.

Let us look at the subject practically. We all know that growing is not a thing of effort, but is the result of an inward life-principle of growth. All the stretching and pulling in the world could not make a dead oak grow; but a live oak grows without stretching. It is plain, therefore, that the essential thing is to get within you the growing life, and then you cannot help but grow. And this life is the "life hid with Christ in God," the wonderful divine life of an indwelling Holy Ghost. Be filled with this, dear believer, and, whether you are conscious of it or not, you must grow, you cannot help growing. Do not trouble about your growing, but see to it that you have the growing life. Abide in the Vine. Let the life from Him flow through all your spiritual veins. Interpose no barrier to His mighty life-giving power, "working in you all the good pleasure of his will." Yield yourself up utterly to His lovely control. Put your growing into His hands as completely as you have put all your other affairs. Suffer Him to manage it as He will. Do not concern yourself about it, nor even think of it. Do not, as children do, keep digging your plants to see if they are growing. Trust the Divine Husbandman absolutely, and always. Accept each moment's dispensation as it comes to you from His dear hands as being the needed sunshine or dew for that moment's growth. Say a continual "Yes" to your Father's will. And finally, in this, as in all the other cares of your life, "be careful for nothing; but in everything, by prayer and supplication, with thanksgiving, let your requests be made known unto God. And the peace of God that passeth all understanding shall keep your hearts and minds through Christ Jesus."

If your "growth in grace" is of this sort, dear reader, you will surely know, sooner or later, a wonderful growing, and you will come to understand, as you cannot now, it may be, what the Psalmist meant when he said, "The righteous shall flourish like the palm-tree: he shall grow like a cedar in Lebanon. Those that be planted in the house of the Lord shall flourish in the courts of our God. They shall bring forth fruit in old age; they shall be fat and flourishing."

Chapter Fifteen

Service

THERE IS, PERHAPS, NO PART OF CHRISTIAN EXPERIENCE where a greater change is known, upon entering into this life hid with Christ in God, than in the matter of service.

In all the ordinary forms of Christian life, service is apt to have more or less of bondage in it; that is, it is done purely as a matter of duty, and often as a trial and a cross. Certain things, which at the first may have been a joy and a delight, become after a while weary tasks, performed faithfully, perhaps, but with much secret disinclination, and many confessed or unconfessed wishes that they need not be done at all, or at least that they need not be done so often. The soul finds itself saying, instead of the "May I?" of love, the "Must I?" of duty. The yoke, which was at first easy, begins to gall, and the burden feels heavy instead of light.

One dear Christian expressed it once to me in this way: "When I was first converted," she said, "I was so full of joy and love that I was only too glad and thankful to be allowed to do anything for my Lord, and I eagerly entered every open door. But after a while, as my early joy faded away, and my love burned less fervently, I began to wish I had not been quite so eager; for I found myself involved in lines of service that were gradually becoming very distasteful and burdensome to me. Since I had begun them, I could not very well give them up without exciting great remark, and yet I longed to do so increasingly. I was expected to visit the sick, and pray beside their beds. I was expected to attend prayer-meetings, and speak at them. I was expected, in short, to be always ready for every effort in Christian work, and the sense of these expectations bowed me down continually. At last it became so unspeakably burdensome to me to live the sort of Christian life I had entered upon, and was expected by all around me to live, that I felt as if any kind of manual labor would have been easier; and I would have infinitely preferred scrubbing all day on my hands and knees to

being compelled to go through the treadmill of my daily
Christian work. I envied," she said, "the servants in the
kitchen, and the women at the washtubs."

This may seem to some like a strong statement; but
does it not present a vivid picture of some of your own
experiences, dear Christian? Have you never gone to your
work as a slave to his daily task, believing it to be your
duty and that therefore you must do it, but rebounding
like an India-rubber ball back into your real interests
and pleasures the moment your work was over?

You have known of course that this was the wrong way
to feel, and have been thoroughly ashamed of it, but still
you have seen no way to help it. You have not *loved* your
work; and, could you have done so with an easy conscience, you would have been glad to give it up altogether.

Or, if this does not describe your case, perhaps another
picture will. You do love your work in the abstract, but
in the doing of it you find so many cares and responsibilities connected with it, and feel so many misgivings
and doubts as to your own capacity or fitness, that it
becomes a very heavy burden, and you go to it bowed
down and weary before the labor has even begun. Then
also you are continually distressing yourself about the results of your work, and greatly troubled if they are not
just what you would like; and this of itself is a constant
burden.

Now, from all these forms of bondage the soul that
enters fully into the blessed life of faith is entirely delivered. In the first place, service of any sort becomes delightful to it, because, having surrendered its will into the
keeping of the Lord, He works in it to will and to do of
His good pleasure, and the soul finds itself really *wanting*
to do the things God wants it to do. It is always very
pleasant to do the things we *want* to do, let them be ever
so difficult of accomplishment, or involve ever so much of
bodily weariness. If a man's *will* is really set on a thing
he regards with a sublime indifference the obstacles that
lie in the way of his reaching it, and laughs to himself at
the idea of any opposition or difficulties hindering him.
How many men have gone gladly and thankfully to
the ends of the world in search of worldly fortunes, or to
fulfil worldly ambitions, and have scorned the thought of
any "cross" connected with it! How many mothers have
congratulated themselves, and rejoiced over the honor
done their sons in seeing them promoted to some place

of power and usefulness in their country's service, although it has involved perhaps years of separation, and a life of hardship for their dear ones! And yet these same men, and these very mothers, would have felt and said that they were taking up crosses too heavy almost to be borne, had the service of Christ required the same sacrifice of home, and friends, and worldly ease.

It is altogether the way we look at things, whether we think they are crosses or not. And I am ashamed to think that any Christian should ever put on a long face and shed tears over doing a thing for Christ which a worldly man would be only too glad to do for money.

What we need in the Christian life is to get believers to *want* to do God's will as much as other people want to do their own will. And this is the idea of the Gospel. It is what God intended for us; and it is what He has promised. In describing the new covenant in Hebrews 8: 6–13, He says it shall no more be the old covenant made on Sinai, —that is, a law given from the outside, controlling a man by force,—but it shall be a law written *within,* constraining a man by love. "I will put my laws," He says, "into their mind, and write them in their hearts." This can mean nothing but that we shall *love* His law; for anything written in our hearts we must love. "And putting it into our minds" is surely the same as God working in us to "will and to do of his good pleasure," and means that we shall will what God wills, and shall obey His sweet commands, not because it is our duty to do so, but because we ourselves want to do what He wants us to do.

Nothing could possibly be conceived more effectual than this. How often have we thought, when dealing with our children, "Oh, if I could only get inside of them, and make them *want* to do just what I want, how easy it would be to manage them then!" How often in practical experience we have found that to deal with cross-grained people we most carefully avoid suggesting our wishes to them, but must in some way induce them to suggest the thing themselves, sure that there will then be no opposition to contend with. And we, who are by nature a stiff-necked people, always rebel more or less against a law from outside of us, while we joyfully embrace the same law springing up within.

God's way of working, therefore, is to get possession of the inside of a man, to take the control and management of his will, and to work it for him. Then obedience is easy and a delight, and service becomes perfect freedom, until the Christian is forced to explain, "This happy service! who could dream earth had such liberty?"

What you need to do, then, dear Christian, if you are in bondage in the matter of service, is to put your will over completely into the hands of your Lord, surrendering to Him the entire control of it. Say, "Yes, Lord, YES!" to everything, and trust Him so to work in you to will as to bring your whole wishes and affections into conformity with His own sweet, and lovable, and most lovely will. I have seen this done often in cases where it looked beforehand an utterly impossible thing. In one case, where a lady had been for years rebelling fearfully against a little act of service which she knew was right, but which she hated, I saw her, out of the depths of despair, and without any feeling whatever, give her will in that matter up into the hands of her Lord, and begin to say to Him, "Thy will be done; *Thy will be done!*" And in one short hour that very thing began to look sweet and precious to her.

It is wonderful what miracles God works in wills that are utterly surrendered to Him. He turns hard things into easy, and bitter things into sweet. It is not that He puts easy things in the place of the hard, but He actually changes the hard thing into an easy one, and makes us love to do the thing we before so hated. While we rebel against the yoke, and try to avoid it, we find it hard and galling. But when we "take the yoke upon us" with a consenting will, we find it easy and comfortable. It is said of Ephraim that at one time he was like "a bullock unaccustomed to the yoke," but that afterwards, when he had submitted to the yoke, he was "as an heifer that is taught, and *loveth* to tread out the corn."

Many Christians, as I have said, love God's will in the abstract, but carry great burdens in connection with it. From this also there is deliverance in the wonderful life of faith. For in this life no burdens are carried, no anxieties felt. The Lord is our burden-bearer, and upon Him we must lay off every care. He says, in effect, "Be careful for nothing, but make your requests known to me, and I will attend to them all." Be careful for *nothing,* He says, not even your service. Above all, I should think, our service, because we know ourselves to be so utterly helpless in regard to it, that, even if we were careful, it would not amount to anything. What have we to do with thinking whether we are fit or not? The Masterworkman surely

has a right to use any tool He pleases for His own work, and
it is plainly not the business of the tool to decide whether
it is the right one to be used or not. He knows; and if He
chooses to use us, of course we must be fit. And in truth,
if we only knew it, our chief fitness is in our utter helplessness. His strength is made perfect, not in our strength,
but in our weakness. Our strength is only a hindrance.

I was once visiting an idiot asylum, and saw the children
going through dumbbell exercises. Now, we all know that
it is a very difficult thing for idiots to manage their movements. They have strength enough, generally, but no skill
to use this strength, and as a consequence cannot do
much. And in these dumbbell exercises this deficiency was
very apparent. They made all sorts of awkward movements. Now and then, by a happy chance, they would
make a movement in harmony with the music and the
teacher's directions, but for the most part all was out of
harmony. One little girl, however, I noticed, who made
perfect movements. Not a jar or a break disturbed the
harmony of her exercises. And the reason was not that
she had more strength than the others, but that she had
no strength at all. She could not so much as close her
hands over the dumbbells, nor lift her arms, and the master had to stand behind her, and do it all. She yielded up
her members as instruments to him, and his "strength
was made perfect" in her weakness. He knew how to go
through those exercises, for he himself had planned
them; and therefore when he did it, it was done right.
She did nothing but yield herself up utterly into his hands,
and he did it all. The yielding was her part; the responsibility was all his. It was not her skill that was needed to
make harmonious movements, but only his. The question was not of her capacity, but of his. Her utter weakness was her greatest strength.

To me this is a very striking picture of our Christian
life, and it is no wonder therefore that Paul could say,
"Most gladly therefore will I rather *glory* in my infirmities,
that the power of Christ may rest upon me." Who would
not glory in being so utterly weak and helpless that the
Lord Jesus Christ should find no hindrance to the perfect
working of His mighty power through us and in us?

Then, too, if the work is His, the responsibility is His,
also, and we have no room left for worrying about results.
Everything in reference to it is known to Him, and He
can manage it all. Why not leave it all with Him, then,

and consent to be "treated like a child and guided where
to go"? It is a fact that the most effectual workers I know,
are those who do not feel the least care or anxiety about
their work, but who commit it all to their dear Master,
and, asking Him to guide them moment by moment in
reference to it, trust Him implicitly for each moment's
needed supplies of wisdom and of strength. To look at
them, you would almost think, perhaps, that they were
too free from care where such mighty interests were at
stake. But when you have learned God's secret of trusting,
and see the beauty and the power of the life that is yielded
up to His working, you will cease to condemn, and will
begin to wonder how any of God's workers can dare to
carry the burdens, or assume the responsibilities, which
He alone is able to bear.

Some may object that the Apostle Paul spoke of the
"care of the churches" coming upon him. But we must
not fail to remember that it was the constant habit of
the Apostle to roll every care off on the Lord, and thus,
while full of care, to be "without carefulness."

There are one or two other bonds in service from which
this life of trust delivers us. We find out that no one individual is responsible for all the work in the world, but
only for a small share. Our duty ceases to be universal,
and becomes personal and individual. The Master does
not say to us, "Go and do everything," but He marks out
an especial path for each one of us, and gives to each one
of us an especial duty. There are "diversities of gifts" in
the kingdom of God, and these gifts are divided to "every
man according to his ability." I may have five talents,
or two, or only one; I may be called to do twenty things, or
only one. My responsibility is simply to do that which
I am called to do, and nothing more. "The *steps* of a good
man are ordered of the Lord," not his way only, but each
separate step in that way.

Many Christians make the further mistake of looking
upon every act of service as of perpetual obligation. They
think because it was right for them to give a tract to one
person in a railway train, for instance, that therefore they
are always to give tracts to everybody, and in this way
they burden themselves with an impossible duty.

There was a young Christian once, who, because she
had been sent to speak a message to one soul whom she
met in a walk, supposed it was a perpetual obligation, and
thought she must speak about his soul to every one she

met in her walks. This was of course impossible, and as a
consequence she was soon in hopeless bondage about it.
She became absolutely afraid to go outside of her own
door, and lived in perpetual condemnation. At last she
disclosed her distress to a friend who was instructed in
the ways of God with His servants; and this friend
told her she was making a great mistake; that the Lord
had His own especial work for each especial workman,
and that the servants in a well-regulated household
might as well each one take it upon himself to try to do
the work of all the rest as for the Lord's servants to
think they were each one under obligation to do everything. He told her just to put herself under the Lord's
personal guidance as to her work, and trust Him to point
out to her each particular person to whom He would have
her speak, assuring her that He never puts forth His own
sheep without going before them, and making a way for
them Himself. She followed this advice, and laid the
burden of her work on the Lord, and the result was a
happy pathway of daily guidance, in which she was led
into much blessed work for her Master, and was able to
do it all without a care or a burden, because He led her
out and prepared the way before her.

I have been very much instructed myself by thinking
of the arrangements of our own households. When we
appoint a servant for an especial part of the work of the
household, we want him to attend to that alone, and
not run all over the house trying to attend to the work
of all the other servants. It would make endless confusion
in any earthly household if the servants were to act in
this fashion, and it makes no less confusion in the Divine
household.

Our part in the matter of service seems to me just like
making the junction between the machinery and the
steam-engine. The power is not in the machinery, but in the
steam. Disconnected from the engine, the machinery is
perfectly useless. But let the connection be made, and the
machinery goes easily and without effort because of the
mighty power there is behind it. Thus the Christian life,
when it is the development of the Divine life working
within, becomes an easy and natural life. Most Christians
live in a strain, because their wills are not fully in harmony
with the will of God, the connection is not perfectly made
at every point, and it requires an effort to move the machinery. But when once the connection is fully made, and

the "law of the Spirit of life in Christ Jesus" can work in
us with all its mighty power, we are then indeed made
"free from the law of sin and death," and shall know the
glorious liberty of the children of God.

Another form of bondage as to service, from which the
life of faith delivers the soul, is in reference to the after-
reflections which always follow any Christian work. These
after-reflections are of two sorts: either the soul con-
gratulates itself upon its success, and is lifted up; or it is
distressed over its failure, and is utterly cast down. One of
these is *sure* to come; and of the two I think the former
is the more to be dreaded, although the latter causes at
the time the greater suffering. But in the life of trust
neither will trouble us; for, having committed ourselves
in our work to the Lord, we shall be satisfied to leave it to
Him, and shall not think about ourselves in the matter at
all.

Years ago I came across this sentence in an old book:
"Never indulge, at the close of an action, in any self-re-
flective acts of any kind, whether of self-congratulation or
of self-despair. Forget the things that are behind, the
moment they are past, leaving them with God." This has
been of unspeakable value to me. When the temptation
comes, as it mostly does to every worker after the performance of any service, to indulge in these reflections,
either of one sort or the other, I turn from them at once
and positively refuse to think about my work at all,
leaving it with the Lord to overrule the mistakes, and to
bless it as He chooses. I believe there would be far fewer
"blue Mondays" for ministers of the Gospel than there
are now if they would adopt this plan; and I am sure all
workers would find their work far less wearing.

To sum it all up, then, what is needed for happy and
effectual service is simply to put your work into the Lord's
hands, and leave it there. Do not take it to Him in prayer,
saying, "Lord, guide me; Lord, give me wisdom; Lord,
arrange for me," and then rise from your knees, and
take the burden all back and try to guide and arrange for
yourself. *Leave* it with the Lord; and remember that what
you trust to Him you must not worry over nor feel anxious
about. Trust and worry cannot go together. If your work
is a burden it is because you are not trusting it to Him. But
if you do trust it to Him you will surely find that the yoke
He puts upon you is easy, and the burden He gives you to

carry is light: and even in the midst of a life of ceaseless activity you shall "find rest to your soul."

If the Divine Master only had a band of such workers as this, there is no limit to what He might do with them. Truly, one such would "chase a thousand, and two would put ten thousand to flight," and nothing would be impossible to them. For it is nothing with the Lord "to help, whether with many, or with them that have no power," if only He can find instruments that are fully abandoned to His working.

May God raise up such an army speedily! And may you, my dear reader, enroll your name among this band, and, yielding yourself unto God as one who is "alive from the dead," may every one of your members be also yielded unto Him as "instruments of righteousness," to be used by Him as He pleases!

Chapter Sixteen

Practical Results in Daily Life

IF ALL THAT HAS BEEN WRITTEN IN THE FOREGOING CHAPters on the life hid with Christ be true, its results in the practical daily walk and conversation ought to be very marked, and the people who have entered into the enjoyment of it ought to be, in very truth, a peculiar people, zealous of good works.

My son, now with God, once wrote to a friend something to this effect: that we are God's witnesses necessarily, because the world will not read the Bible, but they will read our lives; and that upon the report these give will very much depend their belief in the divine nature of the religion we possess. This age is essentially an age of facts, and all scientific inquiries are being increasingly turned from theories to realities. If, therefore, our religion is to make any headway in the present time, it must be proved to be more than a theory, and we must present to the investigation of the critical minds of our age the realities of lives transformed by the mighty power of God, "working in them all the good pleasure of His will."

I desire, therefore, to speak very solemnly of what I conceive to be the necessary fruits of a life of faith such as I have been describing, and to press home to the hearts of every one of my readers their personal responsibility to "walk worthy of the high calling" wherewith they have been called.

I think that I may speak to some of you at least as personal friends, for I feel sure we have not gone thus far together through these pages without there having grown in your hearts, as there has in mine, a tender personal interest and longing for one another, that we may in everything show forth the praises of Him who has "called us out of darkness into His marvelous light." As a friend to friends, then, I speak, and I am sure I shall be pardoned if I go into some details of our daily lives, which may seem of secondary importance, and which make up the largest part of them.

The standard of practical holy living has been so low among Christians that the least degree of real devotedness of life and walk is looked upon with surprise and often even with disapprobation by a large portion of the Church. And, for the most part, the followers of the Lord Jesus Christ are satisfied with a life so conformed to the world, and so like it in almost every respect, that, to a casual observer, no difference is discernible.

But we who have heard the call of our God to a life of entire consecration and perfect trust must do differently. We must come out from the world and be separate, and must not be conformed to it in our characters or in our lives. We must set our affections on heavenly things, not on earthly ones, and must seek first the kingdom of God and His righteousness; surrendering every thing that would interfere with this. We must walk through the world as Christ walked. We must have the mind that was in Him. As pilgrims and strangers, we must abstain from fleshly lusts that war against the soul. As good soldiers of Jesus Christ, we must disentangle ourselves inwardly from the affairs of this life, that we may please Him who hath chosen us to be soldiers. We must abstain from all appearance of evil. We must be kind to one another, tender-hearted, forgiving one another, even as God, for Christ's sake, hath forgiven us. We must not resent injuries or unkindness, but must return good for evil, and turn the other cheek to the hand that smites us. We must take always the lowest place among our fellow men; and seek, not our own honor, but the honor of others. We must be gentle, and meek, and yielding; not standing up for our own rights, but for the rights of others. We must do everything, not for our own glory, but for the glory of God. And, to sum it all up, since He who hath called us is holy, so we must be holy in all manner of conversation; because it is written, "Be ye holy, for I am holy."

Some Christians seem to think that all the requirements of a holy life are met when there is very active and successful Christian work; and because they do so much for the Lord in public they feel a liberty to be cross and ugly and un-Christlike in private. But this is not the sort of Christian life I am depicting. If we are to walk as Christ walked, it must be in private as well as in public, at home as well as abroad; and it must be every hour all day long, and not at stated periods or on certain fixed occasions. We must be just as Christlike to our servants as we are to our minister, and just as "good" in our countinghouse as we are in our prayer-meeting.

It is in daily homely living, indeed, that practical piety can best show itself, and we may well question any "professions" that fail under this test of daily life.

A cross Christian, or an anxious Christian, a discouraged, gloomy Christian, a doubting Christian, a complaining Christian, an exacting Christian, a selfish Christian, a cruel, hard-hearted Christian, a self-indulgent Christian, a Christian with a sharp tongue or bitter spirit, all these may be very earnest in their work, and may have honorable places in the Church; but they are *not* Christlike Christians, and they know nothing of the realities of which this book treats, no matter how loud their professions may be.

The life hid with Christ in God is a hidden life, as to its source, but it must not be hidden as to its practical results. People must see that we walk as Christ walked, if we say that we are abiding in Him. We must prove that we "possess" that which we "profess." We must, in short, be real followers of Christ, and not theoretical ones only. And this means a great deal. It means that we must really and absolutely turn our backs on everything that is contrary to the perfect will of God. It means that we are to be a "peculiar people," not only in the eyes of God, but in the eyes of the world around us; and that, wherever we go, it will be known from our habits, our tempers, our conversation and our pursuits, that we are followers of the Lord Jesus Christ, and are not of the world, even as He was not of the world. We must no longer look upon our money as our own, but as belonging to the Lord, to be used in His service. We must not feel at liberty to use our energies exclusively in the pursuit of worldly means, but must recognize, that, if we seek first the kingdom of God and His righteousness, all needful things shall be added unto us. We shall find ourselves forbidden to seek the highest places, or to strain after worldly advantages. We shall not be permitted to make self, as heretofore, the center of all our thoughts and all our aims. Our days will have to be spent, not in serving ourselves, but in serving the Lord; and we shall find ourselves called upon to bear one another's burdens, and so fulfil the law of Christ. And all our daily homely duties will be more perfectly performed than ever, because whatever we do will be done, "not with eye-service, as men-pleasers, but as the servants of Christ, doing the will of God from the heart."

Into all this we shall undoubtedly be led by the Spirit of God if we give ourselves up to His guidance. But unless we have the right standard of Christian life set before us, we may be hindered by our ignorance from recognizing His voice; and it is for this reason I desire to be very plain and definite in my statements.

I have noticed that wherever there has been a faithful following of the Lord in a consecrated soul, several things have, sooner or later, inevitably followed.

Meekness and quietness of spirit become in time the characteristics of the daily life. A submissive acceptance of the will of God, as it comes in the hourly events of each day, is manifested; pliability in the hands of God to do or to suffer all the good pleasure of His will; sweetness under provocation; calmness in the midst of turmoil and bustle; a yielding to the wishes of others, and an insensibility to slights and affronts; absence of worry or anxiety; deliverance from care and fear,—all these, and many other similar graces, are invariably found to be the natural outward development of that inward life which is hid with Christ in God. Then as to the habits of life: we always see such Christians sooner or later laying aside thoughts of self, and becoming full of consideration for others; they dress and live in simple, healthful ways;

they renounce self-indulgent habits, and surrender all purely fleshly gratifications. Some helpful work for others is taken up, and useless occupations are dropped out of the life. God's glory and the welfare of His creatures become the absorbing delight of the soul. The voice is dedicated to Him, to be used in singing His praises. The purse is placed at His disposal. The pen is dedicated to write for Him, the lips to speak for Him, the hands and the feet to do His bidding. Year after year such Christians are seen to grow more unworldly, more serene, more heavenly-minded, more transformed, more like Christ, until even their faces express so much of the beautiful inward divine life, that all who look at them cannot but take knowledge of them that they live with Jesus, and are abiding in Him.

I feel sure that to each one of you have come some divine intimations or forshadowings of the life I here describe. Have you not begun to feel dimly conscious of the voice of God speaking to you, in the depths of your soul, about these things? Has it not been a pain and a distress to you of late to discover how full your lives are of self? Has not your soul been plunged into inward trouble and doubt about certain dispositions or pursuits in which you have been formerly accustomed to indulge? Have you not begun to feel uneasy with some of your habits of life, and to wish that you could do differently in certain respects? Have not paths of devotedness and of service begun to open out before you, with the longing thought, "Oh that I could walk in them!" All these questions and doubts and this inward yearning are the voice of the Good Shepherd in your heart, seeking to call you out of that which is contrary to His will. Let me entreat of you not to turn away from His gentle pleadings! You little know the sweet paths into which He means to lead you by these very steps, nor the wonderful stores of blessedness that lie at their end, or you would spring forward with an eager joy to yield to every one of His requirements. The heights of Christian perfection can only be reached by each moment faithfully following the Guide who is to lead you there; and He reveals the way to us one step at a time, in the little things of our daily lives, asking only on our part that we yield ourselves up to His guidance. Be perfectly pliable then in His dear hands, to go where He entices you, and to turn away from all from which He makes you shrink. Obey Him perfectly the moment you are sure of His will; and you will soon find that He is leading you out swiftly and easily into such a wonderful life of conformity to Himself that it will be a testimony to all around you, beyond what you yourself will ever know.

I knew a soul thus given up to follow the Lord whithersoever He might lead her, who in a very little while traveled from the depths of darkness and despair, into the realization and actual experience of a most blessed union with the Lord Jesus Christ. Out of the midst of her darkness she consecrated herself to the Lord, surrendering her will up altogether to Him, that He might work in her to will and to do of His own good pleasure. Immediately He began to speak to her by His Spirit in her heart, suggesting to her some little acts of service for Him, and troubling her about certain things in her habits and her life, showing her where she was selfish and un-Christlike, and how she could be transformed. She recognized His voice, and yielded to Him each thing He asked for the moment she was sure of His will. Her swift obedience was rewarded by a rapid progress, and day by day she was conformed more and more to the image of Christ, until very soon her life became such a testimony to those around her that some even who had begun by opposing and disbelieving were forced to acknowledge that it was of God, and were won to a similar surrender. And, finally, in a little while it came to pass, so swiftly had she gone, that her Lord was able to reveal to her wondering soul some of the deepest secrets of His love, and to fulfil to her the marvelous promise of Acts 1: 5 by giving her to realize the baptism of the Holy Ghost. Think you she has ever regretted her whole-hearted following of Him? Or that aught but thankfulness and joy can ever fill her soul when she reviews the steps by which her feet have been led to this place of wondrous blessedness, even though some of them may have seemed at the time hard to take? Ah, dear soul, if thou wouldst know a like blessing abandon thyself, like her, to the guidance of thy divine Master, and shrink from no surrender for which He may call.

> "The perfect way is hard to flesh,
>   It is not hard to love;
> If thou wert sick for want of God,
>   How swiftly wouldst thou move!"

Surely thou canst trust Him! And if some things may be called for that look to thee of but little moment, and not worthy thy Lord's attention, remember that He sees not as man seeth, and that things small to thee may be in His eyes the key and the clue to the deepest springs of thy being. No life can be complete that fails in its little things. A look, a word, a tone of voice even, however small they may seem to human judgment, are often of vital importance in the eyes of God. Thy one great desire is to follow Him fully; canst thou not say, then, a continual "Yes" to all His sweet commands, whether small or great, and trust Him to lead thee by the shortest road to thy fullest blessedness?

My dear friend, whether thou knew it or not, this, and nothing less than this, is what thy consecration meant. It meant inevitable obedience. It meant that the will of thy God was henceforth to be thy will, under all circumstances and at all times. It meant that from that moment thou didst surrender thy liberty of choice, and gave thyself up utterly into the control of thy Lord. It meant an hourly following of Him, whithersoever He might lead thee, without any turning back.

All this and far more was involved in thy surrender to God, and now I appeal to thee to make good thy word. Let everything else go, that thou mayst live out, in a practical daily walk and conversation, the Christ-life thou hast dwelling within thee. Thou art united to thy Lord by a wondrous tie; walk, then, as He walked, and show to the unbelieving world the blessed reality of His mighty power to save, by letting Him save thee to the very uttermost. Thou needst not fear to consent to this, for He is thy Saviour, and His power is to do it all. He is not asking thee, in thy poor weakness, to do it thyself; He only asks thee to yield thyself to Him, that He may work in thee and through thee by His own mighty power. Thy part is to yield thyself, His part is to work; and never, never will He give thee any command that is not accompanied by ample power to obey it. Take no thought for the morrow in this matter; but abandon thyself with a generous trust to the good Shepherd, who has promised never to call His own sheep out into any path, without Himself going before them to make the way easy and safe. Take each little step as He makes it plain to thee. Bring all thy life, in each of its details, to Him to regulate and guide. Follow gladly and quickly the sweet suggestions of His Spirit in thy soul. And day by day thou wilt find Him bringing thee more and more into conformity with His will in all

things; molding thee and fashioning thee, as thou art
able to bear it, into a "vessel unto his honor, sanctified and
meet for his use, and fitted to every good work." So shall
be given to thee the sweet joy of being an "epistle of
Christ, known and read of all men"; and thy light shall
shine so brightly that men seeing, not thee, but thy good
works, shall glorify, not thee, but thy Father which is
in heaven.

"But Thou art making me, I thank Thee, Sire.
    What Thou hast done and doest, Thou knowest well,
And I will help Thee: gently in Thy fire
    I will lie burning; on Thy potter's wheel
    I will whirl patient, though my brain should reel;
        Thy grace shall be enough to quell,
And growing strength perfect, through weakness dire.

"I have not knowledge, wisdom, insight, thought,
    Nor understanding, fit to justify
Thee in Thy work, O Perfect! Thou hast brought
    Me up to this; and lo! what Thou hast wrought,
    I cannot comprehend. But I can cry,
        'O enemy, the Maker hath not done;
One day thou shalt behold, and from the sight shalt run!'

"Thou workest perfectly. And if it seem
    Some things are not so well, 'tis but because
        They are too loving deep, too lofty wise,
    For me, poor child, to understand their laws.
My highest wisdom, half is but a dream;
My love runs helpless like a falling stream;
    Thy good embraces ill, and lo! its illness dies."*

*George Macdonald

Chapter Seventeen

The Joy of Obedience

HAVING SPOKEN OF SOME OF THE DIFFICULTIES IN THIS life of faith, let me now speak of some of its joys. And foremost among these stands the joy of obedience.

Long ago I met somewhere with this sentence, "Perfect obedience would be perfect happiness if only we had perfect confidence in the power we were obeying." I remember being struck with the saying as the revelation of a possible although hitherto undreamed-of, way of happiness; and often afterwards, even when full of inward rebellion, did that saying recur to me as the vision of a rest, and yet of a possible development, that would soothe, and at the same time satisfy all my yearnings.

Need I say that this rest has been revealed to me now, not as a vision, but as a reality; and that I have seen in the Lord Jesus the Master to whom we may yield up our implicit obedience, and, taking His yoke upon us, may find perfect rest?

You little know, dear hesitating soul, of the joy you are missing. The Master has revealed Himself to you, and is calling for your complete surrender, and you shrink and hesitate. A measure of surrender you are willing to make, and think indeed it is fit and proper that you should. But an *utter* abandonment, without any reserves, seems to you too much to be asked for. You are afraid of it. It involves too much, you think, and is too great a risk. To be measurably obedient you desire; to be perfectly obedient appalls you.

Then, too, you see other souls who seem able to walk with easy consciences in a far wider path than that which appears to be marked out for you, and you ask yourself why this need be. It seems strange, and perhaps hard to you, that you must do what they need not, and must leave undone what they have liberty to do.

Ah, dear Christian, this very difference between you is your privilege, though you do not yet know it. Your Lord says, "He that *hath* my commandments, and keepeth them, he it is that loveth me; and he that loveth me shall be loved of my Father, and I will love him, and will mani-

147

fest myself to him." You *have* His commandments; those
you envy have them not. *You* know the mind of your
Lord about many things, in which, as yet, they are walking in darkness. Is not this a privilege? Is it a cause for
regret that your soul is brought into such near and intimate relations with your Master that He is able to tell you
things which those who are farther off may not know? Do
you not realize what a tender degree of intimacy is implied
in this?

There are many relations in life that require from the
different parties only very moderate degrees of devotion.
We may have really pleasant friendships with one another, and yet spend a large part of our lives in separate
interests and widely differing pursuits. When together, we
may greatly enjoy one another's society, and find many
congenial points; but separation is not any especial distress to us, and other and more intimate friendships do
not interfere. There is not enough love between us to give
us either the right or the desire to enter into and share
one another's most private affairs. A certain degree of reserve and distance seems to be the suitable thing in such
relations as these. But there are other relations in life
where all this is changed. The friendship becomes love.
The two hearts give themselves to each other, to be no
longer two, but one. A union of soul takes place, which
makes all that belongs to one the property of the other.
Separate interests and separate paths in life are no longer
possible. Things that were lawful before become unlawful
now because of the nearness of the tie that binds. The reserve and distance suitable to mere friendship become
fatal in love. Love gives all, and must have all in return.
The wishes of one become binding obligations to the
other, and the deepest desire of each heart is that it may
know every secret wish or longing of the other in order
that it may fly on the wings of the wind to gratify it.

Do such as these chafe under this yoke which love im-
poses? Do they envy the cool, calm, reasonable friendships they see around them, and regret the nearness into
which their souls are brought to their beloved one because of the obligations it creates? Do they not rather
glory in these very obligations, and inwardly pity, with a
tender yet exulting joy, the poor far-off ones who dare not
come so near? Is not every fresh revelation of the wishes
of the loved one a fresh delight and privilege, and is any
path found hard which their love compels them to travel?

Ah, dear soul, if you have ever known this, even for a few hours, in any earthly relation; if you have ever loved any of your fellow human beings enough to find sacrifice and service on their behalf a joy; if a whole-souled abandonment of your will to the will of another has ever gleamed across you as a blessed and longed-for privilege, or as a sweet and precious reality, then by all the tender longing love of your Heavenly Lover would I entreat you to let it be so towards Christ!

He loves you with more than the love of friendship. As a bridegroom rejoices over his bride, so does He rejoice over you, and nothing but the bride's surrender will satisfy Him. He has given you all, and He asks for all in return. The slightest reserve will grieve Him to the heart. He spared not Himself, and how can you spare yourself? For your sake He poured out in a lavish abandonment all that He had, and for His sake you must pour out all that you have, without stint or measure.

Oh, be generous in your self-surrender! Meet His measureless devotion for you with a measureless devotion to Him. Be glad and eager to throw yourself unreservedly into His loving arms, and to hand over the reins of government to Him. Whatever there is of you, let Him have it all. Give up forever everything that is separate from Him. Concent to resign, from this time forward, all liberty of choice, and glory in the blessed nearness of union which makes this enthusiasm of devotedness not only possible but necessary.

Have you never longed to lavish your love and attentions upon someone far off from you in position or circumstances, with whom you were not intimate enough for any closer approach? Have you not felt a capacity for self-surrender and devotedness that has seemed to burn within you like a fire, and yet had no object upon which it dared to lavish itself? Have not your hands been full of "alabaster boxes of ointment, very precious," which you have never been near enough to any heart to pour out? If, then, you are hearing the loving voice of your Lord calling you out into a place of nearness to Himself that will require a separation from all else, and that will make an enthusiasm of devotedness not only possible but necessary, will you shrink or hesitate? Will you think it hard that He reveals to you more of His mind than He does to others, and that He will not allow you to be happy in anything that separates you from Himself? Do you *want* to go where He cannot go with you, or to have pursuits which He cannot share?

No! no, a thousand times no! You will spring out to meet His lovely will with an eager joy. Even His slightest wish will become a binding law to you that it would fairly break your heart to disobey. You will glory in the very narrowness of the path He marks out for you, and will pity, with an infinite pity, the poor far-off ones who have missed this precious joy. The obligations of love will be to you its sweetest privileges; and the right you have acquired to lavish the uttermost wealth of abandonment of all that you have upon your Lord will seem to lift you into a region of unspeakable glory. The perfect happiness of perfect obedience will dawn upon your soul, and you will begin to know something of what Jesus meant when He said, "I *delight* to do thy will, O my God."

But do you think the joy in this will be all on your side? Has the Lord no joy in those who have thus surrendered themselves to Him, and who love to obey Him? Ah, my friends, we are not able to understand this; but surely the Scriptures reveal to us glimpses of the delight, the satisfaction, the joy our Lord has in us, which rejoice our souls with their marvelous suggestions of blessedness. That *we* should need Him is easy to comprehend; that *He* should need us seems incomprehensible. That our desire should be toward Him as a matter of course; but that His desire should be toward us passes the bounds of human belief. And yet He says it, and what can we do but believe Him? He has made our hearts capable of this supreme overmastering affection, and has offered Himself as the object of it. It is infinitely precious to Him. So much does He value it that He has made it the first and chiefest of all His commandments that we should love Him with all our might and with all our strength. Continually at every heart He is knocking, asking to be taken in as the supreme object of love. "Wilt thou have me," He says to the believer, "to be thy Beloved? Wilt thou follow me into suffering and loneliness, and endure hardness for my sake, and ask for no reward but my smile of approval and my word of praise? Wilt thou throw thyself, with a passion of abandonment, into my will? Wilt thou give up to me the absolute control of thyself and of all that thou hast? Wilt thou be content with pleasing me, and me only? May I have my way with thee in all things? Wilt thou come into so close a union with me as to make a separation from the world necessary? Wilt thou accept me for thy heavenly Bridegroom, and leave all others to cleave only unto me?"

In a thousand ways He makes this offer of union with Himself to every believer. But all do not say "Yes" to Him. Other loves and other interests seem to them too precious to be cast aside. They do not miss of Heaven because of this. But they miss an unspeakable present joy.

You, however, are not one of these. From the very first your soul has cried out eagerly and gladly to all His offers, "Yes, Lord, yes!" You are more than ready to pour out upon Him all your richest treasures of love and devotedness. You have brought to Him an enthusiasm of self-surrender that perhaps may disturb and distress the so-called prudent and moderate Christians around you. Your love makes necessary a separation from the world, of which a lower love cannot even conceive. Sacrifices and services are possible and sweet to you that could not come into the grasp of a more half-hearted devotedness. The life of love upon which you have entered gives you the right to a lavish outpouring of your *all* upon your beloved One. An intimacy and friendship, which more distant souls cannot enter upon become now not only your privilege, but your duty. Your Lord claims from you, because of your union with Him, far more than He claims of them. What to them is lawful love has made unlawful for you. To you He can make known His secrets, and to you He looks for an instant response to every requirement of His love.

Oh, it is wonderful, the glorious unspeakable privilege upon which you have entered! How little it will matter to you if men shall hate you, and shall separate you from their company, and shall reproach you and cast out your name as evil for His dear sake! You may well "rejoice in that day, and leap for joy," for, behold, your reward is great in heaven; for if you are a partaker of His suffering, you shall also be of His glory.

In you He is seeing of the "travail of his soul," and is satisfied. Your love and devotedness are His precious reward for all He has done for you. It is unspeakably sweet to Him. Do not be afraid, then, to let yourself go in a heart-whole devotedness to your Lord that can brook no reserves. Others may not approve, but He will; and that is enough. Do not stint or measure your obedience or your service. Let your heart and your hand be as free to serve Him as His heart and hand were to serve you. Let Him have all there is of you, body, soul, mind, spirit, time, talents, voice, everything. Lay your whole life open before Him, that He may control it. Say to Him each day, "Lord, enable me to regulate this day so as to please Thee! Give me spiritual insight to discover what is Thy will in all the relations of my life. Guide me as to my pursuits, my friendships, my reading, my dress, my Christian work." Do not let there be a day nor an hour in which you are not consciously doing His will and following Him wholly.

A personal service to your Lord, such as this, will give a halo to the poorest life, and gild the most monotonous existence with a heavenly glow. Have you ever grieved that the romance of youth is so soon lost in the hard realities of the world? Bring Christ thus into your life and into all its details, and a romance, far grander than the brightest days of youth could ever know, will thrill your soul, and nothing will seem hard or stern again. The meanest life will be glorified by this. Often, as I have watched a poor woman at her washtub, and have thought of all the disheartening accessories of such a life, and have been tempted to wonder why such lives need to be, there has come over me, with a thrill of joy, the recollection of this possible glorification of it, and I have realized that even this homely life lived in Christ, and with Christ, following Him whithersoever He might lead, would be filled with a spiritual romance that would make every hour of it grand; while to the most wealthy or most powerful of earthly lives, nothing more glorious could be possible.

Christ Himself, when He was on earth, declared the truth that there was no blessedness equal to the blessedness of obedience. "And it came to pass, as he spake these things, a certain woman of the company lifted up her voice, and said unto him, Blessed is the womb that bare thee, and the paps which thou hast sucked. But he said, Yea rather, blessed are they that hear the word of God, and keep it."

More blessed even than to have been the earthly mother of our Lord, or to have carried Him in our arms and nourished Him in our bosoms (and who could ever measure the bliss of that?), is it to hear and obey His will!

May our surrendered hearts reach out with an eager delight to discover and embrace the lovely will of our loving God!

Chapter Eighteen

Divine Union

ALL THE DEALINGS OF GOD WITH THE SOUL OF THE believer are in order to bring it into oneness with Himself, that the prayer of our Lord may be fulfilled: "That they all may be one; as thou, Father, art in me, and I in thee, that they also may be one in us. . . . I in them, and thou in me, that they may be made perfect in one; and that the world may know that thou hast sent me, and hast loved them, as thou hast loved me."

This Divine union was the glorious purpose in the heart of God for His people before the foundation of the world. It was the mystery hid from ages and generations. It was accomplished in the death of Christ. It has been made known by the Scriptures; and it is realized as an actual experience by many of God's dear children.

But not by all. It is true of all, and God has not hidden it or made it hard; but the eyes of many are too dim, and their hearts too unbelieving for them to grasp it. It is therefore for the purpose of bringing His people into the personal and actual realization of this that the Lord calls upon them so earnestly and so repeatedly to abandon themselves to Him, that He may work in them all the good pleasure of His will.

All the previous steps in the Christian life lead up to this. The Lord has made us for it; and until we have intelligently apprehended it, and have voluntarily consented to embrace it, the "travail of His soul" for us is not satisfied, nor have our hearts found their destined and real rest.

The usual course of Christian experience is pictured in the history of the disciples. First they were awakened to see their condition and their need, and they came to Christ, and gave their allegiance to Him. Then they followed Him, worked for Him, believed in Him, and yet how unlike Him! Seeking to be set up one above the other; running away from the cross; misunderstanding His mission and His words; forsaking their Lord in time of danger; but still sent out to preach, recognized by Him as His disciples, possessing power to work for Him. They knew Christ only "after the flesh," as outside of them, their Lord and Master, but not yet their life.

Then came Pentecost, and these same disciples came to know Him as inwardly revealed, as one with them in actual union, their very indwelling life. Henceforth He was to them Christ within, working in them to will and to do of His good pleasure, delivering them, by the law of the Spirit of His life, from the bondage to the law of sin and death under which they had been held. No longer was it between themselves and Him a war of wills and a clashing of interests. One will alone animated them, and that was His will. One interest alone was dear to them, and that was His. They were made *one* with Him.

And surely all can recognize this picture, though perhaps as yet the final stage of it has not been fully reached. You may have left much to follow Christ, dear reader; you may have believed on Him, and worked for Him, and loved Him, and yet may not be like Him. Allegiance you know, and confidence you know, but not yet union. There are two wills, two interests, two lives. You have not yet lost your own life that you may live only in His. Once it was "I and not Christ." Next it was "I and Christ." Perhaps now it is even "Christ and I." But has it come yet to be Christ only, and not I at all?

If not, shall I tell you how it may? If you have followed me through all the previous chapters in this book, you will surely now be ready to take the definite step of faith which will lead your soul out of self and into Christ, and you will be prepared to abide in Him forever, and to know no life but His.

All you need, therefore, is to understand what the Scriptures teach about this marvelous union that you may be sure it is really intended for you.

If you read such passages as I Corinthians 3: 16, "Know ye not that ye are the temple of God, and that the Spirit of God dwelleth in you?" and then look at the opening of the chapter and see to whom these wonderful words are spoken, even to "babes in Christ" who were "yet carnal," and walked according to men, you will see that this soul-union of which I speak, this unspeakably glorious mystery of an indwelling God, is the possession of even the weakest and most failing believer in Christ; so that it is not a new thing you are to ask for, but only to realize that which you already have. Of every believer in the Lord Jesus it is absolutely true, that his "body is the temple of the Holy Ghost, which is in him, which he has of God."

But although this is true, it is also equally true that unless the believer knows it, and lives in the power of it, it is to him as though it were not. Like the treasures under a man's field, which existed there before they were known or used by him, so does the life of Christ dwell in each believer as really before he knows it and lives in it as it does afterward, although its power is not manifested until, intelligently and voluntarily, the believer ceases from his own life, and accepts Christ's life in its place.

But it is very important not to make any mistakes here. This union with Christ is not a matter of emotions, but of character. It is not something we are to *feel,* but something we are to *be.* We may feel it very blessedly, and probably shall; but the vital thing is not the feeling, but the reality.

No one can be one with Christ who is not Christlike. This is a manifest truth, yet I fear it is often too much overlooked and very strong emotions of love and joy are taken as signs and proofs of Divine union in cases where the absolutely essential proofs of a Christlike life and character are conspicuously wanting. This is entirely contrary to the Scripture declaration that "he that *saith* he abideth in him ought himself also to *walk,* even as he walked." There is no escape from this, for it is not only a Divine declaration, but is in the very nature of things as well.

We speak of being one with a friend, and we mean that we have a union of purposes and thoughts and desires. No matter how enthusiastic our friends may be in their expressions of love and unity, there can be no real oneness between us unless there are, at least in some degree, the same likes and dislikes, the same thoughts and purposes and ideals. Oneness with Christ means being made a "partaker of his nature," as well as of His life; for nature and life are, of course, one.

If we are really one with Christ, therefore, it will not be contrary to our nature to be Christlike and to walk as He walked, but it will be in accordance with our nature. Sweetness, gentleness, meekness, patience, long-suffering, charity, kindness, will all be natural to the Christian, who is a partaker of the nature of Christ. It could not be otherwise.

But people who live in their emotions do not always see this. They *feel* so at one with Christ that they look no farther than this feeling, and often delude themselves with thinking they have come into the Divine union, when all the while their nature and dispositions are still under the sway of self-love.

Now, we all know that our emotions are most untrustworthy, and are largely the result of our physical condition or our natural temperaments. It is a fatal mistake, therefore, to make them the test of our oneness with Christ. This mistake works both ways. If I have very joyous emotions, I may be deluded by thinking I have entered into the Divine union when I have not; and if I have no emotions, I may grieve over my failure to enter, when I really have entered.

Character is the only real test. God is holy and those who are one with Him will be holy also. Our Lord Himself expressed His oneness with the Father in such words as these: "The Son can do nothing of himself, but what he seeth the Father do: for what things soever he doeth, these also doeth the Son likewise." "If I do not the works of my Father, believe me not. But if I do, though ye believe not me, believe the works; that ye may know, and believe, that the Father is in me, and I in him."

The test Christ gave, then, by which the reality of His oneness with the Father was to be known, was the fact that He did the works of the Father; and I know no other test for us now.

It is forever true in the nature of things that a tree is to be known by its fruits; and if we have entered into the Divine union we shall bear the Divine fruits of a Christlike life and conversation: for "he that saith, I know him, and keepeth not his commandments, is a liar, and the truth is not in him. But whoso keepeth his word, in him verily is the love of God perfected: hereby know we that we are in him."

"Hereby know we," that is, by the "keeping of his word." Pay no regard to your feelings, therefore, in this matter of oneness with Christ, but see to it that you have the really vital fruits of a oneness in character and walk and mind. Your emotions may be very delightful, or they may be very depressing. In neither case are they any real indications of your spiritual state. Very undeveloped Christians often have very powerful emotional experiences. I knew one who was kept awake often by the "waves of salvation," as she expressed it, which swept over her all night long, but who yet did not tell the truth in her intercourse with others, and was very far from honest in her business dealings. No one could possibly believe that she knew anything about a real Divine union, in spite of all her fervent emotions in regard to it.

Your joy in the Lord is to be a far deeper thing than a mere emotion. It is to be the joy of knowledge, of perception, of actual existence. It is a far gladder thing to *be* a bird, with all the actual realities of flying, than only to *feel* as if you were a bird, with no actual power of flying at all. Reality is always the vital thing.

But now, having guarded against this danger of an emotional experience of Divine union, let us consider how the reality is to be reached. And first I would say that it is not a new attitude to be taken by God, but only a new attitude to be taken by us. If I am really a child of God, then of necessity my heart is already the temple of God, and Christ is already within me. What is needed, therefore, is only that I shall recognize His presence and yield fully to His control.

It seems to me just in this way: as though Christ were living in a house, shut up in a far-off closet, unknown and unnoticed by the dwellers in the house, longing to make Himself known to them, and to be one with them in all their daily lives, and share in all their interests, but unwilling to force Himself upon their notice, because nothing but a voluntary companionship could meet or satisfy the needs of His love. The days pass by over that favored household, and they remain in ignorance of their marvelous privilege. They come and go about all their daily affairs, with no thought of their wonderful Guest. Their plans are laid without reference to Him. His wisdom to guide and His strength to protect are all lost to them. Lonely days and weeks are spent in sadness which might have been full of the sweetness of His presence.

But suddenly the announcement is made, "The Lord is in the house!" How will its owner receive the intelligence? Will he call out an eager thanksgiving, and throw wide open every door for the entrance of his glorious Guest? Or will he shrink and hesitate, afraid of His presence, and seek to reserve some private corner for a refuge from His all-seeing eye?

Dear friend, I make the glad announcement to thee that the Lord is in thy heart. Since the day of thy conversion

He has been dwelling there, but thou hast lived on in ignorance of it. Every moment during all that time might
have been passed in the sunshine of His sweet presence,
and every step have been taken under His advice. But because thou knew it not, and did not look for Him there,
thy life has been lonely and full of failure. But now that
I make the announcement to thee, how wilt thou receive
it? Art thou glad to have Him? Wilt thou throw wide open
every door to welcome Him in? Wilt thou joyfully and
thankfully give up the government of thy life into His
hands? Wilt thou consult Him about everything, and let
Him decide each step for thee, and mark out every path?
Wilt thou invite Him into thy innermost chambers, and
make Him the sharer in thy most hidden life? Wilt thou
say "Yes" to all His longing for union with thee, and
with a glad and eager abandonment hand thyself and all
that concerns thee over into His hands? If thou wilt, then
shall thy soul begin to know something of the joy of
union with Christ.

But words fail me here! All that I can say is but a faint
picture of the blessed reality. For far more glorious than
it would be to have Christ a dweller in the house or in the
heart is it to be brought into such a real and actual union
with Him as to be one with Him—one will, one purpose,
one interest, one life. Human words cannot express such
a glory as this. And yet it ought to be expressed, and our
souls ought to be made so unutterably hungry to realize
it, that day or night we shall not be able to rest without
it. Do you understand the words "one with Christ"? Do you
catch the slightest glimpse of their marvelous meaning?
Does not your whole soul begin to exult over such a
wondrous destiny? It seems too wonderful to be true that
such poor, weak, foolish beings as we are should be created for such an end as this; and yet it is a blessed reality.
We are even *commanded* to enter into it. We are exhorted
to lay down our own life that His life may be lived in us;
we are asked to have no interests but His interests, to share
His riches, to enter into His joys, to partake of His sorrows,
to manifest His likeness, to have the same mind as He
had, to think and feel and act and walk as He did.

Shall we consent to all this? The Lord will not force it
on us, for He wants us as His companions and His friends,
and a forced union would be incompatible with this. It
must be voluntary on our part. The bride must say a will-

ing "Yes" to the bridegroom, or the joy of their union is wanting. Can we not say a willing "Yes" to our Lord?

It is a very simple transaction, and yet very real. The steps are but three: first, we must be convinced that the Scriptures teach this glorious indwelling of God; then we must surrender our whole selves to Him to be possessed by Him; and, finally, we must believe that He *has* taken possession, and is dwelling in us. We must begin to reckon ourselves dead, and to reckon Christ as our only life. We must maintain this attitude of soul unwaveringly. It will help us to say, "I am crucified with Christ: nevertheless I live, yet not I, but Christ liveth in me," over and over, day and night, until it becomes the habitual breathing of our souls. We must put off our self-life by faith continually, and put on the life of Christ; and we must do this not only by faith, but practically as well. We must continually put self to death in all the details of daily life, and must let Christ instead live and work in us. I mean we must never do the selfish thing, but always the Christlike thing. We must let this become, by its constant repetition, the attitude of our whole being. And as surely as we do, we shall come at last to understand something of what it means to be made one with Christ as He and the Father are one. Christ left all to be joined to us; shall we not also leave all to be joined to Him in this Divine union which transcends words, but for which our Lord prayed when He said, "Neither pray I for these alone, but for them also which shall believe on me through their word: that they all may be one; as thou, Father, art in me, and I in thee, that they also may be one in us"?

Chapter Nineteen

The Chariots of God

IT HAS BEEN WELL SAID THAT "EARTHLY CARES ARE a heavenly discipline." But they are even something better than discipline,—they are God's chariots, sent to take the soul to its high places of triumph.

They do not look like chariots. They look instead like

enemies, sufferings, trials, defeats, misunderstandings, disappointments, unkindnesses. They look like Juggernaut cars of misery and wretchedness, which are only waiting to roll over us and crush us into the earth. But could we see them as they really are, we should recognize them as chariots of triumph in which we may ride to those very heights of victory for which our souls have been longing and praying. The Juggernaut car is the visible thing; the chariot of God is the invisible. The King of Syria came up against the man of God with horses and chariots that could be seen by every eye, but God had chariots that could be seen by none save the eye of faith. The servant of the Prophet could only see the outward and visible; and he cried, as so many have done since, "Alas, my master! how shall we do?" But the Prophet himself sat calmly within his house without fear, because his eyes were opened to see the invisible; and all he asked for his servant was, "Lord, I pray thee open his eyes that he may see."

This is the prayer we need to pray for ourselves and for one another, "Lord, open our eyes that we may see"; for the world all around us, as well as around the Prophet, is full of God's horses and chariots, waiting to carry us to places of glorious victory. And when our eyes are thus opened, we shall see in all the events of life, whether great or small, whether joyful or sad, a "chariot" for our souls.

Everything that comes to us becomes a chariot the moment we treat it as such; and on the other hand, even the smallest trials may be a Juggernaut car to crush us into misery or despair if we so consider them. It lies with each of us to choose which they shall be. It all depends, not upon what these events are, but upon how we take them. If we lie down under them and let them roll over us and crush us, they become Juggernaut cars, but if we climb up into them, as into a car of victory, and make them carry us triumphantly onward and upward, they become the chariots of God.

Whenever we mount into God's chariots the same thing happens to us spiritually that happened to Elijah. We shall have a translation. Not into the heavens above us, as Elijah did, but into the heaven within us; and this, after all, is almost a grander translation than his. We shall be carried away from the low, earthly, groveling plane of life, where everything hurts and everything is unhappy, up into the "heavenly places in Christ Jesus," where we can ride in triumph over all below.

These "heavenly places" are interior, not exterior; and the road that leads to them is interior also. But the chariot that carries the soul over this road is generally some outward loss or trial or disappointment, some chastening that does not indeed seem for the present to be joyous, but grievous, but that nevertheless afterward "yieldeth the peaceable fruits of righteousness to them that are exercised thereby."

In the Canticles we are told of "chariots paved with love." We cannot always see the love-lining to our own particular chariot. It often looks very unlovely. It may be a cross-grained relative or friend; it may be the result of human malice or cruelty or neglect; but every chariot sent by God must necessarily be paved with love, since God is love; and God's love is the sweetest, softest, tenderest thing to rest one's self upon that was ever found by any soul anywhere. It is His love, indeed, that sends the chariot.

Look upon your chastenings then, no matter how grievous they may be for the present, as God's chariots sent to carry your souls into the "high places" of spiritual achievement and uplifting, and you will find that they are, after all, "paved with love."

The Bible tells us that when God went forth for the salvation of His people, then He "did ride upon His horses and chariots of salvation." And it is the same now. Everything becomes a "chariot of salvation" when God rides upon it. He maketh even the "clouds his chariot," we are told, and "rideth on the wings of the wind." Therefore the clouds and storms that darken our skies and seem to shut out the shining of the sun of righteousness are really only God's chariots, into which we may mount with Him, and "ride prosperously" over all the darkness. Dear reader, have you made the clouds in your life your chariots? Are you "riding prosperously" with God on top of them all?

I knew a lady who had a very slow servant. She was an excellent girl in every other respect, and very valuable in the household; but her slowness was a constant source of irritation to her mistress, who was naturally quick, and who always chafed at slowness. This lady would consequently get out of temper with the girl twenty times a day, and twenty times a day would repent of her anger and resolve to conquer it, but in vain. Her life was made miserable by the conflict. One day it occurred to her that she had for a long while been praying for patience, and that perhaps this slow servant was the very chariot the Lord had sent to carry her soul over into patience. She immediately accepted it as such, and from that time used the slowness of her servant as a chariot for her soul; and the result was a victory of patience that no slowness of anybody was ever after able to disturb.

I knew another lady, at a crowded convention, who was put to sleep in a room with two others on account of the crowd. *She* wanted to sleep, but *they* wanted to talk; and the first night she was greatly disturbed, and lay there fretting and fuming long after the others had hushed and she might have slept. But the next day she heard something about God's chariots, and at night she accepted these talking friends as her chariots to carry her over into sweetness and patience, and was kept in undisturbed calm. When, however, it grew very late, and she knew they all ought to be sleeping, she ventured to say quietly, "Friends, I am lying here riding in a chariot!" The effect was instantaneous, and perfect quiet reigned! Her chariot had carried her over to victory, not only inwardly, but at last outwardly as well.

If we would ride in God's chariots instead of our own we should find this to be the case continually.

Our constant temptation is to trust in the "chariots of Egypt," or, in other words, in earthly resources. We can *see* them; they are tangible, and real, and look substantial, while God's chariots are invisible and intangible, and it is hard to believe they are there.

We try to reach high spiritual places with the "multitude of our chariots." We depend first on one thing and then on another to advance our spiritual condition, and to gain our spiritual victories. We "go down to Egypt for help." And God is obliged often to destroy all our own earthly chariots before He can bring us to the point of mounting into His.

We lean too much upon a dear friend to help us onward in the spiritual life, and the Lord is obliged to separate us from that friend. We feel that all our spiritual prosperity depends on our continuance under the ministry of a favorite preacher, and he is mysteriously removed. We look upon our prayer-meeting or our Bible-class as the chief source of our spiritual strength, and we are shut up from attending them. And the "chariot of God" which alone can carry us to the places where we hoped to be taken by the instrumentalities upon which we have been depending is to be found in the very deprivations we have so mourned over. God must burn up with the fire of His love every chariot of our own that stands in the way of our mounting into His.

We have to be brought to the place where all other refuges fail us before we can say, "He only." We say, "He and—something else," "He and my experiences," or "He and my church relationships," or "He and my Christian work"; and all that comes after the "and" must be taken away from us, or must be proved useless, before we can come to the "He only." As long as visible chariots are at hand the soul will not mount into the invisible ones.

Let us be thankful, then, for every trial that will help to destroy our earthly chariots, and that will compel us to take refuge in the chariot of God which stands ready and waiting beside us in every event and circumstance of life. We are told that "God rideth upon the heavens," and if we would ride with Him there we need to be brought to the end of all riding upon the earth.

When we mount into God's chariot our goings are "established," for no obstacles can hinder His triumphal course. All losses, therefore, are gains that bring us to this. Paul understood this, and he gloried in the losses which brought him such unspeakable rewards. "But what things were gain to me, those I counted loss for Christ. Yea doubtless, and I count all things but loss for the excellency of the knowledge of Christ Jesus my Lord: for whom I have suffered the loss of all things, and do count them but dung, that I may win Christ, and be found in him."

Even the "thorn in the flesh," the messenger of Satan sent to buffet him, became a "chariot of God" to his willing soul, and carried him to the heights of triumph which he could have reached in no other way. To "take pleasure" in one's trials, what is this but to turn them into the grandest of chariots?

Joseph had a revelation of his future triumphs and reigning, but the chariots that carried him there looked to the eye of sense like dreadful Juggernaut cars of failure and defeat. Slavery and imprisonment are strange chariots to take one to a kingdom, and yet by no other way could Joseph have reached his exaltation. And

our exaltation to the spiritual throne that awaits us is
often reached by similar chariots.

The great point, then, is to have our eyes opened to see
in everything that comes to us a "chariot of God," and to
learn how to mount into these chariots. We must recognize each thing that comes to us as being really God's
chariot for us, and must accept it as from Him. He does
not command or originate the thing, perhaps; but the
moment we put it into His hands it becomes His, and He
at once turns it into a chariot for us. He makes all things,
even bad things, work together for good to all those who
trust Him. All He needs is to have them entirely committed to Him.

When your trial comes, then, put it right into the will
of God, and climb into that will as a little child climbs
into its mother's arms. The baby carried in the chariot of
its mother's arms rides triumphantly through the hardest
places, and does not even know they are hard. And how
much more we who are carried in the chariot of the "arms
of God!"

Get into your chariot, then. Take each thing that is
wrong in your lives as God's chariot for you. No matter
who the builder of the wrong may be, whether men or
devils, by the time it reaches your side it is God's chariot
for you, and is meant to carry you to a heavenly place of
triumph. Shut out all the second causes, and find the Lord
in it. Say, "Lord, open my eyes that I may see, not the
visible enemy, but thy unseen chariots of deliverance."

No doubt the enemy will try to turn your chariot into a
Juggernaut car by taunting you with the suggestion that
God is not in your trouble, and that there is no help for
you in Him. But you must utterly disregard all such suggestions, and must overcome them with the assertion of a
confident faith. "God *is* my refuge and strength, a very
present help in time of trouble," must be your continual
declaration, no matter what the seemings may be.

Moreover, you must not be half-hearted about it. You
must climb wholly into your chariot, not with one foot
dragging on the ground. There must be no "ifs," or "buts,"
or "supposings," or "questionings." You must accept God's
will fully, and must hide yourself in the arms of His love,
that are always underneath to receive you, in every circumstance and at every moment. Say, "Thy will be done,
Thy will be done," over and over. Shut out every thought
but the one thought of submission to His will and of trust

in His love. There can be no trials in which God's will has not a place somewhere; and the soul has only to mount into His will as in a chariot, and it will find itself "riding upon the heavens" with God in a way it had never dreamed could be.

The soul that thus rides with God "on the sky" has views and sights of things that the soul which grovels on the earth can never have. The poor crushed and bleeding victim under the car of Juggernaut can see only the dust and stones and the grinding wheels, but the triumphant rider in the chariot sees far fairer sights.

Do any of you ask where your chariots are to be found? The psalmist says, "The chariots of God are twenty thousand, even thousands of angels." There is never in any life a lack of chariots. One dear Christian said to me at the close of a meeting where I had been speaking about these chariots: "I am a poor woman, and have all my life long grieved that I could not drive in a carriage like some of my rich neighbors. But I have been looking over my life while you have been talking, and I find that it is so full of chariots on every side that I am sure I shall never need to walk again."

I have not a shadow of doubt, dear readers, that if all our eyes could be opened to-day we should see our homes, and our places of business, and the streets we traverse, filled with the "chariots of God." There is no need for any one of us to walk for lack of chariots. That cross inmate of your household, who has hitherto made life a burden to you, and who has been the Juggernaut car to crush your soul into the dust, may henceforth be a glorious chariot to carry you to the heights of heavenly patience and long-suffering. That misunderstanding, that mortification, that unkindness, that disappointment, that loss, that defeat,— all these are chariots waiting to carry you to the very heights of victory you have so longed to reach.

Mount into them, then, with thankful hearts, and lose sight of all second causes in the shining of His love, who will "carry you in his arms" safely and triumphantly over it all.

Chapter Twenty

The Life on Wings

THIS LIFE HID WITH CHRIST IN GOD HAS MANY ASPECTS, and can be considered under a great many different figures. There is one aspect which has been a great help and inspiration to me, and I think may be also to some other longing and hungry souls. It is what I call the life on wings.

Our Lord has not only told us to consider the "flowers of the field," but also the "birds of the air"; and I have found that these little winged creatures have some wonderful lessons for us. In one of the Psalms, the Psalmist, after enumerating the darkness and bitterness of his life in this earthly sphere of trial, cries out, "Oh that I had wings like a dove! for then would I fly away, and be at rest. Lo, then would I wander far off, and remain in the wilderness. I would hasten my escape from the windy storm and tempest" (Psalm 55: 6–8).

This cry for "wings" is as old as humanity. Our souls were made to "mount up with wings," and they can never be satisfied with anything short of flying. Like the captive-born eagle that feels within it the instinct of flight, and chafes and frets at its imprisonment, hardly knowing what it longs for, so do our souls chafe and fret, and cry out for freedom. We can never rest on earth, and we long to "fly away" from all that so holds and hampers and imprisons us here.

This restlessness and discontent develop themselves generally in seeking an outward escape from our circumstances or from our miseries. We do not at first recognize the fact that our only way of escape is to "mount up with wings," and we try to "flee on horses," as the Israelites did, when oppressed by their trials (see Isaiah 30: 16).

Our "horses" are the outward things upon which we depend for relief, some change of circumstances, or some help from man; and we mount on these and run east or west, or north or south, anywhere to get away from our trouble, thinking in our ignorance that a change of our environment is all that is necessary to give deliverance to our souls. But all such efforts to escape are unavailing, as we have each one proved hundreds of times; for the soul is not so made that it can "flee upon horses," but must make its flight always upon wings.

Moreover, these "horses" generally carry us, as they did the Israelites, out of one trouble only to land us in another. It is as the Prophet says, "As if a man did flee from a lion, and a bear met him; or went into the house, and leaned his hand on the wall, and a serpent bit him."

How often have we also run from some "lion" in our pathway only to be met by a "bear," or have hidden ourselves in a place of supposed safety only to be bitten by a "serpent"! No; it is useless for the soul to hope to escape by running away from its troubles to any earthly refuge, for there is not one that can give it deliverance.

Is there, then, no way of escape for us when in trouble or distress? Must we just plod wearily through it all and look for no relief? I rejoice to answer that there is a glorious way of escape for every one of us if we will but mount up on wings and fly away from it all to God. It is not a way east or west, or north or south, but it is a way upwards. "They that wait upon the Lord shall renew their strength; they shall mount up with wings as eagles; they shall run, and not be weary; and they shall walk, and not faint."

All creatures that have wings can escape from every snare that is set for them if only they will fly high enough; and the soul that uses its wings can always find a sure "way to escape" from all that can hurt or trouble it.

What, then, are these wings? Their secret is contained in the words, "They that wait upon the Lord." The soul that waits upon the Lord is the soul that is entirely surrendered to Him, and that trusts Him perfectly. Therefore we might name our wings the wings of Surrender and of Trust. I mean by this, that if we will only surrender ourselves utterly to the Lord, and will trust Him perfectly, we shall find our souls "mounting up with wings as eagles" to the "heavenly places" in Christ Jesus, where earthly annoyances or sorrows have no power to disturb us.

The wings of the soul carry it up into a spiritual plane of life, into the "life hid with Christ in God," which is a life utterly independent of circumstances, one that no cage can imprison and no shackles bind.

The "things above" are the things the soul on wings cares about, not the "things on the earth," and it views life and all its experiences from the high altitude of "heavenly places in Christ Jesus." Things look very different according to the standpoint from which we view them. The caterpillar, as it creeps along the ground, must have a widely different "view" of the world around it from that which the same caterpillar will have when its wings are developed, and it soars in the air above the very places where once it crawled. And similarly the crawling soul must necessarily see things in a very different aspect from the soul that has "mounted up with wings." The mountain top may blaze with sunshine when all the valley below is shrouded in fogs, and the bird whose wings can carry him high enough may mount at will out of the gloom below into the joy of the sunlight above.

I was at one time spending a winter in London, and during three long months we did not once see any genuine sunshine because of the dense clouds of smoke that hung over the city like a pall. But many a time I saw that above the smoke the sun was shining, and once or twice through a rift I had a glimpse of a bird, with sunshine on its wings, sailing above the fog in the clear blue of the sunlit sky. Not all the brushes in London can sweep away the fog; but could we only mount high enough we should reach a region above it all.

And this is what the soul on wings does. It overcomes the world through faith. To overcome means to "come over," not to be crushed under; and the soul on wings flies over the world and the things of it. These lose their power to hold or bind the spirit that can "come over" them on the wings of Surrender and Trust. That spirit is made in very truth "more than conqueror."

Birds overcome the lower law of gravitation by the higher law of flight; and the soul on wings overcomes the lower law of sin and misery and bondage by the higher law of spiritual flying. The "law of the spirit of life in Christ Jesus" must necessarily be a higher and more dominant law than the law of sin and death; therefore the soul that has mounted into this upper region of the life in Christ cannot fail to conquer and triumph.

But it may be asked how it is, then, that all Christians do not always triumph. I answer that it is because a great many Christians do not "mount up with wings" into this higher plane of life at all. They live on the same low level with their circumstances; and instead of flying over them, they try to fight them on their own earthly plane. On this plane the soul is powerless; it has no weapons with which to conquer there; and instead of overcoming, or coming over, the trials and sorrows of the earthly life it is overcome by them and crushed under them.

We all know, as I have said, that things look differently to us according to our "point of view." Trials assume a very different aspect when looked down upon from above than when viewed from their own level. What seems like an impassable wall on its own level becomes an insignificant line to the eyes that see it from the top of a mountain; and the snares and sorrows that assume such immense proportion while we look at them on the earthly plane become insignificant little motes in the sunshine when the soul has mounted on wings to the heavenly places above them.

A friend once illustrated to me the difference between three of her friends in the following way. She said if they should all three come to a spiritual mountain which had to be crossed, the first one would tunnel through it with hard and wearisome labor; the second would meander around it in an indefinite fashion, hardly knowing where she was going, and yet, because her aim was right, getting around it at last; but the third, she said, would just flap her wings and fly right over. I think we must all know something of these different ways of locomotion; and I trust, if any of us in the past have tried to tunnel our way through the mountains that have stood across our pathway, or have been meandering around them, that we may from henceforth resolve to spread our wings and "mount up" into the clear atmosphere of God's presence, where it will be easy to overcome, or come over, the highest mountain of them all.

I say "spread our wings and mount up," because not the largest wings ever known can lift a bird one inch upward unless they are used. We must *use* our wings, or they avail us nothing.

It is not worth while to cry out, "Oh that I had wings and then I would flee," for we *have* the wings already, and what is needed is not more wings, but only that we should use those we have. The power to surrender and trust exists in every human soul, and only needs to be brought into exercise. With these two wings we *can* "flee" to God at any moment; but, in order really to reach Him, we must actively use them. We must not merely want to use them, but we must *do* it definitely and actively. A passive surrender or a passive trust will not do. I mean this very practically. We shall not "mount up" very high if we only surrender and trust in theory, or in our especially religious moments. We must do it definitely and practically about each detail of daily life as it comes to us. We must meet our disappointments, our thwartings, our persecutions, our malicious enemies, our provoking friends, our trials and temptations of every sort, with an active and experimental attitude of surrender and trust. We must spread our wings and "mount up" to the "heavenly places in Christ" above them all, where they will lose their power to harm or distress us. For from these high places we shall see things through the eye of Christ, and all earth will be glorified in the heavenly vision.

> "The dove hath neither claw nor sting,
>   Nor weapon for the fight,
> She owes her safety to the wing,
>   Her victory to flight.
> The bridegroom opes His arms of love,
>   And in them folds the panting dove."

How changed our lives would be if we could only fly through the days on these wings of surrender and trust! Instead of stirring up strife and bitterness by trying, metaphorically, to knock down and walk over our offending brothers and sisters, we should escape all strife by simply spreading our wings and mounting up to the heavenly region, where our eyes would see all things covered with a mantle of Christian love and pity.

Our souls were made to live in this upper atmosphere, and we stifle and choke on any lower level. Our eyes were made to look off from these heavenly heights, and our vision is distorted by any lower gazing. It is a great blessing, therefore, that our loving Father in heaven has mercifully arranged all the discipline of our lives with a view to teaching us to fly.

In Deuteronomy we have a picture of how this teaching is done: "As an eagle stirreth up her nest, fluttereth over her young, spreadeth abroad her wings, taketh them, beareth them on her wings: so the Lord alone did lead him, and there was no strange god with him."

The mother eagle teaches her little ones to fly by making their nest so uncomfortable that they are forced to leave it and commit themselves to the unknown world of air outside. And just so does our God to us. He stirs up our comfortable nests, and pushes us over the edge of them, and we are forced to use our wings to save ourselves from fatal falling. Read your trials in this light, and see if you cannot begin to get a glimpse of their meaning. Your wings are being developed.

I knew a lady whose life was one long strain of trial by a cruel, wicked, drunken husband. There was no possibility of human help, and in her despair she was driven to use her wings and fly to God. And during the long years of trial her wings grew so strong from constant flying that at last, as she told me, when the trials were at their hardest, it seemed to her as if her soul was carried over them on a beautiful rainbow and found itself in a peaceful resting-place on the other side.

With this end in view we can surely accept with thankfulness every trial that compels us to use our wings, for only so can they grow strong and large and fit for the highest flying. Unused wings gradually wither and shrink and lose their flying power; and if we had nothing in our lives that made flying necessary we might perhaps at last lose all capacity to fly.

But you may ask, Are there no hindrances to flying, even where the wings are strong, and the soul is trying hard to use them? I answer, Yes. A bird may be imprisoned in a cage, or it may be tethered to the ground with a cord, or it may be loaded with a weight that drags it down, or it may be entrapped in the "snare of the fowler," and hindrances which answer to all these in the spiritual realm may make it impossible for the soul to fly until it has been set free from them by the mighty power of God.

One "snare of the fowler" that entraps many souls is the snare of doubt. The doubts look so plausible and often so humble that Christians walk into their "snare" without dreaming for a moment that it is a snare at all, until they find themselves caught and unable to fly; for there is no more possibility of flying for the soul that doubts than there is for the bird caught in the fowler's snare.

The reason of this is evident. One of our wings, namely,

the wing of trust, is entirely disabled by the slightest doubt; and just as it requires two wings to lift a bird in the air, so does it require two wings to lift the soul. A great many people do everything but trust. They spread the wing of surrender, and use it vigorously, and wonder why it is that they do not mount up, never dreaming that it is because all the while the wing of trust is hanging idle by their sides. It is because Christians use one wing only, that their efforts to fly are often so irregular and fruitless.

Look at a bird with a broken wing trying to fly, and you will get some idea of the kind of motion all one-sided flying must make. We must use both our wings, or not try to fly at all.

It may be that for some the "snare of the fowler" is some subtle form of sin, some hidden want of consecration. Where this is the case the wing of trust may seem to be all right, but the wing of surrender hangs idly down; and it is just as hopeless to try to fly with the wing of trust alone as with the wing of surrender alone. Both wings must be used, or no flying is possible.

Or perhaps the soul may feel as if it were in a prison from which it cannot escape, and consequently is debarred from mounting up on wings. No earthly bars can ever imprison the soul. No walls however high, or bolts however strong, can imprison an eagle so long as there is an open way upward; and earth's power can never hold the soul in prison while the upward way is kept open and free. Our enemies may build walls around us as high as they please, but they cannot build any barrier between us and God; and if we "mount up with wings" we can fly higher than any of their walls can ever reach.

If we find ourselves imprisoned, then, we may be sure of this, that it is not our earthly environment that con-stitutes our prison-house, for the soul's wings scorn all paltry bars and walls of earth's making. The only thing that can really imprison the soul is something that hin-ders its upward flight. The Prophet tells us that it is our iniquities that have separated between us and our God and our sins that have hid His face from us. Therefore, if our soul is imprisoned, it must be because some indulged sin has built a barrier between us and the Lord, and we cannot fly until this sin is given up and put out of the way.

But often where there is no conscious sin the soul is still unconsciously tethered to something of earth, and so struggles in vain to fly. A party of my friends once got into a boat in Norway to row around one of the fiords there. They took their seats and began to row vigorously, but the boat made no headway. They put out more strength and rowed harder than before, but all in vain, not an inch did the boat move. Then one of the party suddenly recollected that the boat had not been unmoored, and he exclaimed, "No wonder we could not get away when we were trying to pull the whole continent of Europe after us!" And just so our souls are often not unmoored from earthly things. We must cut ourselves loose. As well might an eagle try to fly with a hundred-ton weight tied fast to its feet as the soul try to "mount up with wings" while a weight of earthly cares and anxieties is holding it down to earth.

When our Lord was trying to teach His disciples concerning this danger, He told them a parable of a great supper to which many who were invited failed to come because they were hindered by their earthly cares. One had bought a piece of ground, another a yoke of oxen, and a third had married a wife; and they felt that all these things needed their care.

Wives, or oxen, or land, or even very much smaller things, may be the cords that tether the soul from flying, or the weights that hold it down. Let us, then, cut every cord, and remove every barrier, that our souls may find no hindrance to their mounting up with wings as eagles to heavenly places in Christ Jesus.

We are commanded to have our hearts filled with songs of rejoicing and to make inward melody to the Lord. But unless we mount up with wings this is impossible, for the only creature that can sing is the creature that flies. When the Prophet declared that though all the world should be desolate, yet he would rejoice in God and joy in the God of his salvation, his soul was surely on wings. Paul knew what it was to use his wings when he found himself to be "sorrowful, yet always rejoicing." On the earthly plane all was dark to both Paul and the Prophet, but on the heavenly plane all was brightest sunshine.

Do you know anything of this life on wings, dear reader? Do you "mount up" continually to God, out of and above earth's cares and trials, to that higher plane of life where all is peace and triumph, or do you plod wearily along on foot through the midst of your trials and let them overwhelm you at every turn?

Let us, however, guard against a mistake here. Do not think that by flying I mean necessarily any very joyous emotions or feelings of exhilaration. There is a great deal of emotional flying that is not real flying at all. It is such flying as a feather accomplishes which is driven upward by a strong puff of wind but flutters down again as soon as the wind ceases to blow. The flying I mean is a matter of *principle*, not a matter of *emotion*. It may be accompanied by very joyous emotions, but it does not depend on them. It depends only upon the facts of an entire surrender and an absolute trust. Every one who will honestly use these two wings, and will faithfully persist in using them, will find that they *have* mounted up with wings as an eagle, no matter how empty of all emotion they may have felt themselves to be before.

For the promise is sure: "They that wait upon the Lord SHALL mount up with wings as eagles." Not "may perhaps mount up," but "SHALL." It is the inevitable result. May we each one prove it for ourselves!

> "The lark soars singing from its nest,
>   And tells aloud
>   His trust in God, and so is blest
>   Let come what cloud.
>
> "He has no store, he sows no seed,
>   Yet sings aloud, and doth not heed.
>   Through cloudy day or scanty feed,
>   He sings to shame
>   Men who forget in fear of need
>   A Father's name.
>
> "The heart that trusts forever sings,
>   And feels as light as it has wings;
>   A well of peace within it springs.
>   Come good or ill,
>   Whate'er to-day or morrow bring,
>   It is His will."

MORE CHALLENGING READING
FROM YOUR FAVORITE AUTHORS
Complete and Unabridged

GOD'S PSYCHIATRY by Charles L. Allen   1.75
An actual working manual which can change your life in just seven days. From Biblical lessons come ways to banish fear, acquire confidence, and face life with new enthusiasm and peace of mind.

THE BURDEN IS LIGHT! by Eugenia Price   1.50
The amazing autobiography of a successful, sophisticated writer whose empty personal life was transformed when she took the Word of God literally!

A MAN CALLED PETER by Catherine Marshall   1.75
The glowing story of the acclaimed minister and Senate chaplain whose messages touched the heartstrings of the whole world.

PEACE WITH GOD by Billy Graham   1.75
Written by one of the century's most influential religious figures, here is inspiration and comfort for the man in the street.

ANGEL UNAWARE by Dale Evans Rogers   1.25
The poignant story of the birth, and death, of Roy and Dale Rogers' own little girl. A lasting victory over great sorrow.

THROUGH GATES OF SPLENDOR by Elisabeth Elliot   1.95
An on-the-scene account of the martyrdom of five American missionaries in the steaming jungles of Ecuador, an epic of unmatched courage and faith.

Order From Your Bookstore

If your bookstore does not stock these books, return this Order Form to:

SPIRE BOOKS
Box 150, Old Tappan, New Jersey 07675

Enclosed is my payment plus $.35 mailing charge on first book ordered, $.10 each additional book.

Name _____

Street _____

City _____ State _____ Zip _____

_____ amount enclosed ____ cash ____ check ____ money order (no C.O.D.)

SB-28

"Come on, Danny. Aren't you going to tell me how beautiful I look?"

Abby took a step back, waiting while he drank in the whole delectable picture.

He deserved this. The torture of dragging his gaze up her long, tanned legs cut at his core. Her curved hips, trim waist and slim belly taunted him so that he nearly squeezed his eyes shut once before he reached her sweet, round breasts. But as much as he wanted to look away, he couldn't.

The flavor of her skin was one he'd never forget. The sound of her pleasured moans echoed through his dreams. The feel of her lips lingering on every intimate part of him was like a chained ghost, haunting him with the sins of his past.

The irony that Abigail Albertini would show up in New Orleans tonight couldn't be denied. He glanced at the stupid ring his brother had shoved onto his finger. Michael had spouted some nonsense about how the two-hundred-year-old heirloom would change his life, but Danny hadn't believed it.

Now, he wasn't so sure.

Abby sidled closer, dancing the tips of her fingers up his shirt, from his waistband to his collar. "I have a job for you. And I'm counting on you being the same low-life thief you used to be."

Karma could really be a bitch sometimes....

Dear Reader,

I remember the first time I fell in love with a scoundrel. I was eleven years old. His name was Han Solo. I liked the way Princess Leia pushed him around, but he pushed back. I liked the way he shot first and made no apologies later. I loved how in the end, everyone thought he'd abandon them, but instead, he came back in the nick of time and saved the day.

The scoundrel is a wily hero. He's hard to justify, but even harder to resist. He's charming and clever and when he's bad, he's oh-so-bad. He's Rhett Butler. He's Danny Ocean. Or even better, he's Danny Burnett, the hero of this book and the third brother in my Legendary Lovers series.

Danny isn't your typical good guy. He doesn't have an implacable moral code, and the only time he deals with law enforcement is when they're after him. Now he's inherited the infamous Murrieta ring—which means his life is about to undergo a serious change.

And, of course, that means a woman!

I hope you enjoy the story, especially the sweet antics of Black Jack and Lady, two real cats who are looking for their forever home (check out the Blaze Authors' Pet Project at www.blazeauthors.com for details). As the owner of a rescued cat, I know the joy animals can bring. Please stop by and see me on Facebook (http://www.facebook.com/readjulieleto) or Twitter (@JulieLeto) and, as always, at www.plotmonkeys.com.

Enjoy!

Julie Leto

Julie Leto

TOO WICKED TO KEEP

TORONTO NEW YORK LONDON
AMSTERDAM PARIS SYDNEY HAMBURG
STOCKHOLM ATHENS TOKYO MILAN MADRID
PRAGUE WARSAW BUDAPEST AUCKLAND

Recycling programs
for this product may
not exist in your area.

ISBN-13: 978-0-373-79643-4

TOO WICKED TO KEEP

Copyright © 2011 by Book Goddess, LLC

ABOUT THE AUTHOR

Over the course of her career, *New York Times* and *USA TODAY* bestselling author Julie Leto has published more than forty books—all of them sexy and all of them romances at heart. She shares a popular blog—www.plotmonkeys.com—with her best friends Carly Phillips, Janelle Denison and Leslie Kelly and would love for you to follow her on Twitter, where she goes by @JulieLeto. She's a born and bred Floridian homeschooling mom with a love for her family, her friends, her dachshund, her lynx-point Siamese and supersexy stories with a guaranteed happy ending.

Books by Julie Leto

HARLEQUIN BLAZE

To get the inside scoop on Harlequin Blaze and its talented writers, be sure to check out blazeauthors.com.

Don't miss any of our special offers. Write to us at the following address for information on our newest releases.

Harlequin Reader Service
U.S.: 3010 Walden Ave., P.O. Box 1325, Buffalo, NY 14269
Canadian: P.O. Box 609, Fort Erie, Ont. L2A 5X3

To all the families who adopt pets...
either from roadsides or shelters like
Furry Friends in Barrie, Ontario. Animals bring
pure joy and light into the lives of so many.

1

Five Years Earlier...

REACHING BEHIND HER, Abigail Albertini tried to snag the tiny crystal dangling from the zipper of her white silk cocktail dress. Her shoulders ached. Her neck twinged, and her artfully arranged hair lay heavy at her nape. The day had been so long. Appointments at the salon. Lunch with her bridesmaids. A last-minute meeting with the wedding planner before a pre-rehearsal cocktail hour, a trek to the church and several run-throughs with her family and friends. Then the wedding party had endured a five-course meal at Charlie Trotter's and a final round of champagne and aperitifs at her father's Lake Shore mansion, where she was now shedding the last vestiges of her life as a single woman in the room she'd slept in as a child. No wonder people wanted to only get married once. It was hard work.

She bent her arm back farther, trying not to snag her newly polished nails on the metal clasp, when she heard the deep male voice from behind her.

"Need help?"

She spun, her heart hammering.

"David!"

He emerged from the shadows beside her window looking more delicious and debonair than any man had a right to. Dressed in a tuxedo with a loosened collar and tie, he would have fit right in with the guests at tonight's pre-wedding soiree. Had he been there, blended with the crowd of out-of-town guests, family friends and Chicago elite? Her father had given the security team strict instructions to detain him if he got within two-hundred yards of her, but what chance did former military police have against a man like him?

She'd learned the hard way that what David Brandon wanted, David Brandon got—no matter the danger. No matter the cost.

As he swaggered closer and closer, she thought about screaming or running for the door. Thought, but didn't act. In that instant of indecision, his nearness ensnared her. Her exhausted nerve endings exploded with keen awareness of his body, of his hands encased in soft kid leather. Of his skin, devoid of cologne, yet rich with an intoxicating scent that was his and his alone.

David Brandon was an expert at getting into places he shouldn't. He'd breached Abby's heart that way— what was one Gold Coast bedroom to a thief like him?

"You have to go."

"Not without you," he whispered.

She stumbled backward, forcing herself out of the fog his body heat injected into her brain. "Have you lost your mind? You betrayed me, David. You took advantage of me and used me to get your hands on my grandmother's painting. You used me."

"I know. I'm sorry. And trust me, I'm never sorry."

It wasn't his confession that stopped her retreat, but the pleading in his voice. She shook her head, knowing she must have heard wrong. Why would he beg? Why would he care? He'd taken what he wanted. She had nothing more to give.

"Then don't be sorry now. I don't need your pity and I don't accept your pathetic apology."

"It may be pathetic, but it's sincere."

"What the hell do you know about sincere? Nothing about you is real. Nothing."

This much she'd learned the hard way. David Brandon, the man who'd come into her life at a time when she was vulnerable and afraid that she was making all the right choices for all the wrong reasons, had been a fraud. A con. He'd crafted his persona specifically to get close to her, to get access to the painting. She knew that now. She knew it all.

He wasn't sweepingly romantic or achingly suave or deliciously wicked…he was a filthy, thieving liar who'd stolen everything she'd ever valued, from her grandmother's cherished painting to her faith in her ability to tell the difference between a man who loved her and a man who was out to exploit everything she treasured.

He smoothed a lock of hair off her cheek.

His gloves were cold. "My feelings for you are real. Maybe the first real emotions I've ever felt."

She squeezed her eyes shut, determined not to listen, determined not to make the same mistakes with David just because her body quaked and her breasts felt heavy and tingly with his chest so near to hers.

"Why are you doing this?" she asked, hating the tears blurring her vision as she fought to look him in the eye. "You took what you wanted. There's nothing left. If I scream, my father won't just have you arrested. He'll kill you."

Despite her threat, David stepped closer until their

bodies touched. She whimpered, remembering with intimate clarity how this contact had once made her weak in the knees—how it still took every ounce of her shame not to grab on to him to steady her balance.

"I'm not afraid of your father," he said, his intense green eyes boring into her like a drill. "I'm not afraid of jail. But if I'm arrested, I won't be able to get your painting back. And I will, Abby. I swear."

The empty promise broke the spell. She pushed him away and scrambled to the other side of the room.

"When? And how? If you want to prove something to me, why don't you have it with you now?"

She didn't know why she bothered grilling him with questions. Even if he had answers, they'd be lies. A week ago, she would not have doubted him. A week ago, she would have hung on his every utterance, convinced he was on the verge of rescuing her from her privileged, but staid and predictable life. He'd promised to sweep her into an epic romantic adventure where they'd spend their days exploring the world's finest art museums and their nights making love in penthouses from Paris to Morocco to Prague.

But those dreams had been nothing but pretty pictures painted to earn her trust—and access to the portrait she'd refused to ever part with.

"It's already been fenced," he said. "I had to finish the job. But I'll track it down. I'll return it to you, I promise. It'll be my wedding gift to you."

Her stomach roiled. Even if David made good on his promise, Marshall would never allow the painting into their home now that he knew the truth about her own part in this grand betrayal.

"Haven't you given us enough? Like pain? Misery?"

David skewed his face in disgust. "I'm not talking about you and that stiff."

"That stiff has a name—a real name," she defended. "He inherited it from his grandfather and it stands for integrity and honesty and, remarkably, for forgiveness. Tomorrow, it will be my name, too. I'll spend the rest of my life making up for what I did, David. Will you?"

He answered her question with a curse.

"You can't marry him."

His voice was so definitive, Abby couldn't help but laugh.

"I not only can," she said, determination straightening her spine in ways it hadn't in a long time, "I will. I love him. And I don't know why he didn't toss me to the curb when I told him about us, but I'm taking this second chance, and this time, I'll get it right."

His eyes widened. "You confessed?"

"Of course I confessed! Did you think I'd cover up because I was ashamed? You probably counted on that. But I couldn't do it. I couldn't lie anymore. I told him everything. I told him how we met at the foundation fundraiser. I told him how you knew so much about me, how you plied me with champagne and lured me into the museum's Renaissance art collection. I even told him how you compared me to Titian's Diana and you to the brave Actaeon, and how I couldn't think straight and how I forgot all my promises and responsibilities and got caught up until I didn't know how to stop from ruining everything."

The words tumbled from her as if spiked with shards of shattered glass. She covered her mouth with her hands.

David dropped onto the edge of her bed. "I can't believe you told him everything."

His voice was a whisper, not of surprise, but shock. Maybe even hurt.

She didn't care. She couldn't care. His strategy had been artfully planned and executed, playing to her every weakness, her every fantasy.

But she'd learned the hard way that life wasn't about schoolgirl dreams or grand romantic affairs. It was about living. Loving.

Trusting.

"I couldn't live with the lies. Unlike you, I believe people should have the whole truth about someone before they make a serious decision. Marshall didn't have to honor our engagement. He could have...he *should* have called the whole thing off. But he didn't. He's a real man who loves me enough to forgive me. And I love him. I always have and I always will."

David stood, his head shaking from side to side as if he was trying to process all she'd said. But how could he? He didn't have the capacity to understand things like love and compassion and honesty and forgiveness. If he had, he never would have sought her out in the first place.

Then he went still, took a deep breath and met her confused stare with clear, determined eyes.

"My name's not David."

Her heart fell, even though this news came as no surprise, not after all the searches she'd done after he'd disappeared with her painting.

"Who are you, then?"

He hesitated.

The momentary pause acted like an explosion of awareness. She'd made the right choice in confessing to Marshall. She'd made the right choice in accepting his forgiveness and pushing her leftover feelings for David Brandon—or whatever his name was—out of her heart.

The truth did not come easily to this man—and it never would.

He'd come into her life at precisely the wrong time. Just out of graduate school and only a few months into her first job, she was staring down at a future that had been mapped out for her from before she was born. Until she'd met him, she'd never questioned any of it. She'd willfully stepped onto the path of her life, never straying, never questioning, never *doing* anything her family would be ashamed of, even if she had fantasized about dangerous adventures and sensual sins.

Then he'd shown up. He'd offered her a taste of the very things that had always been forbidden—and for that, she'd paid a high price.

"Tell me your real name."

"Daniel," he replied. "Daniel Burnett."

"And you're from?"

"Anywhere," he said, shaking his head. "Nowhere. Doesn't matter, Abby. Nothing matters. Not if you're really going to marry him. I made a lot of mistakes, but the worst was falling in love with you."

She snorted, not caring that it was unattractive and unladylike. "That was your biggest error? The so-called falling-in-love part? Not the lying or the scheming or the fact that you took the one thing my grandmother left me when she died?"

"No, that's not what I meant. That was wrong, too. All of it. But it's what I do. It's who I am...or who I was, before I met you."

She glared at him, willing herself to ignore how sincere he looked, how broken.

"And you expect me to believe that after all those

carefully crafted lies, you're now telling me the truth? You're reformed? Just like that?"

"No. I mean, yes, I want you to believe me. I need you to believe me. I'm not reformed. I don't know if that's even possible, but I do love you."

She contained a bitter chuckle. God, how had she become so jaded so fast?

Falling for a liar like Daniel Burnett had definitely helped.

"And why should I believe anything you say, Daniel?" she asked, putting a searing emphasis on the name the first time it passed her lips.

"I can't stop thinking about you."

"That's just your conscience."

"No, that can't be it."

"Probably not, since I doubt you even have a conscience."

"I probably don't. At least, not one I've paid any attention to for a long time. When I do a job, I do a job. I get what I came for, I sell it for the highest price and I walk away. It's what I do. It's what I've done my whole life. But suddenly, that's changed. I can't get you out of my mind. I can't stop thinking about what I did. Remorse is an emotion I've avoided my entire life, and yet that's gotta be what I'm feeling, right? That has to mean something."

Abby took a bold, if shaky, step toward the door. This conversation was over. This situation was over. "It means you crossed the line this time, Daniel. It means you went too far. If you want to find my grandmother's painting and return it, that's up to you. But I want no part of it—no part of you."

She reached for the doorknob, but he intercepted her.

"You loved me," he insisted.

Just a short time ago, his hand on hers would have felt exciting, wicked, thrilling.

Now, it just felt foreign.

And wrong.

"I loved the idea of you. I loved the secrecy and the illicit sex. It was like a drug. But I never meant to hurt anyone. You did. If not for this sudden burst of conscience, you would have walked away without a second thought. I may never forgive myself for my part in this mess, but Marshall has forgiven me. He trusts me to never make that mistake again. That's what love is, David or Daniel or whoever you are. Maybe someday, you'll learn about real love, but it won't be from me."

Though she didn't want to, she took one last look at him, with his dark, swarthy skin, close-cropped hair and twinkling green eyes—which had, in the uncertain light, lost their clever confidence. Every muscle, every fiber, every bone in her body ached for him, but she pushed the empathy aside. She couldn't care about his pain. She couldn't even believe it existed. Nothing about him was real.

"I'm going to go ask my mother to help me out of this dress. If you're not gone by the time we get back, I will call the police and I will make sure you're prosecuted to the fullest extent of the law."

"Abby, please," he began, but he stopped when she turned her back and snatched the doorknob.

And with more power and will than she ever thought she possessed, Abby walked away.

2

Present Day...

"IF YOU NEED SOMETHING slick to rub on there, I think I have just the thing."

Daniel Burnett stopped tugging at the ring caught on his knuckle. He must have looked like a moron, sitting in a New Orleans casino, tugging at his finger as if the gold band was cutting off his circulation. He couldn't imagine why any woman would proposition him under these circumstances, especially since he probably looked like a schmo trying to hide the evidence of his marital status.

But when he looked up at the woman behind the sultry proposition, he nearly slid right off the bar stool.

Everything about her was different. Her hair, once a straight, unadorned brown, now glimmered with striking copper highlights. Amber eyes once muted behind square-shaped red-framed glasses now flashed from the center of long, dark lashes. Lips she'd once coated only with balm or a pale gloss were now outlined and plump with a rich cognac shade that made him crave a burning, fortifying sip.

"Abby?"

She arched a brow. "Wow, and here I thought you wouldn't recognize me after all these years."

"I'd know you anywhere."

The words were out before he could stop them, before he could put a lid on the Pandora's box of emotions flying through him. He never thought he'd see her again—never wanted to. He'd avoided taking any jobs in Chicago—hell, he avoided the whole Midwest altogether. He'd survived Abby once, but barely. A woman like her was lethal.

Dangerous.

Gorgeous.

He grabbed his jacket from the back of his chair and shrugged into it. He eyed the door. His flight wasn't leaving for another six hours, but maybe he'd be smart to head out to the airport now. Maybe he'd rent a car and drive back to California.

Or maybe he'd just crawl under a rock.

She leaned in close so that her breath, sweet with mint, caressed the skin on his neck and ear. "Come on, Daniel. After all these years, you're not going to at least tell me how beautiful I look?"

This was the advantage of meeting up again with a woman who already knew you were an asshole. He could look his fill and she wouldn't think any less of him—it wasn't possible. She took a step back, hooked one hand onto her slim waist and waited while he drank in the whole delectable picture.

He deserved this. The torture of dragging his gaze up her long, tanned legs cut at his core. Her curved hips, trim waist and slim belly taunted him so that he nearly squeezed his eyes shut before he reached her sweet, round breasts. But as much as he wanted to look away, he couldn't.

The flavor of her skin danced on the memory of his tongue. The sound of her pleasured moans echoed through his dreams. The feel of her lips lingering on every intimate part of him was like a chained ghost, haunting him with the sins of his past.

The irony that Abigail Albertini would show up in New Orleans the very night Danny had done the first good deed in his life couldn't be denied. He glanced at the stupid ring his brother had shoved onto his finger less than an hour ago, as a reward for Danny's help in rescuing Michael's lover from a crazed rapist. His younger brother had spouted some nonsense about how the two-hundred-year-old heirloom would change his life, but Danny hadn't believed a word.

Now he wasn't so sure.

"Like what you see?" she asked boldly.

He tried not to groan as she twisted sideways so that the full impact of her curves hit him like a battering ram.

He reached for his drink.

"Marriage agrees with you," he muttered.

The edge of her mouth quirked at the corner. "Thank you."

As much as he didn't want to look, Danny made a quick survey of the bar. He'd never met Marshall Chamberlain, so he just looked for any man whose veins were popping out of the side of his skull. That's what he'd look like if the guy who'd tempted his fiancé to cheat on him had suddenly appeared in their vicinity. But none of the guys nursing their beers or strolling through the casino looked the least bit interested in him or Abby.

Danny clicked his tongue. The guy really was a

moron. If he had a wife as passionate, beautiful and barely reined as Abby, he'd never let her out of his sight.

Of course, he didn't have a wife like Abby and that was no one's fault but his own.

"So," he said, wanting to put himself out of his misery sooner rather than later. "Where is the lucky guy? I never did offer my congratulations on your nuptials."

"That's probably best, don't you think?"

"I'm not known for doing what is best," he reminded her.

"Sure you are," she said, sliding on the bar stool beside him and signaling for the bartender. "As long as it's best for you. Trust me, you and Marshall running into each other would not have been good for anyone."

While she ordered a bottle of champagne, Danny swigged the last of his scotch and wondered how the hell the past couple of days had gone from bad to worse. First, he'd left California for Louisiana, hoping to find his brother Michael and maybe make good on his plan to steal their father's ring, sell it and use the profit to start a new life somewhere fresh...or at least, somewhere that didn't have Wanted posters with his name on them.

The Netherlands, perhaps? Outer Botswana?

But once he'd arrived in the Crescent City, he'd ended up helping his brother, an FBI agent, solve a case and save the woman he loved. On top of that mess, Michael had ended up giving Danny the damned ring voluntarily, which took all the fun out of it.

For revenge, the stupid gold-and-emerald heirloom was now nearly cutting off the circulation in his right hand. And as the pièce de résistance, the one woman who'd broken his heart had, for some unknown reason, now traveled cross-country to rub his nose in her long and happy marriage.

This was karma. It had to be.

"So, what are you doing here, so far from the man who stole you away from me?"

She laughed, but there was no trace of humor in those brandy-colored irises.

"Is that how you remember things? Because as I recall, you were the one who did *all* the stealing."

Five years of time and distance, plus wearing, even under duress, his infamous ancestor's ring, gave him the balls to snag her by the waist and pull her in close.

Five years of marriage gave her the confidence to remain still, a curious grin playing on her lips while she waited to see what he'd do next.

Those five years did not, however, protect him from the instantaneous slam of need that exploded through his system from the scent of her perfume and the silky warmth of her skin.

"You stole my heart," he murmured.

She twisted away from him, but she probably hadn't even heard him over the music and clanging sounds of the casino. "You lost the right to touch me a long time ago."

He leaned back into his chair. Maybe if he exuded his typical casual air, the heartbeat ramming against his chest wouldn't be so obvious.

She hadn't meant to lose her cool. Danny could see the combination of anger and shock in her eyes. But her intense reaction proved one thing—she hadn't gotten over him. Maybe she still hated him. Maybe she spent every day cursing his name. But at least she hadn't forgotten him. That was something.

"You're right." He took another drink, grateful for the smooth burn of the scotch as it slid down his throat. "But you know exactly who I am, Abby. If you wanted to rub my face in how hot you look after five years of marriage, then you've accomplished your goal. If you want to slap my face or have me arrested, then go ahead." He leaned forward, his newly acquired ring glittering on his hand. "But don't parade that luscious body of yours so close to mine and expect me to keep my hands off. Every man has his limits. Even me."

"I'm counting on you to push past those limits, then," she said stiffly.

For the first time, he caught a glimpse of the haughty, privileged princess he'd met five years ago. But only a glimpse.

"What are you talking about?"

"I came here to find you."

"And your husband let you? What is he, a moron?"

"Don't speak that way about Marshall," she shot back. "He was a good man who didn't deserve what I did to him."

Was?

Danny stood. "No, he didn't deserve any pain we caused him."

She pressed her mouth into a tight line—a line Danny couldn't help but want to breach. On a normal day, at a normal hour, Abigail was a classic Mediterranean beauty, with her thick, dark hair, smooth olive skin and expressive amber eyes. But when she was angry—when she let her control slip even a little—she knocked the breath from his lungs.

"Very true," she conceded. "But I didn't expect to hear compassion from Daniel Burnett, or is it David Brandon again?"

"I haven't been David Brandon for—" He cut his claim short. He'd actually used the name the day before. He'd developed a habit of trying it every so often, to see if the pain of losing Abby had lessened any in the years since she'd kicked him out of her life.

It hadn't.

"Why'd you come looking for me?"

His voice was as strangled as the skin beneath his ring finger. Her mouth curved into a tiny smile—the first one that flashed all the way up to her irises. His pain gave her pleasure. He couldn't blame her.

She sidled closer, then danced the tips of her fingers up his shirt, from his waistband to his collar. "I have a job for you."

With a flick of her nail up the underside of his chin, a fire sparked through Danny's body that made him want to drown himself in the moisture of her mouth. She was taunting him. Making him pay, one hormone at a time, for nearly destroying her future.

He not only didn't blame her—he wanted more.

His brain might have registered all the reasons why he should stay half a country away from Abigail Albertini Chamberlain, but his dick hadn't gotten the memo. Blood rushed down so fast, Danny had to grab the edge of the bar to keep from losing his balance.

"No way."

"You owe me," she said.

"So? You're playing with fire, Abby. I can't promise you won't get burned again. And this time, Marshall won't forgive you. I wouldn't."

"You wouldn't have the first time."

She took her time tracing her fingers up his neck and then tousling the strands of hair at his temples. When her gaze locked with his, he saw none of the naive, uncertain girl she used to be.

She was all woman now—and she had something up

her sleeve, figuratively speaking. Something that wasn't going to be good—at least, not for him.

"No," he conceded. "I wouldn't have forgiven you."

"Good," she said, pushing away from him and snatching the flute of champagne the bartender had delivered. "Then you haven't changed. I'm counting on you being the same lowlife, conscienceless thief you used to be."

He forced a chuckle. "Why would you hope for that?"

She sipped her champagne. After enjoying half the glass, replete with appreciative hums and slides of her tongue over her rich, luscious lips, she put the flute back onto the bar and stretched up onto her tiptoes to whisper in his ear.

When she did, her breasts brushed against his chest. The sensation caused a domino effect of ignitions that sparked his every nerve ending.

"Because I've found my painting and I need you to make good on your promise and steal it back."

3

ABBY SPUN ON HER four-inch heels, grabbed the bottle of champagne out of the ice bucket and started her hip-swinging parade out of the hotel bar. She measured her steps and the rhythm of her walk. She needed him to follow. She needed him to prove he wasn't so much of a scoundrel that he'd break the last promise he made to her before he'd disappeared.

She supposed she could have offered him money. She had plenty of it, not that it had helped her thus far in averting a scandal for her family. She'd thought about offering her forgiveness, but she wasn't sure he cared about it or that she had any to give. Time, distance and four years of marriage to a man who loved her had less-ened the sting. She was still pissed off at Danny for nearly wrecking her life, but she no longer wanted to curl into a whimpering ball of loss and regret.

But he probably didn't need her money, and if he cared one bit about forgiveness, he would have made good on his vow to retrieve the painting years ago. If she wanted him to follow now, she was going to offer him something she hoped he still craved—a chance to win her back.

It wasn't going to happen, of course. She might have put on her sexiest dress and flown across the country to lure him back to Chicago, but she wasn't going to sleep with him. She'd been there, done that and had the heartache to prove it.

Though she had to admit—he was still hot.

She knew better than anyone that any living, breathing woman within close proximity to David Brandon, aka Daniel Burnett, would be subject to a raging surge of lust. But while she'd come here anticipating a tug of attraction from the leftover riptides of their fast and furious affair, she hadn't expected to nearly drown.

The minute she'd seen him from across the crowded casino, she'd fallen backward in time. Her nerve endings had sizzled and her brain, conditioned over the past five years to block out the memory of the night he'd approached her for the first time in a darkened museum gallery, had betrayed her with images vibrant with sex and sensuality. From that first whispered innuendo, he'd turned her inside out, exposing the desires she'd kept so carefully hidden from everyone in her life, her fiancé included.

But she was older now. Stronger. She'd tried other avenues to reclaim her painting before it exposed her family—mostly her father—to derision and ridicule.

Lust aside, she couldn't allow her fears to stop her plan. It wasn't a wise plan. It certainly wasn't remotely ethical. But that ship had sailed a long time ago. Trying to reclaim her good-girl status now was like trying to win back her virginity. The only thing she had left from her days before Daniel had charmed his way into her life was her reputation. If she didn't act soon, that would be at risk, too.

"Abby, wait."

His voice traveled over the retreating sounds of the casino, but she didn't break her stride. The doors from the lobby to the street slid open, blasting her head to toe with cool night air that had, only hours before, clung to her with the warm, wet heat that made Louisiana so infamous. Tracking Daniel down to New Orleans had been no small feat. She might never have found him if he hadn't made the unexpected mistake of getting himself arrested in California. "Abby!"

He grabbed her arm and his touch was electric. The sensation of his palm wrapped around her wrist ratcheted up her heartbeat until she was certain he could feel her pulse. She tried to yank herself free, but he held her fast.

"Let go of me."

"We need to talk."

He pressed his thumb intimately on her pulse point. The pounding intensified in her ears and heat suffused her system until tiny beads of sweat trickled at her nape and between her breasts. Her brain flashed with a memory. The two of them, naked, in front of her fireplace. Ice cubes. His thirsty tongue.

She pulled harder. "Don't touch me."

His face twisted with confusion, but he instantly let her go.

"What the hell, Abby? You came on to me back there, not the other way around. Now I can't lay a hand on you just to stop you from running?"

"I wasn't running," she said, gulping in air. "And yes, that's the deal."

"What if I don't agree to the terms?"

She took another deep breath and released it slowly. She hadn't come here to give him an ultimatum. She'd meant to entice him to do this one favor, to repay her for what he'd put her through. She'd expected residual chemical attraction to him, but she hadn't expected fear.

"If you won't help me, I'll find someone else who will."

He eyed her warily, but didn't immediately walk away. She had to get herself together. Remember her endgame. Stick to her plan. She'd banked on Daniel still caring about her. She'd hoped, stupidly perhaps, that he'd cultivated a bit of real remorse since she'd left her bedroom the night before her wedding with her dress unzipped and Daniel long gone.

"Why do you need the painting all of a sudden?"

"The man who owns it now plans to not only display it, but auction it off. I have less than a week to get it back before everyone knows about my grandmother and her affair with that artist."

"I don't get it," Daniel said, his voice doubtful. "You're the original owner. If he puts it on display, the whole world will know it was stolen."

"After you took it, I never reported it stolen. My father hated that portrait. To him, it's salt in the wound of his mother cheating on his father and all the years of bullying and taunting he suffered through as a kid because of it. He's had years to forget about that pain, and now it's going to be dragged up again because I let you steal it. My grandmother gave the painting to me to keep it safe, to keep our family secrets just that."

"Why didn't she destroy it?"

Abby's blood heated. "I don't know," she lied. "Maybe she appreciated the artist's talent. Maybe she intended to keep it as financial insurance. All I know is that I was supposed to keep the painting out of the public eye. Once this collector shows it, art historians will trip over themselves trying to figure out who the subject is. She was the wife of a prominent Chicago businessman. Her picture dominated the society columns every other day. It won't take long for our family secrets to be made very public—including mine."

Daniel snorted. "No one cares about scandals anymore, sweetheart. With the publicity, your father can probably double the per-square-foot price of his properties."

"Do you know how hard it is, still, for someone with the last name Albertini in a city like Chicago? Italian last name? Whispered ties to the old mob? It never really stops, no matter how many charities you fund or legitimate businesses you own and operate without so much as a fine from the IRS. And how do you think my father will feel, personally, when a nude portrait of his mother is all over the papers?"

"As I recall, she was a gorgeous woman."

Abby growled. "That's not the point. The painting is proof of an affair my grandmother had with the artist— an affair that has been a family secret for a long time. But people gossiped like crazy and my grandmother's greatest regret was how those whispers hurt my father, who was just a little kid. I can't let my mistakes drag out all that old pain again. Besides, once art experts start digging into the painting's authenticity and history, someone is going to connect the dots about us, too. Ever consider what that kind of publicity will do to your business?"

His eyebrows shot up, but only for a second. "You had an affair with some jerk named David Brandon. No one will connect him to me."

"Oh, really? I did."

"I told you who I was."

"And the police in California made note of that same

alias when you were arrested for attempted murder. It won't take long for a good reporter to make the connections. And I expect it will be hard to sneak into people's homes or famous museums when your face is splashed all over the latest news feeds. You have as much on the line as I do."

She turned back to the street, hoping to spot her limousine from the line outside the casino entrance. Maybe this was a mistake. Five years felt like five seconds with Daniel standing so near. The emotions he provoked, from lust to anger to passion to betrayal, rushed at her from every direction.

The deeper she tried to dig herself out of this mess, the worse it got. She'd managed to keep the details of her relationship with Daniel secret from everyone, even her parents. They knew that she'd been duped by a con man, but she'd never told them that she'd slept with him or that she'd practically handed over the safe's combination when he'd coaxed the story of her grandmother's rebellious affair with the artist, Bastien Pierre-Louis, out of her.

The only person who knew the whole truth had been Marshall. To him, she'd confessed everything. Not the sordid details—she'd spared him that pain—but she'd been brutally honest about her weaknesses and how Daniel had played to every single one.

And yet, for reasons she'd never completely understand, he'd forgiven her. They'd had to work hard to rebuild their relationship, but in the end, they'd been happy. If her past sins came to light, Marshall's memory would be tarnished, too. She couldn't allow that to happen.

She cursed, unable to spot her driver. The delay gave Daniel a chance to walk around in front of her. Though he'd slipped his hands casually into his pockets, his tight jaw and focused stare were anything but relaxed.

"I'm the last person you should ask for help."

"No, you're the only person I can ask. You already know the painting's history and you owe me. It was hard to track you down, but no harder than asking you for help."

"Do you think staying away from you has been easy? For five years, I've pretended you didn't exist. I let you have your perfect marriage with your perfect man. Now you show up here acting like a sex goddess on the prowl, make me an offer I can't refuse, but then freak out after one innocent touch? I'm a thief, Abby. Not a monster. I hurt you once. I won't do it again."

She swallowed deeply, then straightened her spine, determined to regain her control. He sounded so sincere, but she knew better than to fall for his line, no matter how artfully he delivered it. Daniel Burnett couldn't be trusted with her emotions. She wasn't even sure she could trust herself with them.

"I have no reason to believe you," she said. "But if you agree to help me, I have no choice but to take you at your less-than-reliable word."

"So we're both backed into a corner."

He stretched out his right hand, but stopped just a millimeter shy of touching her cheek. In the span of a heartbeat, his attention shifted from her to the ring on his right hand, the one he'd been trying desperately to get off when she'd first seen him in the bar.

She grabbed the opportunity to change the subject.

"What is that?"

"Recently inherited family treasure."

He turned his hand so she could see the stone. As jewelry went, it was fairly pathetic. The black opals on the sides were brilliant with bright blues and greens, but the center stone, which caught the marquee lights with more brilliance than she expected, had a huge, zig-zagged scratch.

"Maybe you can barter with the collector who has my painting," she suggested. The two items were nowhere near equal value, but she couldn't ignore the irony that he now possessed a family treasure when he'd been re-sponsible for stealing hers.

"If I could get the damned thing off my finger. But it's supposed to bring luck, so to speak, to the men in my family. Could come in handy while I'm breaking my rule of never stealing the same piece of art twice."

Her heart skipped a beat. "You're going to help me?"

"Yes, and not because of the threat to my livelihood. You may not believe me, but I'm helping you because it's the right thing to do."

His voice inflected with his obvious disbelief, but before she could question his sincerity, he gestured gal-lantly toward the line of limousines and gave her a little bow, as if inviting her to lead the way.

Her shoes were rooted to the sidewalk.

"Without any expectations?"

He looked up at the dark night sky as if asking for divine intervention. "Really, woman, when you have the advantage, take it and run."

Abby opened her mouth to object, but then decided to quit while she was ahead. The hard part of this opera-tion, apparently, was not getting Daniel on board—but keeping him from running roughshod over her.

She had to stay focused. Eyes on the prize.

And hands off the merchandise.

She finally spotted her limo. With a nod to the driver, she slid into the backseat, adjusting her skirt as the car dipped slightly while Daniel climbed in beside her. Despite the roominess of the interior, he sat as close to her as he could.

The driver slammed the door.

"There's space in this car for eight people," she said. "Feel free to spread out."

He made that clicking sound with his tongue. "Thanks, but I'm fine here."

She'd had no illusions that he'd make this easy, but she was up to the challenge. She had to be.

She gave the driver instructions to take them straight to the airport, and then didn't object when Daniel closed the glass partition.

"Should we stop anywhere to retrieve your things?" she asked.

"You can buy me whatever I need."

"What you need most can't be bought," she quipped.

He chuckled. "Clever. So you've developed a sharp tongue since last we met?"

"I've developed a lot of things. I was a child when last we met."

He turned so that his body, so close, faced hers. "You were a lot of things, Abigail Alexandra Albertini, but a child you were not."

She didn't remember ever telling him her alliterative middle name, but his casual use of it reminded her how much more he knew about her than she did about him.

To find Daniel Burnett, she'd had to employ several private investigators. Each one had provided tidbits of his past, disjointed and disconnected, until she'd pieced them together into an incomplete picture of his life.

His mother had turned him over to family services when he was five years old. She'd died of a drug overdose about a year later. He'd been shuttled from foster home to foster home until he was ten, when he'd landed with the Burnett family, who'd adopted him. His juvenile record included multiple counts for petty theft and trespassing, but by the time he turned eighteen, his name disappeared from arrest records. He'd been interviewed about a few cases in his early twenties and the name Daniel Burnett had dominated watch lists for museums, collectors and auction houses worldwide since, but he had never been prosecuted, not even after a security guard was seriously injured at the site of his last job.

When she combined what she'd learned from her private investigators with what she knew from their affair, the idea that he'd nearly killed someone struck her as unlikely. Even after he'd betrayed her trust in the worst possible way, Daniel was a lover, not a fighter. She couldn't believe he'd try to kill someone.

"What happened in California?" she asked.

"I grew up in California," he answered. "Many things happened there."

"I mean your arrest."

"Rethinking your decision to tap me for the honor of retrieving your stolen property?" he asked, his eyes glittering with his tease—one likely meant to divert her line of questioning.

"No," she said. "It's just that part of your appeal as a thief is that up until a couple of months ago, you'd never seen the inside of a jail cell for more than a few hours. And you definitely never hurt anyone."

"You've checked up on me?"

"Of course," she replied.

"Smart girl," he admitted. "You probably won't believe this, but I was set up for that mess in California."

"By whom?"

He leaned back into the seat and eyed her again, this time warily. Had he not expected her to take him at his word?

"Might have been you, now that I think about it. You couldn't see me jailed for what I did to you, so maybe you arranged for me to be railroaded for something else."

She shook her head. "There's a huge flaw in that logic."

"Really?"

"Oh, yes. If I was going to frame you for a crime, I'd do it in Illinois, not California. We don't have the death penalty, so you'd have to suffer longer."

He snickered at her joke and she was surprised she'd made it. She was supposed to be angry at him, or at least wary of him. But in the span of twenty minutes, she'd already started meeting his teases with her own.

"Do you think the person who set you up is still out to get you?" she asked, returning the conversation to her most serious concern.

"Nah," he said. "But it's sweet that you're worried about me."

This time, her laugh was a burst of genuine humor. "I'm not worried about you. I'm worried about someone getting in the way of you retrieving my painting. The collector has already sent out invitations to art lovers all around Chicago, promising to reveal an unknown work by Bastien Pierre-Louis next week. The buzz in local circles is getting louder every day. This operation needs to be quick and simple. No complications."

Daniel laughed, retrieved two glasses from the limousine's bar and then commandeered the champagne she'd taken from the casino and poured. "Then you're out of luck, sweetheart. If you don't want complications, you picked the wrong man."

4

FROM A SEAT IN the back of Abigail's private jet, Danny watched her move up the aisle and marveled at how much she'd changed—and how much she had stayed the same. She was still beautiful and slim, still graceful and minimal in her movements, still sweet and charming as she spoke in hushed tones to her pilot and copilot, who nodded and smiled with deferential respect when she was facing them, but checked out her ass when she left the cockpit.

Shifting in his seat, Danny made eye contact. Their hungry grins vanished. The captain tipped his hat and then quickly shut the door.

Danny had no right to feel territorial. He had no business thinking about how smooth Abby's skin had been underneath his touch for that brief moment, or how her aversion to contact now reminded him of how skittish she'd been five years ago, how hard he'd had to work to get past her considerable defenses. Even after he'd tempted her into his bed, she would have rather bitten through her lip than make too much noise. Her idea of down-and-dirty sex was doing it standing up.

He had a hard time reconciling that shy, repressed

young woman with the vixen now sashaying up the aisle as if she meant to torture him with what he could not have.

And on this, she was succeeding.

She slid into the leather seat across from his, her skirt riding up an extra inch or two that the dress simply didn't have to give.

"Want anything before we take off?" she asked.

Oh, he wanted a lot of things—none of which he was going to get anytime soon.

Still, he made a show of glancing around the cabin. "No flight attendants?"

"Just the pilot and copilot." She clicked her seat belt and waited for Danny to do the same. "We have a lot to talk about. I didn't want to be disturbed."

He stretched out his legs so that they were inches from hers. "Sure that's the only reason you wanted to be alone? To talk?"

She ignored his question. "Who hired you to steal the painting five years ago?"

"Why?"

"Anatomy of a crime," she explained. "By the time we arrive in Chicago, I want to know everything you do about what happened to my painting."

"I thought you knew who had it."

"I do. Or at least, I think I do," she clarified. "His name is Harris Liebe."

Danny shrugged. He'd never heard the name before— and this was odd. The fraternity of art collectors who purchased off the black market wasn't that extensive.

"Never heard of him."

"Neither have a lot of people. But his little announcement has piqued the interest of the legitimate art world. Bastien Pierre-Louis's work has been experiencing a resurgence in the last decade. Every year leading up to what would have been the man's one-hundredth birthday increases the value of his pieces, particularly the unsigned ones he gave away during his lifetime."

"Like your grandmother's."

"Precisely like hers. She was the daughter of a wealthy New York businessman with supposed ties to the mob. My great-grandfather, her father-in-law, had similar connections in Chicago, though his son was legitimate. The whole twisted tale makes the painting worth more than even I could afford."

"And that's why your family never insured it?"

"I wanted to. Because I curate for so many private collectors, I have contacts with people who would have been very discreet. But my father wanted no connection to it and asked me not to do anything that would officially connect the painting to our family. And after you took it," she said, the words shooting out of her mouth like bullets from a twenty-two, "my father asked me not to call the police. He hated that painting. I think he was glad someone took it."

Now, this was a piece of information Danny would file away for later. He'd never met Abby's parents, but assumed they'd hate him on sight. If he were a father, he certainly would. But maybe there was a chance, even if it was a long shot, that he'd find a way into the real estate titan's good graces. Everything about this situation was doomed for failure, but he'd survived most of his life because of his inability to take no for an answer.

"How does your father feel now that the painting is going to be publicly displayed?"

She looked askance. "He doesn't exactly know."

"How'd you pull that off?"

"I arranged for my mother to have a sudden need to

spend alone time with him in their Italian villa. They'll be gone for two more weeks."

Danny leaned back in his seat. "Impressive."

"I've learned to cover all my bases, which is why I need to know everything you know about the collector who paid you to seduce me."

Danny shook his head. He'd deflect blame for a lot of his misdeeds, but not that one. "That part was entirely my idea. I mean, look at you. Can you blame a guy?"

Her sneer wasn't nearly as biting as she intended. "Tell me what you know about the first collector."

He gave up trying to postpone this part of the conversation. He wasn't used to discussing his business practices with anyone, much less someone he'd used them against.

"The story isn't that exciting. A collector contacted me, told me about the painting and offered me a shit-load of money to steal it."

"And how does one go about contacting you?"

"Word of mouth."

"Whose word? Whose mouth?"

That secret he wasn't sharing. "An associate who takes care of moving my merchandise to the collectors who've requested it."

"So this person is a fence?"

He arched a brow. Abby was nothing if not thorough.

"She's also a legitimate art appraiser," he explained, "so she runs in a lot of circles, maybe even some of yours. The collector got word to her that he was interested in hiring me for a job. I met with his representative, who paid my retainer after we negotiated a timetable and a total price. The deal was sealed with a handshake."

She chuckled humorlessly. "Sounds so clean and professional."

"It is what it is," he shot back.

Danny had never defended his lifestyle to anyone before. He'd never needed to. Approval or disapproval of how he made his living had never mattered to him. And even though Abby was now hiring him for the very reasons she sneered at, he knew she'd never approve. How could she, after what he'd done?

"Does your husband know you tracked me down?" he asked, wondering why a smart guy like Marshall Chamberlain would allow his wife to seek him out, particularly while wearing that little black dream of a dress.

He watched her cheek hollow as she sucked on the inner flesh.

That would be a no.

And yet, she replied, "I'd like to think so."

He glanced at her hand.

She wasn't wearing a ring.

"Wait a minute."

Since she'd shown up at the casino, she hadn't answered a single question about her husband. Until now, he'd figured she was on a secret mission, hoping to keep Marshall from having to relive the incident that almost waylaid their wedding.

But she hadn't mentioned Marshall at all. In fact, the only time the man had come up in conversation was when Danny had asked.

He leaned forward and gazed purposefully into her eyes, his chest tightening as she tried to keep her face impassive and cool. She was biting the inside of her mouth again, but instead of making her mouth look pinched or prissy, her lips puckered in a way that tugged at his heart.

"What aren't you telling me?" he asked.

"About a gazillion things that are none of your business," she snapped.

"I mean about Marshall."

When Abby had thrown him out of her room on the night before her wedding, Danny had taken the rejection hard. He always spent the weeks after a job underground, but after Chicago, he'd gone completely off the grid in Mexico. After a few cases of tequila and more beer than a man should drink in a lifetime, he'd finally decided that Abby was better off without him. If Marshall Chamberlain loved her enough to forgive her indiscretion, then he must have loved her more than Danny could even comprehend.

So how the hell could he have left her a short five years later?

"I can't believe he dumped you."

"He didn't," she said, her eyes flaring.

"Then where the hell is he? Or is thievery just beneath him, so he's left it all to you?"

"There isn't anything much beneath him anymore except dirt," she choked out. "He's dead."

She made the callous statement, then instantly turned away. She flattened her left palm on the window, as if she needed contact with the glass to cool her emotions. Or maybe she was mourning the absence of her ring. A slight shadow encircled her fourth finger, a reminder of where the band had been. She'd taken it off, but only recently.

"I'm sorry. When?"

She gave a tiny shrug, as if she hadn't been counting the days, when he guessed she could probably calculate the man's last breath to the minute.

"A little over a year ago. He was on his way to his

office and a semi lost control on the highway and he was gone."

The crack in the foundation of her voice tore at his insides, but Danny had no right to share her grief. No right to try and comfort her.

But he still had to say something.

"I really am sorry."

"So am I. But if there was one thing I knew about Marshall, and I knew everything about him," she said, skewering him with a glare that dared him to challenge her, "it was that he'd want me to move forward. Put the past behind me, once and for all. That was the entire basis for our marriage. He never once threw our affair in my face. He didn't make me pay for how I betrayed him with you, even though he probably should have."

Danny couldn't believe how easily she talked about this. The Abby he'd known had always shied away from discussing anything painful or unpleasant. Despite his offers to meet her out of town, even a suggestion they fly up to Toronto for a rendezvous, their liaisons had only taken place at night, in locked rooms or shadowed corners.

Even when they were alone, she'd been conditioned to keep her deepest thoughts to herself. He'd had to pull out all the stops to sneak behind her private walls. But he'd succeeded, or at least, he'd thought he had. By the time he'd finally learned how to retrieve the painting without triggering her security system, he'd discovered all sorts of things about her that he hadn't really wanted to know.

Her secret passions.

Her most erotic fantasies.

Her deepest, most desperate dreams.

She'd also confessed how desperately she wanted

a man who understood the real her. Not the cool, controlled young lady of wealth that she'd been trained to be, but the innately curious, impassioned lover of sensual beauty that she kept so well hidden.

Before him, she hadn't revealed that woman to anyone, not even to her fiancé. She'd been too embarrassed, too self-conscious, too afraid that Marshall would run in the other direction quicker than he could say *scandal*.

David Brandon, on the other hand, knew precisely how to coax that side of her out of hiding. He'd cultivated her need for freedom with honeyed words and wicked suggestions spoken to burn through the layers of her fears. David Brandon did not judge her. How could he, when his whole persona was one big fat lie?

The plane began to move, so they were quiet while the pilot taxied down the runway, gained speed and then altitude. When a ding indicated they'd reached their cruising height, Danny caught Abby staring at him, her eyebrows scrunched tightly together.

"I don't understand you," she declared.

"Welcome to the club. I can't figure me out, and I am, hands down, the smartest guy I know."

She didn't crack a smile.

"I mean, I get that you're all complicated and tragic. Charming on the outside and brooding and miserable on the inside." She waved her hand, as if her gesture could dismiss the very core of him, which he'd never heard so succinctly summarized. "But why would you come with me so easily? Is it just because you might be exposed?"

"Nope," he said breezily. "I'm in it for the cash."

"I didn't offer you any money. And even if I did, you don't need it. You have a very wealthy brother who paid a king's ransom for the criminal attorney who got you out of jail. And you and I both know that you have to have a boatload of cash stashed somewhere. International art thieves don't come cheap."

"You've certainly learned a lot over the last five years."

"To say the least," she replied.

"Care to share some of your wisdom?"

He didn't know why he was asking. In his entire life, he'd never once asked for anyone's advice. Sure, he'd watched people he admired and listened carefully whenever they spoke to glean whatever nugget of information he could mine for a greater take, but he'd never out-and-out asked anyone to share their insight about... well, about anything.

Unfortunately, from Abby's frown, she didn't look anxious to share.

"I'm sure the things I've learned you committed to memory by the age of eight."

"That everyone is a liar and a thief, you mean. In one way or another?"

"Yeah," she acknowledged. "That."

"You're not," he argued.

"Not what? A liar? Please, Daniel. Don't sugarcoat on my account."

"I'm not," he insisted. "You told Marshall the truth about us, didn't you?"

"Only after lying to him for weeks. And I colluded with my mother to get my father out of the country. And I expect that by this time next week, I'll have lied enough to match your level of expertise."

She unbuckled her seat belt and retreated to the galley at the back of the plane. She tugged open the built-in wine cooler and extracted a bottle without giving the label a second glance. When her hunt for a corkscrew escalated from frustrated to frantic, he joined her.

"I should have kept the champagne," she said with a slightly maniacal laugh. "It was already open."

"Let me." He reached out to touch her shoulder, but pulled back. She didn't want him to touch her—she'd made that clear. And right now, he didn't think she needed one more reason to hate him.

She didn't turn around, but clutched the countertop in front of her.

"I loved Marshall."

"I know."

From their first contact, their first kiss, their first hot, frantic sexual encounter in a darkened corner of the museum after hours, Danny had known that Abby had only gravitated to him because of excitement and exploration and lust. He was a man unlike any she'd ever encountered—one who had been tailored to her needs, her wants, her desires. In giving her what she so secretly craved, he'd taken what he'd come for and then counted on her loyalty to the man she really loved in order to cover up his own crime.

What Danny hadn't factored into the equation was that once he delivered the painting to his buyer, he hadn't been able to follow his usual routine, which was to disappear until the heat from the crime wore off. Instead, he'd walked right back into the fire, determined to steal Abby, too.

But not to fence her for someone else to enjoy—she was a treasure he'd wanted for himself.

One he could never have.

He wished he could define what it was about her that was so enthralling. Despite her sexier packaging, he still sensed her reined-in wildness, her continued struggle between doing what was expected of her and acting on her raging need to be free.

In a lot of ways, she lived a double life the same as he did.

Once upon a time, Abby had been as simple to figure out as a game of Three Card Monty. Now, she was more like Omaha Hi/Lo Hold'Em Poker—complex and challenging, with variations the average player wouldn't understand.

Luckily, Danny was well above average.

"I'm sorry for what I did to you, Abby. I'm sorry that I took something you valued so much. I have no good excuse, I just have the truth. I'm a thief. Stealing is what I do. It's what you're counting on me to do when we get to Chicago."

At this, she spun around. Her eyes were dry, but streaked with red. "And you agreed with hardly a second thought."

He clasped his hands behind his back to keep from grabbing her by the shoulders and kissing her. The action was all levels of wrong, but the need to backtrack out of this conversation was powerful.

"Of course I agreed. Stealing is what I do. Besides, I only steal from people who can afford it," he explained with a wink. "And my expertise is in stealing *things*. The value we put on tangible items in our society is the real crime."

She snorted, then pushed past him, abandoning the wine. "Philosophy? Not your forte."

"Clearly," he said wryly.

She marched down the aisle and threw herself back into her seat. Danny took a quick look through a drawer, found a corkscrew, grabbed the wine bottle and joined her. As he had not thought to pack a parachute, he had nowhere to run and a lot of air space to endure before they reached Chicago. The whole experience would be a hell of a lot better after a few glasses of Pinot Noir.

He settled in across from her and popped the cork.

She didn't speak until he offered her a glass, which she accepted, though she didn't take a sip. "You stole more than a thing from me, Daniel."

Her voice was barely audible, yet sharp as a knife.

"I know."

"I want it back," she said.

"I told you. I'll do whatever it takes to get the painting for you."

She stared at him with such intense focus, he nearly looked away. "That's not what I meant. I want what you took from my heart. Think you can find that, too?"

5

THE MINUTE THEY LANDED, Abby wrapped herself up in the minutiae of getting them from the airport to her apartment without more than minimal conversation. Though she'd tried to dig a little deeper into what had transpired five years ago between her and Daniel, he'd skillfully spun the topics away from anything personal. For the duration of their two-hour flight, they'd exchanged little more than small talk.

But that, in itself, was revealing.

Time had not made him cavalier about what had happened between them. He had regrets, which was only fair, since she had them, too.

Outside the casino, Daniel's touch had blown apart the emotional containment built by Marshall's unconditional forgiveness. Questions she'd set aside in order to concentrate on her marriage now exploded in her brain. What vulnerabilities had Daniel noticed about her first? How had he breached her understanding of right and wrong so easily? Why had *he* learned about her secret fantasies when she'd never confessed them to anyone else?

Had he ever really loved her?

For so long, she hadn't cared about what Daniel felt. She'd concentrated only on Marshall's love, which she'd cherished. But now she needed answers. Moving on would require them, and more than anything, she wanted to put her past to rest so she could live again—and hopefully, someday, love again. And since the collector who had her painting would show the work to the public in a little over a week, she only had until then to close this chapter of her life for good.

But instead of deconstructing the foundation of their affair, she and Daniel had spent the rest of the flight sipping wine and talking about his newly discovered brothers.

Or rather, his newly acknowledged brothers. He'd actually known about them both long before either Alejandro, the Spanish auction-house owner, and Michael, the FBI agent, learned about him—a fact that pretty much summed up the man she was counting on to save her family from humiliation. To keep the upper hand, Daniel made it his business to know everything he could about any nemesis, even when his "nemesis" was a blood relative...or a woman he'd once claimed to love.

Luckily, she had honed her own information-gathering skills since they'd last met. From her private investigators, she'd learned about his arrest and subsequent release from jail. But from Daniel, she'd found out that he no longer thought Alejandro was a stuck-up prick, and that he'd gone to New Orleans to steal the ring he was now wearing, but instead had helped Michael rescue two women from a psychotic rapist.

"So are you going to tell your brothers where you are?" she asked, hunting in her clutch bag for the keys as her driver pulled up to the covered awning in front of her apartment. Though she'd downsized from the brownstone Marshall's parents had leased to them during her marriage, she was eternally grateful that she'd picked a place with more than one bedroom. Inviting Daniel into Marshall's house would not have been right. Putting Daniel up in a hotel would make planning his theft too difficult. She needed to keep him close—but not too close.

"No," he replied, folding his arms against the blast of Chicago cold.

She hurried to the front entrance so they could get out of the frigid wind. "Don't you think you should?"

"Why?"

Abby keyed in the code to her building, then waited while Daniel swung open the door. At nearly three in the morning, the doorman had left his post and the chilled October air sliced through her skin. She rubbed the gooseflesh from her arms while they hurried across the marble lobby to the elevators.

"I don't know," she said. "I don't have siblings."

"What about that friend of yours?"

She stopped up short. "You remember Erica? You never met her."

"No, but you talked about her all the time. As I recall, she's like a sister and I bet you don't check in with her every time you go somewhere."

"Yes, I do."

"Did she know you were going to New Orleans?"

"Yes," she replied haughtily.

"Did she know *why?*"

She frowned and punched the arrow pointing up. "Not exactly."

He smirked, and then held back the doors after they slid open.

"Why the secrecy?"

Abby scowled. She'd meant for tonight to be about her eking out painful answers from Daniel—not the other way around.

"I never told her about you."

She hurried inside, slid her resident key in the slot and programmed the elevator to go to the twenty-first floor. It was late and she was tired. Her mouth felt dry and cottony, a result of two glasses of wine, a high altitude and a lot of talking. She didn't want to confess to him how she'd hidden her worst mistake from her best friend, even after all these years. They had more important things to discuss—things that weren't so much about her.

As the elevator shot upward, she grappled with the fact that after researching her thoroughly before he'd gone after the painting, Daniel had obviously not picked up a single newspaper or searched her name through Google since he'd left. He'd had no idea that Marshall had died. He'd had no clue that she'd taken a job as a curator for several private art collections and spent the rest of her time leading tours of Chicago's great museums for kids from working-class and struggling neighborhoods who might not otherwise have a chance to experience the city's many artistic and architectural treasures. She led a simple, unexciting life, but one with purpose and meaning.

At least, that's what he'd said when she told him.

And she wasn't exactly sure how she felt about his reaction. In a way, she was disappointed that he hadn't been more…disappointed.

They arrived on her floor and she quietly padded down the carpeted hallway and unlocked her door. The minute she stepped inside, she felt the warm softness of fur curling around her ankles. Lady, her short-haired, dark tortoiseshell cat, had immediately come to greet her while Black Jack, her long-haired male, stared at her from atop her antique china cabinet with his assessing amber eyes.

"Jack! Get down from there."

The cat, predictably, ignored her.

She tossed her purse aside and scooped Lady into her arms. The loud purring made her smile. When she turned, Daniel stood rooted in the doorway, eyeing her as if she were some sort of alien.

She glanced down at her pet. "Are you allergic?"

"To cats specifically? No. To pets in general? Yeah."

"But you're a cat burglar," she said, snuggling Lady's furry head beneath her chin. "I assumed you'd love my sweet babies."

"Nobody says *cat burglar* anymore."

"I just did," she corrected him.

The cat's soft vibrations of contentedness soothed Abby's frazzled nerves. She was glad to be home, even if she'd had to bring Daniel with her—even if her life could fall apart in a thousand different ways if her crazy plan to save her family from humiliation failed.

She slipped into the kitchen and checked the food and water bowls, which were full. She grabbed a pouch of cat treats out of the pantry and endured Lady's impatient mewls on her way back into the living area, where she intended to coax Black Jack down from his perch. She was a little surprised to see Daniel still standing in the hallway warily eyeing her and her cat.

She smirked as she approached him, Lady cradled in her arms. "I can bring you a pillow and blankets if you prefer to sleep in the hall."

With a grimace, he entered the apartment and shut the door behind him. Lady instantly struggled out of her arms, bounced to the ground and made a beeline for the new guy. Her internal motor turned up to its highest setting, Lady coiled around his legs, basting his pants with her soft, dark fur. He sidestepped with an amazing amount of grace, but he'd met his match. The cat anticipated his moves, and no matter how much dancing he did in the foyer, Lady wouldn't let him get away.

"What is she, in heat or something?"

"You do have that effect on women," Abby quipped, shaking the bag of treats up at Black Jack, who seemed much more interested in his companion's obsession with the new guy than he did in the tuna-flavored crunchies.

"It's a curse," Daniel said, balancing on one foot to avoid stepping on Lady's serpentine tale. "Know how to break it?"

She snorted. If she knew how to fight the allure that was Daniel Burnett, she wouldn't be in this situation at all, would she?

"Just pet her," she advised. "If cats think you don't like them, they never leave you alone."

"So if you like them, they ignore you?"

"Pretty much." She slid a footstool to the cabinet and climbed up to collect Black Jack, but he had no interest in coming down. He lifted his big furry body and backed into a corner with a hiss.

"Oh, really?" she challenged, annoyed. Her pets weren't accustomed to guests of the male persuasion, but she didn't expect open hostility. "No treats for you, you nasty traitor."

"Talking to me or the cat?"

Daniel was directly behind her. She gasped, surprised he'd come so near without her hearing him—without her feeling him. He had Lady curled up in his arms, her eyes at half-mast while he scratched her chin. Abby couldn't remember her cat ever looking quite so hypnotized.

She remembered the sensation very well.

"Give me a second and I'll get you set up in the guest room," she said, turning so she could back her way down the stool—but not before he took a bold look at her ass, which was right at his eye level.

"Is that my only option?"

His voice was silk and sensuality, not unlike the sound emanating from the back of her cat's throat. She allowed herself a split second to fantasize about him caressing her as he did her pet, but then skewered him with an exasperated look that was more for herself than for him.

Daniel exuded sex to strangers. To a woman who'd experienced the skill of his sly hands, wicked tongue and generous mouth, his allure was doubly powerful.

With their shared past, her attraction to him wasn't rational. It was chemical.

"Unless you want to sleep out here on the couch with the cats, yes, Daniel, that's your only option."

"If we skip the sleeping part, do my choices expand?"

His shamelessness was both infuriating and exhilarating. He had no boundaries, no limits. She couldn't help but laugh. She'd never met anyone like him and she doubted that once he left, she'd ever meet anyone like him again.

At least, not if she could help it.

"Sorry, but that's the best I can offer."

He eyed her couch and then the cat, who was now stretching up and burrowing her head beneath his chin. "The guest room will be fine."

"Good choice. Make yourself at home and I'll show you around in a few minutes."

Abby went into her bedroom, kicked off her high heels, then unhooked her earrings as she sauntered into her bathroom to take off her makeup and brush her teeth. Thinking it might not be a good idea to show Daniel into the bedroom while she was still wearing the sexy black dress, she pulled out her most modest pajamas, a full-length top and pants in a hazy pearl silk that she'd gotten from her mother for her last birthday.

She kept the lights off, her ear tuned for any sound of Daniel moving around her apartment, maybe looking through her things, trying to find some clue about her current life that he could use to his advantage.

He could look all he wanted—he wouldn't find much. When she'd moved out of the brownstone she'd shared with Marshall, she'd left most of her possessions behind. The house had belonged to his family and most of the furnishings had been theirs, too. Shamed by her behavior before the wedding, she'd wrapped herself up in his world, in his things. When he died, she realized how much of herself she'd lost.

Once she'd started to come out of the fog of sadness, she'd decided to get her own place. She'd ignored her mother's offer to pay for an interior designer, opting instead to fill the apartment herself with furniture and knickknacks that she'd picked out on her own. Even the cats were new, adopted from a shelter. She still had a few things to remind her of Marshall—like the T-shirt he used to wear to bed that she kept in a tissue-lined box in her closet—but mostly, this places was hers and hers alone.

But now, Daniel was here. In her life. In her home. Was he still in her heart, too?

She reached behind to undo the zipper of her dress

and nearly jumped out of her skin when her hand met his.

"Here, let me."

She moved to step away, but stopped. She couldn't keep running. She'd found Daniel not only so he could help her retrieve her grandmother's painting, but also so she could face his part in her crazy past and put it to rest. If she couldn't endure his touch, how would she ever prove to herself that he no longer held sway over her heart, body or soul?

After taking a deep breath, she lifted her hair off her nape.

For a long minute, he didn't move, but his warmth prickled her exposed skin.

She glanced over her shoulder.

"Everything okay back there?" she asked, trying not to sound as if her nerve endings were about to burn out at the tips.

The heat of his hand hovered inches from her flesh. "I didn't expect you to let me get this close."

She held her hair higher. "I'm too tired to twist myself into a pretzel so I can put on my pajamas. I'm just being practical."

He hummed as he mulled over her claim. "I can work with that."

"Why don't you just work my zipper while you tell me why you think it's okay to be in my bedroom?"

He slid the fastener down her body, but didn't reply. The pad of his finger only struck against her skin once, at the spot where her lower back arched.

Then he was gone.

At least, his hand was gone. He hadn't moved.

Slowly, she let her hair down, the strands fanning down her exposed back, providing scant protection against her body's keen awareness of his. So close. So warm. So…solid. She swayed a little. He cupped her elbows to keep her from losing her balance.

"Daniel," she pleaded.

"Danny," he corrected. "No one calls me Daniel. No one who really knows me."

"There are people who really know you?"

He released her. "A few. Maybe one or two."

"Like your brothers? The ones you won't call to tell where you are?"

She crossed her arms to keep her loosened dress from sliding off her body, but she wanted to hear his answer. In all the reports she'd read from her private investigators, she'd never once run across the name of anyone Daniel—Danny—had become close with. She'd assumed he was either an inveterate loner or he kept the people he cared about protected from his work.

Or both.

"Just because I don't want them in my business doesn't mean they're not important to me. Alex and I have gotten kind of tight."

"You mean Alejandro?"

Danny smirked. "Yeah, him."

"And what about Michael. You said on the plane that you've known him longer. Aren't you close?"

He rolled his eyes. "Hello? FBI agent. He's not exactly cool with my profession."

"Your older brother is an art expert," she pointed out. "As you steal art, I can't imagine he's too thrilled about your choice of jobs, either."

"He's not," he conceded. "But he's willing to overlook my past misdeeds in the name of brotherhood. He's Spanish. They're really big on family blood and loyalty and all that."

She sniffed in amusement, snatched her pajamas and headed back to the dressing area. "Yeah, I know about *famiglia*."

She didn't expect him to leave the room, so she wasn't surprised when she heard her mattress squeak under his weight. She chuckled hopelessly and changed as quickly as possible out of her dress and into the silky pj's. Even covered from head to toe, she still felt exposed when she slid back into the bedroom. One layer of filmy material between her bare breasts and Danny's assessing eyes didn't seem like nearly enough.

"Interesting look," he commented.

He'd bunched her throw pillows against the headboard and was lying across her comforter as if he owned the place.

"What did you expect me to wear? Flannel?"

"Seemed to be the direction you were going in."

"I don't own flannel."

"Then this is the next best thing."

Against his chest, he held her favorite pillow. In the darkness, he couldn't see the saying embroidered into the cover. *Well-behaved women rarely make history.* Like the painting, it had been a gift from her grandmother. Like the painting, it was a present her parents had been glad to see taken from their house. She couldn't help but wonder what her parents would think if they knew who was lying on her bed with a half-expectant look in his dreamy green eyes.

She snatched the pillow away.

"Time for me to show you where you're sleeping."

"I could sleep here."

"You could," she said, "but then I'd have to sleep in the guest room and that just doesn't seem right somehow."

He moved as if to get up, but instead, planted his elbows on his knees and eyed her with that cocky assuredness of his that she never could decipher. Was he about to tease her? Or hit her with an undeniable truth? Or both?

"Come on, Abby. Your husband has been gone for a year. A guy like him, willing to forgive what you—what *we* did. He wouldn't want you to be lonely."

"I'm not lonely."

"This from the woman with two cats?"

"Exactly," she said. "I have two cats not because I am lonely, but so that I won't be. At least I know they're going to stick around. At least I know they're not going to steal from me or lie to me."

"I won't lie to you."

"But you have."

"Yes, and I apologized. And now I have a chance to prove to you that I won't hurt you again."

"By sleeping with me?"

He scooted to the other side of the bed, where no one had ever slept except Black Jack and Lady, and flipped back the covers.

"Great idea," he said. "It's been a long day, and to be honest, I've been spending way too many nights alone. And maybe, if I manage to sleep next to you all night long without doing anything you don't want me to, you'll start trusting me a little."

She narrowed her gaze. He was trying to pull something. A guy like Danny Burnett was always running a scam, always working an angle.

"Define *doing anything you don't want me to*," she asked.

He chuckled. "Sharp as always. Okay, that could be too open for interpretation. How about, I won't do

anything that I might have done during our previous…
interactions. Unless you verbally ask me to."

She quirked a brow.

"Okay, unless you beg."

"That's not going to happen."

He grinned. "Not tonight."

She swallowed what little moisture was in her mouth
and considered how this could play out. She could order
him into the guest bedroom, lock her door behind her
and spend the rest of the night wondering if she'd lost a
key opportunity to see just how far she could trust the
man she'd recruited to save her family's reputation. Or,
she could show him how much *she'd* changed by accepting the gauntlet he'd thrown.

"Fine," she said, sliding between the sheets. "The
bathroom's in there if you want to take a shower or
whatever. I have extra toothbrushes in the drawer."

Surprisingly, he took her up on her offer. He bounded
off the bed and made such quick work of prepping himself for bed that she hardly had time to close her eyes
when he came back in with his shirt untucked, his pants
unbuckled and his socks removed. He grabbed a throw
blanket from her chair and then slid on top of her bed
beside her.

She rolled over. "That's cheating."

He arched a brow. "And you expect more from a guy
like me?"

She turned over with a huff, punched her pillow and
then slid her right arm firmly underneath it. "No, I guess
I don't."

"Good, because I'd hate to disappoint you again. The
first time nearly ripped me apart."

6

FOR AN HOUR, MAYBE TWO, Abby slept. Her dreams had been a confusing kaleidoscope of shapes and colors, most of them more like smears of slick oils on canvas rather than actual images she could identify. But they hadn't woken her up. Danny's voice had done that. Even as she rubbed her face and her eyes adjusted to the darkness, she could hear him muttering in his sleep. She couldn't understand him until he said, "Abby."

She rolled over and pushed aside the comforter that had bunched up like a cushioned wall between them. He'd turned onto his side, facing away from her. Though it was cold outside her floor-to-ceiling windows, Danny's skin glistened with a thin layer of sweat. The slight muskiness shot Abby's tired mind straight back to the hot summer nights she'd tried so hard to forget.

"Please, Abby."

She scooted closer. Was he really dreaming about her? She bit her lip, as afraid to believe him as she was to doubt him. If he was murmuring her name in the middle of the night, that meant he still cared about her—still wanted her. Even after all these years. Even when she had nothing left for him to steal.

But what if he was faking, pretending to be so wrapped up in her that she invaded his dreams? She'd never be able to trust him. He'd manipulated her once. She couldn't allow him to do it again.

With a minimum of movement, she rolled out of bed. Crouched, she remained beside the bed for a minute, pondering her choices. She really didn't have many. She could, she supposed, take her pillow and retreat to the guest room. There, at least, she'd be safe from either scenario. If he was really sleeping, then she wouldn't hear anything that he wouldn't want her to—anything that might reveal the truths locked away in his subconscious mind.

And if he was acting, he couldn't play her if she wasn't around.

But she didn't want to run. She wasn't that girl anymore. She couldn't be.

Instead, she padded softly around the bed. A streak of silver moonlight stretched across the length of his body. The light dazzled through his chest hair, drawing Abby's eyes to his lean, flat abs, which tapered into his unbuckled pants. It was too dark to distinguish the source of the bulge in his crotch. It could have been the blanket, she supposed. Or a trick of the light.

Or an erection.

Her mouth watered.

She covered her face with her hands. This was wrong. So wrong. The man had lied to her, stolen from her, nearly wrecked her whole life, starting with her impending marriage. He'd used her in the worst possible way, luring her out of her comfortable, respectable life with promises of sensual experiences that he had, admittedly, made good on up until the very end.

While married to Marshall, she couldn't remember

ever fantasizing about Danny or even wondering what had happened to him. She'd done her very best to put him entirely from her mind. And her husband, whether out of his own insecurities or a genuine desire to keep their marriage strong, had gone out of his way to spice up their sex life. She was never bored. They never fell into a rut.

But as a result, Marshall's death meant she missed sex more than ever. She missed the intimacy. She missed the mindlessness. She missed the conflagration of sensations that stripped away every pretense, every fear, every regret.

Could Danny give her that?

Did she want him to?

This time when he spoke, his words were unintelligible, a tangle of sounds that spoke of hot sex and utter surrender. He shifted, turning so that he was lying flat on his back. There was no mistaking his erection now. He'd not only unbuckled his pants, he'd unzipped them.

And he wasn't wearing underwear.

Unconsciously, she stepped closer, then looked away.

She didn't have to peek at him to remember his naked body. The images had remained burned into her brain. With him, she'd discovered so much about her sexuality—things she never would have been brave enough to explore with Marshall, who'd known her since she was a child and who'd treated her, up until her affair with Danny, like a china doll that might break if he loved her too roughly.

But Danny had never treated her gently. From the first moment they'd met, he'd come on to her with whispered innuendos just shy of crass to pique her curiosity without frightening her or turning her off. He'd orchestrated every word, every touch, to her vulnerabilities so that she'd had no choice but to fall and fall hard.

With him, she'd explored the true depths of passion and physical need and expression. He'd scorched away her inhibitions until all that was left was raw, unfulfilled desires, which he'd then satisfied one by one by one.

"No, don't," he said. "Don't go. No."

He grunted and groaned, and in the sounds, Abby heard the timbre of true supplication. He was begging her for something...or at least, he was begging someone. She knew how quickly characters could morph when someone was asleep.

Then he said her name again.

She dropped to her knees beside the bed. Heat suffused his skin, curling the dark hair at his temple and forehead. She lifted her hand to brush the moisture aside, but stopped. If she touched him, he might wake up. And if he did, then what would she do? He was more than ready to slide his thick and rigid length right into her. He was so primed, so fevered, the act of copulation might take a minute, maybe more, to bring him to the edge.

But she'd want more than a minute.

No, wait.

She didn't want anything at all.

She couldn't want him.

Could she?

His eyes fluttered open, but they were sightless, still trapped in a madness she could not allow herself to join.

"You came back," he said before his eyelids drifted closed again and he launched into another string of nonsense words—each more erotic than the last.

She had no idea what he was saying, but God help her, she knew what he meant. From the way his tongue rolled and his lips buzzed, he was reciting a collection of sensual promises that only he could fulfill. Her mind flew back in time, to the night he'd first kissed her, to the night she'd surrendered to passions she'd kept locked inside since the first time she'd seen a nude portrait at the Art Institute or read a romance novel.

But with Danny, no lock on her sensuous nature would hold. He'd awakened her like no other man had before.

Or since.

Forgive me, Marshall.

She reached out and risked running her fingers over Danny's rough cheek. His skin was as hot and sharp as the tears suddenly streaming down her face. The thought of the sandpaper sensations grazing over her naked body stole her breath. Fiery heat flooded her veins, sparking a gentle throb between her thighs.

The sweet tattoo of pleasure synched with the beat of her heart. She refused to be ashamed. She refused to feel regret. She didn't want Danny because she was still hung up on him—she wanted him because even while asleep, he brought to the surface pieces of herself she kept buried deep inside, pieces she needed to find and nurture or she might never be whole.

Risking everything, she leaned over until her face was inches from Danny's. She hesitated, not breathing, caught in the twilight world between hoping he'd wake up and praying he'd remain asleep. From his rapid breaths and undulating eyelids, she could imagine the eroticism of his dreams. She wished she could see them. She wished she could live them.

Like a feather floating in a curved cushion of air, Abby lowered her lips. His warmth intoxicated her. Like a key in a keyhole, his taste opened the store of memories she'd tried so hard to repress. Floodgates of sensation nearly drowned her, but she remained still, applying only enough pressure to his mouth so that she could experience the flavors that were his and his alone.

"Abby."

At the sound of her muffled name, she shot back into the darkness. She waited for him to open his eyes, maybe laugh at her for falling for him again…or drive home the fact that she was the one who couldn't keep away from him, not the other way around.

Instead, he rolled over onto his stomach, moved erotically against the mattress for a second, then stilled. He hadn't come, but he'd dreamed about it. Probably with her underneath, accepting his silky hot erection into her wet, tight body…her legs wrapped around his waist… his name bursting from her lips.

She slid into the chair by the window and curled into a ball, wishing it was daylight so she could forget, just for a minute, everything she was missing while Danny slept in her bed alone.

THE WEIGHT ON Danny's chest was not a good sign.

He was under forty. He was in excellent shape. He'd just spent the night next to a beautiful woman and, shockingly, he'd kept to his promise to not touch her.

At least, not while he was awake.

That wasn't entirely true, either. Just after she'd finally fallen asleep, he'd turned over to watch her. Unable to resist, he'd smoothed a lock of hair out of her face. The texture of her skin had struck him like a match and lit a continuous stream of erotic dreams that might have resulted in wet sheets if he'd been younger.

Could the heightened frustration of having her so close and yet being totally unable to act on the fantasies playing out in his subconscious have caused him to have a heart attack?

Then the weight sitting on the center of his chest swatted his nose with its paw.

He cracked one eye open. The amber eyes staring at him did not belong to Abby, but to her massive, long-haired, pissed-off-looking male cat.

Danny scooted back onto the pillows. The cat flew off the side of the bed, but his companion was curled contentedly in the crook of Danny's arm. Black Jack pounced atop the mattress again and hissed.

Jeez, what was it with him and the Albertinis? Could he never go after a female in this family who wasn't already spoken for?

"You're awake."

He turned to find Abby standing in the doorway, her pretty, petite hands wrapped around a quirky mug with a handle that looked like the marquee outside the old Chicago theater. She looked well rested, her complexion bright, as if she'd just gotten back from the gym.

He pushed Black Jack away, then gingerly coaxed Lady off his wrist so he could rub his face with his hands. Prickly stubble bit into his palms, and though he'd only had one glass of wine last night on the plane, he felt as if he'd drunk everyone in a biker bar under the table.

"If you say so," he said.

She came around to his side of the bed, sat near his feet and handed him her mug. He sniffed. She drank her brew with cream and sweetener, but he needed caffeine and wasn't about to be choosy.

"How'd you sleep?" she asked.

He tested the temperature and then finished what was left of her coffee in a couple of gulps. "Like a baby."

She took back the empty mug, a smile teasing the corners of her mouth. "A baby Casanova, maybe."

"Excuse me?"

She waggled her eyebrows.

"Crap. I didn't do anything, did I?"

The humorous twinkle in her eyes dropped off her face, taking the tilted corners of her mouth down with it. He untangled the blanket from his legs and looked down, half afraid he'd shed his clothes during the night before doing something he'd sworn he wouldn't do.

But he was fully dressed. His zipper was lowered, but his johnson was tucked safely away. He grunted with relief.

"You should see your face!" Abby said, dissolving with laughter. "I never knew skin could fade to that particular shade of green."

He glared at her. So she thought this was funny, did she?

He'd show her funny.

He tackled her.

She squealed. The coffee mug went flying, bouncing first on the mattress and then onto her plush, carpeted floor. The cat screeched and ran.

Then his body made full contact with hers and he wasn't aware of anything else happening in the room. Was there sunlight? Was there air? He could feel nothing but her softness against his hardness and then, incrementally, her heartbeat thrumming against his chest.

"Danny," she said.

"Hmm, that sounds suspiciously like a plea to me. What do you want me to do, Abby? Or maybe I should ask where you prefer me to start? I mean, your neck has always been a favorite spot of mine, especially that little curve right beneath your ear where you…"

"Danny, please."

He lowered his head, but stopped short of kissing her on the sensitive area that he couldn't tear his gaze from.

"Remember what I said about begging, Abby."

She folded her lips together, then speared him with a determined glare.

"Please, Danny. Please get off me."

She sounded serious. Damn it.

"First, I think I should get some credit for keeping my hands to myself last night. I kept my end of the deal."

"Yes, you did," she confirmed. "You lived up to your word. And from what I could gather about your dreams, it wasn't an easy task."

"Nothing about you has ever been easy."

"Except getting me into bed the first time."

He grinned. "We didn't do it in a bed the first time."

In her bid to free herself, she shifted beneath him. He winced as the teeth of his zipper scraped against his naked flesh.

"You know what I mean."

"Of course I do. What do you think I was dreaming about all night?"

Pushing past the pain of knowing he'd get no more contact than this, Danny concentrated on the feel of Abby underneath him. Their natural curves fit together like the tongues and grooves of a masterfully carved frame. No gaps. No space.

No room for uncertainty.

"You said you wouldn't do anything unless I begged you to," she reminded him, even as her nipples pebbled beneath her T-shirt. "And the only thing I'm begging you to do right now is let me up."

She sounded so reasonable, so calm, he had no choice but to comply. He might have tricked a few women—including her—into doing things they might not have done otherwise, but he'd never forced anyone.

Still, he couldn't help himself from prolonging the situation for a bit longer. "The sun's up now, sweetheart. That means the rules have to change. And I happen to know that as much as I was dreaming about you last night, you were doing the same about me."

He was guessing, of course. He'd been too caught up in his own fantasies to have picked up on any of hers. But the instantaneous blush of her cheeks told him his theory was dead-on.

The truth knocked him senseless long enough for her to scramble out from under him. Stunned, he rolled over and folded his hands behind his head while she attempted to straighten her yoga pants and zip up her hoodie.

Her skin was still pink and she was a little breathless. He supposed he should feel a measure of remorse after what he'd promised her last night, but he didn't. High from the prolonged contact of his body against hers, his blood zinged through his system and made him feel as if he could take on the world.

Or at the very least, one questionable art collector.

"So if we're not going to spend all day in bed, what is on the agenda?"

"Strategizing," she replied, snatching up her empty mug.

From the outer room, the doorbell rang.

"Who's that?" he asked.

"Delivery. Take a shower in the guest room and stay out of sight. I don't want to explain you to anyone just yet."

"As if you could," he teased.

She frowned, then disappeared out the door.

Curiosity piqued, Danny followed her into the hall and found a spot that was both hidden and had fairly good acoustics to the entryway.

"Are you going to tell me why you need men's clothes and toiletries?" a sharply feminine voice asked.

"Not yet," Abby answered. "But thanks for coming through for me. Did you do the other thing, too?"

"Of course," the woman replied, her annoyance evident, as if the thought of her not doing something that Abby had asked was utterly repugnant. "But you need to tell me what's going on. The last time you were so secretive…"

"Yeah," Abby said quickly.

Interesting. Danny wasn't normally so vain as to think that all conversations were about him…well, maybe he was. But in either case, this one certainly seemed to fit. He was, after all, Abby's biggest mistake. From what he knew of her life, she'd been the perfect child, the perfect daughter, the perfect student and the perfect wife. Except for the part where she cheated on her fiancé—thanks to him.

He ducked farther back into the hall. Somehow, he didn't think that inserting himself into the conversation was a good idea.

He heard the rustle of plastic coming nearer. He dashed into the guest room and removed his shirt seconds before Abby stopped dead in the doorway.

"Who's that?" he asked.

His voice popped her out of her frozen state. She scurried inside and shut the door behind her.

"My friend Erica. She lives on the Magnificent Mile, so I asked her to pick up some clothes for you—well, not for you specifically, but for a man your size—as soon as the stores opened so we didn't have to go out in public together before we had a plan."

"I am perfectly capable of shopping for myself."

"I'm sure you are, but I prefer to keep an eye on you until this business is handled." She tossed him the bag. Inside were jeans, a shirt, a sweater and underwear.

Tighty whities?

As if.

"And she did this favor for you without asking questions?"

"Just because she asks doesn't mean I have to answer," Abby countered. "It's just the basics, but we'll pick up more later."

"No reason why we can't plan a heist in the buff," he suggested, handing her back the bag. He had no real objection to the clothes inside. He didn't have many preferences when it came to fashion. But he did like teasing her, especially when she skewered him with one of her dangerous looks.

Five years ago, he never would have imagined Abigail Albertini had any dangerous looks. She'd been secretly passionate and publicly malleable. But in the time since him, she'd grown a backbone lined with steel that glinted straight through her cognac-colored eyes.

He took the bag back.

"Right. No naked strategizing. It was just a suggestion."

She groaned and marched—quietly—out of the room.

He dumped the contents onto the bed, then pawed through them to see that her friend had indeed purchased the right sizes. As he tested the softness of a dark gray cashmere sweater, the Murrieta ring caught the eastern light streaming in through the guest-room windows. He tried once again to remove it from his hand, but it was stuck. The ring he'd been so keen to own for so long was now starting to piss him off.

He'd only met his biological father, Ramon Murrieta, once, but he distinctly remembered the moment he'd first noticed the man's ring. About five seconds into his explanation that Danny's mother had never told him she was pregnant, he'd lifted his hand to wipe sweat from his temple and the ring had sparkled green in more ways than one.

But Danny hadn't had a chance to take it. He'd dismissed Ramon's offer for a relationship. Already adopted into the Burnett family, Daniel hadn't seen any need to know more about the man who'd done nothing for him except provide half of his DNA.

At sixteen, Danny had not been interested in the history. He'd seen right away that the center stone was scratched and the gold showed signs of sloppy repair. Both then and now, the only things that kept the signet from being a total piece of junk were the brilliant black opals. But the ring had meant something special to Ramon. He turned it while he talked, as if contact gave him a measure of comfort or a jolt of courage.

From that moment, Danny had dreamed about stealing it. Not because he needed courage or comfort, but because the ring meant something to his father. He'd considered holding it for ransom or keeping it as punishment for his father's oblivious neglect. He'd considered selling it and destroying the family legacy he'd never be a part of.

As he'd done none of the above, now he was stuck with the thing.

And what was worse, he'd seen with his own eyes what had happened to his brothers when they'd worn the damned thing. Alejandro, a confirmed bachelor, was now planning his marriage to Lucy Burnett, Danny's adopted sister and the only woman he'd ever trusted. And upstanding, reliable Michael had chucked his law-enforcement career aside to remain in New Orleans with a sexy private investigator who had a reputation for bending laws until just before they snapped in two.

And he was no better. Danny had been wearing the ring for less than twenty-four hours and he'd already spent the night in Abigail Albertini's bed without touching her once.

What the hell kind of magic did this thing have?

Determined to use the soap in the shower to coax the ring off his finger, he stripped off the rest of his clothes and headed into the bathroom, where he found a disposable razor and the toothbrush he'd scored last night from her drawer, along with a travel-size shaving cream, toothpaste and deodorant. The precision of Abby's thought processes took him by surprise. Apparently, she'd prepped the room for his use sometime before he woke up. He thought he was always ready for any contingency, but she had him beat. What she probably saw as basic hospitality and preparedness, he saw as careful attention to detail.

Maybe planning a heist with her wouldn't be so bad.

Maybe winning her back would be better.

The thought was insane.

Impossible.

And yet, Danny had pulled off unlikely heists before. His reputation for taking on the most difficult schemes and breaking through the most sophisticated security had not been unearned. And who knew? Maybe the ring would help him.

Stranger things had happened.

7

"SO, WHO IS HE?"

Abby cursed under her breath, then trudged into the living room. Instead of leaving quietly, as she'd hoped, Erica had planted herself on the couch, ankles crossed demurely and hands folded beatifically in her lap. She'd poured herself a cup of coffee in one of Abby's china cups and waited for her friend to dish.

Abby pushed aside her annoyance. If her best friend had sent her on such a mysterious errand first thing on a Monday morning, there was no way she'd scoot out without learning as many details as she could. She and Erica were peas-in-a-pod—two young ladies of wealth and privilege raised to be smart and capable. They'd both gone from their small, exclusive private school to Northwestern. They'd both collected master's degrees and now had low-key, but respectable jobs: Abby as an art curator and Erica as an event designer. While Erica had never married, she'd had three long-term relationships with three of Chicago's most eligible bachelors.

Although Erica disappointed her mother daily because she hadn't produced at least one grandchild by now, she was as close to perfect as Abby could stand.

Time and again, she'd proven to be an ideal friend—mostly because she didn't ask too many deep and probing questions, waiting instead for Abby to come clean on her own.

Except today.

Erica already knew Abby had a man in the house. What she didn't know was who—or why.

"He's a friend who is helping me out on a project."

Erica's blue eyes narrowed. "I know all your friends."

Abby grinned. "You don't know this one."

"Do I want to?"

"No," Abby answered, remaining standing as a not-so-subtle hint that she wasn't in the mood to chat. "But thanks for bringing the clothes. I'm sure his luggage will be delivered sometime today. Airlines."

Erica snorted, the sound unapologetically unladylike. "What do you know about airlines? Even when you fly commercial, you ship your things to your destination ahead of time."

"I only did that once! And I wasn't the one flying into O'Hare. He was."

"Really? Then why wasn't Captain Brennan available to fly my grandfather to Dallas for an emergency shareholder meeting yesterday? Sucks that our families lease the same jet, doesn't it?"

Abby opened her mouth, but Erica cut her denial short with a raised palm.

"Save the excuses, Abigail. You're up to something. And since this is a rare and noteworthy occurrence, please don't lie to me about it. You're acting like you did right before your wedding, remember? All secretive and bending the truth in little ways. Please don't shut me out again."

Guilt pressed Abby into the chair across from Erica.

They'd been close friends since high school, when she'd been a junior and Erica a sophomore. Together, they'd run a successful campaign for the top two jobs in student government. Then they'd attended the same college, a year apart, and when Abby pledged Alpha Delta Pi, Erica joined her the next fall semester. They'd spent a thousand early Saturday mornings attending teas and fundraisers with their mothers and another thousand late nights holed up in Abby's apartment drinking beer from the bottle and watching Farrelly brothers movies.

And yet, she'd never told Erica about Danny.

"I'm sorry," Abby said. "I don't mean to shut you out of anything. I'm just in the middle of something I haven't really figured out yet."

Erica leaned forward. "I can help."

"I know." Abby grabbed her friend's hand and gave it a squeeze. "And I'll take you up on it soon, I promise. But not until we have some real privacy, okay?"

She glanced over her shoulder toward the guest room. Erica followed her stare, then nodded and stood. "Okay, but call me soon. Honestly, I don't care if it's four o'clock in the morning. Whatever trouble you've gotten yourself mixed up in will be infinitely more interesting than anything I'm doing in the middle of the night." She sighed. "Lately, even my dreams have been about tablecloths and floral arrangements."

As a premiere party planner, Erica had skillfully put together society weddings, celebrity fundraisers and intimate dinner parties for the mayor. But for the past month, she'd been organizing an event that would rip through even the most confident woman's latent insecurities—her ten-year high-school reunion.

"Read any interesting RSVPs?"

Erica waved her hand and headed toward the door.

"First responses never come from anyone interesting. Just the same old crowd who will be showing off the same old pictures of their same old spouses, their same old little darlings and their same old winter homes."

Abby slid her hand over Erica's shoulder. "Not that you're bitter."

Erica screwed up her face. "Sounds that way, doesn't it?"

"Just a little," Abby said, pinching her fingers together.

Erica's usually bright eyes darkened as she contemplated the doorknob. Abby had hit a raw nerve, something she'd ordinarily insist on deconstructing over large amounts of coffee or, later in the day, martinis.

But today, she had to put her own needs first. She had an ex-lover showering in her guest bedroom and her family on the brink of public embarrassment. Her friend was strong and capable and resourceful. Whatever had Erica off-kilter could wait until Abby had her own house in order.

"Can I ask you one question before you get back to your big secret?" Erica asked.

"Of course, honey."

"Do you think nice men are overrated?"

Abby nearly choked. The unexpected and wholly apropos question hit her straight in the center of her stomach. "Of course they are. But for girls like us, what other choice is there?"

DANNY SHAVED QUICKLY before jumping in the shower. Being naked—something he was ordinarily comfortable with—felt off, as if stripping down while alone was deeply and intrinsically wrong. Even while he made short work of soaping up and rinsing off, images from his dreams filtered through his brain. They were at once disturbing and erotic. No matter how he tried, he couldn't remember precisely what fantasies he'd had while he slept, but he knew they'd trapped him and, even now, weren't letting go.

By nature, he was a light sleeper. He'd adopted the same techniques used by soldiers on the battlefield, only allowing his mind and awareness to shut down enough to rest, but not enough to be caught unaware. Unless he was holed up in a safe house where he knew no one could get the jump on him, he never allowed his brain to go far enough into REM sleep to produce powerful dreams.

But last night, he'd fallen into a deep and constraining slumber. He'd clung to the images like a lifeline, fighting to remain asleep so he could continue to hold Abby, touch Abby, feel Abby underneath him, even if it wasn't real.

While he couldn't conjure the exact images, the sensations locked on to him, even now when he was wide-awake. The only clear picture he could recall was Abby, standing over the bed in her prim, buttoned-up, satiny pajamas, her mouth close enough so that he could smell the sweet spearmint of her toothpaste mingling with the earthy herbal scent of rosemary in her shampoo. If he closed his eyes really tight and blocked out the rest of the world, he could almost remember the feel of her lips on his—a whisper of a kiss and then, oddly, the taste of a teardrop.

None of it had happened, but it had him rattled and he did not do his best work when he was halfway out of his skin.

He toweled off, dressed and then listened at the door. He could hear music playing, but no voices other than the singer's. Abby's friend must have left, or else she was using the radio to keep him from overhearing a private conversation.

Either way worked for him. He had his own private conversation to have.

He hadn't brought much with him when Abby had made her unexpected appearance, but he did have his cell phone. He moved to the other end of the room near the window and dialed one of the five programmed numbers.

"Danny? Where the hell are you?"

Leave it to Lucy to cut to the chase.

"Chicago."

"Chicago? You hate Chicago."

In the past five years, Lucy had had interest from several Chicago collectors who'd wanted to hire him for jobs in the Windy City, but he'd turned them all down. He'd never told her why...and he wasn't keen on confessing now, either.

"I felt like going to a Cubs game."

"You hate baseball."

"I don't hate baseball."

"Well, you don't like it enough to travel to see it. What's going on?"

"So is this what a committed relationship does to you? Turns you into a mother hen?"

"Maybe," she confessed, not sounding the least bit doubtful, "or maybe I'm concerned because the last time you did a job without me making the arrangements, you ended up in jail for murder."

"I was never officially charged with murder," he corrected. "The man is alive and well and convalescing at home with his wife and grandchildren."

"You checked up on him?" she asked, sounding a

little more surprised than he would have liked. He might
be a thief and a con man, but he wasn't a coldhearted
killer. He'd always taken care to avoid security guards
when timing his heists. The mark of a good cat burglar,
as Abby called him, was not escaping capture, but not
being detected at all.

"My lawyer told me," he lied.

"Oh," she said. "But I still don't understand why
you're in Chicago. Michael told us what you did to help
him with his case in New Orleans. I thought you'd stick
around there awhile."

"Why? Michael's got his hands full, or didn't he tell
you that part?"

"Actually, Alex has arranged for us to stop in New
Orleans on our way to Madrid. He wants to meet the
woman who, um, inspired Michael to quit the Bureau."

Danny groaned. "Meet her or bulldoze over her?
Claire's cool, Luce. Michael's damned lucky to have
her."

"You're just glad he's not a cop anymore."

"That's a definite plus, but seriously, Michael needs
some loosening up and Claire's the woman to do it."

Lucy whistled into the phone. "Wow. Is that a romantic sentiment I hear, coming from you?"

Danny glanced at the door. Though Lucy knew him
better than anyone, he'd never told her a thing about Abigail. Up until recently, she'd shared his skewed view of
right and wrong when it came to moving stolen goods,
but when it came to relationships, she was fairly tradi-
tional. Before she'd hooked up with Alex, she'd kept her
business and private lives separate. She wouldn't understand how Danny had blurred the lines with Abby—
especially since both of them had ended up getting hurt.

"I like Claire, okay? She's cool and doesn't deserve

to get grief from your fiancé. But I didn't call to talk about Michael and Claire. I need information. Are you alone?"

He heard a door shut.

"Alex is downstairs, arranging for our luggage to be transported to the airport."

"Good," he said. "I need you to tell me everything you remember about that job I did in Chicago five years ago."

"You mean the job where you stole that nude and then disappeared for six months? Yeah, I remember."

"I didn't disappear," he snapped. "I was lying low."

"So low even I couldn't find you?"

"Yeah, well, it was a rough job."

"So rough you never wanted to talk about it after it was done."

God, women could be so frustrating. Couldn't she just tell him what he needed to know without prying into his past?

"The collector who hired me, do you remember his name?" he asked, trying to keep the conversation on a straight and narrow path.

"That was the art deco piece, right? It had to have been Bosco Reese. He was obsessed with the stuff."

"Bosco," he said, remembering the name for the first time in years. "I haven't heard a whisper about him in quite a while. I wouldn't even know how to track him down."

"Neither would anyone else. He's dead."

Danny mined his memory, vaguely aware of an invitation to a funeral he'd declined to attend. Bosco Reese had been a well-known dealer in stolen art, jewels and cars. His personal interest had been in deco pieces, so he must have wanted Abby's painting for himself. But if he was six feet under, then anyone could have gotten their hands on the portrait since.

"Do you know what happened to his personal stash?"

"I think I remember his partner holding an underground auction and moving most of his collection outside of the United States, though I'm sure some of it is back since art deco is so hot here. Wait…is that why you're in Chicago again? Something to do with that painting you stole from that woman?"

"Something like that," he said.

"I never liked that job," she snapped. "It never felt right."

She didn't know the half of it.

"Can you put out a feeler, try and find out where the painting ended up after Bosco kicked it?"

"I can try," she said, but he could hear the reluctance in her voice. When she'd fallen in love with his brother—his uptight, upstanding brother—she'd decided to go legit. Lucy had adopted a new name, a new persona, a new outlook on life and love and business. She wouldn't deny Danny anything—her loyalty ran too deep—but in her new circumstances, he was asking a lot. More than he had a right to.

"Never mind," he said, grimacing at the ring on his hand. He'd never felt guilty for involving Lucy in his schemes before. Why now? "I'll figure it out."

"No, I'll help," she said hurriedly. "It's just that Alex and I are leaving the country and it might be a while before I can make the calls."

Danny cursed under his breath. "Holy crap. He's taking you to meet his mother, isn't he?"

Raised in Madrid with his mother and grandparents, Alejandro had lived a life that was the polar opposite of his and Lucy's. The Aguilars owned a respected,

eponymous auction house on par with Christie's and
Sotheby's, and honor was their most prized possession.
They gave Superman a run for his money when it came
to respecting truth and justice. Alex had only helped
Danny get out of jail because he'd been genuinely con-
vinced of his innocence.

And because they were brothers. As much as Danny
tried to deny their family connection, Alex had been
good to him—and good to Lucy. Right now, she had a
hell of a lot more to worry about than him and the mess
with Abby's painting.

"Look, forget I called. I'll find out what I need to
know about the painting another way. You concentrate
on impressing Alex's mother. From the stories I've
heard, she's a force to be reckoned with."

Lucy whimpered. Strong, implacable, cunning Lucy
whimpered. That's what love did to a person. It broke
them down. It yanked out their deepest insecurities and
broadcast them to the world. That's why he'd tried so
hard to stay away from the emotion entirely. Even now,
he was paying the price of falling for Abby. When she'd
asked for his help, even five years after he'd put her out
of his mind, he'd been powerless to refuse.

"She's going to hate me," Lucy said.

"She can't hate you. Nobody can hate you. You're
like the least hateable person I know, and I know a lot
of hateable people."

"But what if she finds out I'm a former fence who
made a living trafficking in exactly the same kind of
treasures that her family has sold legitimately for three
generations? Or what if she decides I'm not good enough
for her son because I'm not Spanish? A woman like her
wants a wife for her son who comes from a good family
and went to the right schools and—"

"You're better than any of that, Luce," he interrupted. Though he was thankful to focus on her problems, he hated hearing her sound so unsure of herself.

Lucy's kindness and loyalty had saved his life more than once. Her resourcefulness and brains had helped keep him out of jail. He owed her more than he could ever repay. And besides, he could only pay back one woman at a time.

"You're beautiful and smart, and for whatever crazy reason, you're head over heels in love with her son. She's a Spanish mother and he's no spring chicken. She's probably overjoyed that he's finally settling down."

In a million years, he could never have imagined him and Lucy—who now officially went by the name Lucienne to distance herself from her past—would be having this conversation. As one of countless foster kids who'd come in and out of the Burnett home, he'd connected instantly with their one "natural" child. Each for different reasons, they'd bonded in their bid to please her father. Lucy had wanted her dad's attention and Danny had wanted his knowledge.

As the respected curator of a university's varied collections, the man was brilliantly connected to amazing pieces of art and artifacts. As someone with a gambling habit, he'd figured out how to navigate the underworld trade in such items to feed his addiction. From him, Danny and Lucy had learned all they'd needed. He stole the art. She fenced it.

But now, everything was changing. To marry his brother, she'd have to quit trafficking in stolen goods. And Danny was now doing a job not for the money or the challenge, but because Abby had asked him to. Because it was the right thing to do. He glanced outside the window to check if the sky was still blue and hovering above the earth. From where he was standing, the whole world had turned upside down.

"I've never met any guy's mother before," Lucy said. "And this one's a matriarch, for God's sake. She's going to see right through me."

"Which means she'll see that you're a genuinely sweet person with a giving heart."

Lucy didn't respond for a long moment, then he heard a sound, as if she were tapping the phone with her fingernail.

"Hello? Who are you and what have you done with the flippant, unsentimental Daniel Burnett I've counted on all these years?"

"He's still here," Danny reassured her, though he wasn't entirely certain his claim was true. In the past, he would have advised Lucy to get out of the relationship before she got hurt, but that ship had sailed. She was head over heels in love with Alex and vice versa. And Alex wasn't the type to let her go easily—if at all. Once he committed to something, or someone, he was in for life.

Even though he was losing Lucy as a partner, Danny knew that going straight was the right thing for her.

Was it, however, the right thing for him?

Was it even possible?

To get Abby back, he had to steal for her. But as a thief, he'd never get her back.

"Danny, what's really going on?" Lucy asked. "Why are you in Chicago again? We never talked about it, but I always knew something bad went down there last time. You never, ever wanted to go back. Now you're there and I'm worried."

As much as he liked the idea that someone cared enough about him to be concerned, Danny didn't need

Lucy—or worse, Alex—interfering. He had to work through this dilemma on his own—and he thought he had an idea how to do it.

"You have nothing to worry about, Luce," he said, twisting his father's ring. "For the first time in a while, I think I know what I want out of the rest of my life."

She groaned. "Now you're really scaring me."

Danny laughed. "That makes two of us."

8

"YOU CLEAN UP NICE."

Abby curled her legs under her on the couch. Black Jack, who'd been lounging on her lap, hopped down, gave Danny a disapproving mewl, then scampered to his favorite hiding place behind her decorative Chinese screen. Lady, who'd shot toward Danny the minute he'd emerged from the guest room, marched around in a confused circle, then disappeared with her buddy.

The cats were either really smart, or seriously missing out.

"Your friend has good taste," Danny said, spreading out his arms to indicate his clothes.

Abby couldn't argue. Though she'd texted Erica sizes and had made suggestions about what to buy, her friend had chosen soft denim jeans just loose enough to give the man room to move and snug enough in the seat and thighs that she had to swallow a sigh of appreciation. The gray sweater, worn over a black T-shirt, looked exceedingly lush, and the dark colors did amazing things to his swarthy skin and emerald-green eyes.

It was no wonder she'd fallen for the guy. From her first visit to the Art Institute when she was only four, she'd developed an insatiable appreciation for beauty, form and style. Danny had all of the above. His rugged jawline and athletic build counterbalanced the innate grace with which he moved. He was contradictions and perfection, all rolled up into one irresistible, macho male package.

"She's not the only one," she muttered.

"Excuse me?"

"Good taste," she said. "You're a stunningly good-looking man."

He hesitated as he reached across the table to the carafe of coffee and assessed her with his penetrating eyes. "Are you trying to butter me up for something?"

She shook her head and pushed beyond the eruption of butterflies in her stomach.

"I think it's time for me to be honest with you. Completely and totally honest."

"That sounds dangerous."

"I thought you loved danger."

"No, I love a challenge. There's a subtle, but very important difference."

"Didn't you just help your brother bring down a serial rapist? That couldn't have been a walk in the park."

"Compared with being honest about my emotions, it was child's play."

"Yeah," she agreed. "You're probably right, but that doesn't mean we shouldn't give it a go. To get my grandmother's painting back, we're going to have to do some serious lying to a lot of people. But we might as well tell each other the truth first. Clear the air."

He poured his coffee, then took his time sprinkling in a half teaspoon of sugar and stirring. "The truth is a fluid thing, Abby. Your truth may not be the same as mine."

"I'm not talking about the past. We both know what

happened and why. I'm talking about now. Five years ago, we never even had a conversation during daylight hours unless we were on the phone. We never once slept in the same bed all night long. One of us always left before the sun rose."

"Then today wasn't any different," he said.

She sipped her coffee, which had grown as lukewarm as her enthusiasm for honesty and confessions. But she had to do this. She only had Danny in her life as long as it took to steal back her painting. If she wanted to come to terms with his influence on her life, she had to pull out all the stops—and stop all the lies, even the little white ones.

"Actually, I stayed until the sun came up, though I was in the chair across from you."

"The chair? I thought you said I didn't try anything."

"You didn't," she confessed, the heat of a blush blooming on her cheeks. "But when I heard you muttering my name in your sleep, I almost tried something. I even kissed you."

He set his coffee down and leaned on his elbows, his expression inscrutable.

"That wasn't part of my dream?"

She shook her head.

Moments after Erica left, Abby had made the decision to lay her cards on the table. Her friend had asked if nice guys were overrated and Abby had said yes. Marshall had been an exception to the rule, but that wasn't the point. Nice guys were as overrated as bad boys. The labels on either side of the spectrum were limiting and oversimplified the human condition. Yes, she believed saints and sinners existed, but not in great numbers. The majority of human beings were somewhere in the middle.

Like Danny.

Yes, he skewed toward bad boy. He made a living on thievery and lies. Even when he'd claimed to love her, he'd still gone through with the unforgivable act of stealing her grandmother's painting and then had the audacity to beg her to run away with him on the eve of her wedding to a man whose capacity for forgiveness could not be measured.

And yet, Danny wasn't so entirely corrupt that he hadn't kept his promise to leave her alone. He hadn't checked up on her or otherwise interfered with her life— and the minute she'd asked him to come back and help her retrieve her painting, he'd said yes. And despite the chemistry sizzling between them, despite the way she'd infiltrated his dreams, he'd kept his hands to himself last night.

She was the one who'd breached the barrier.

And it had been nice.

Very, very nice.

Danny put down his coffee and joined her on the couch, his mouth set in an emotionless line and his eyes narrowed with suspicion. With his hand braced behind her, he slid into her personal space. Instantly, his scent ensnared her. Warm and male and potent, wrapped up in the herbal scents of her favorite soap and shampoo.

"You kissed me while I was sleeping?"

"I did," she confessed.

"And how was it?"

She shook her head. "Too brief to tell."

"We can fix that," he said, leaning even closer so that he ratcheted up her body heat.

Her eyes drifted closed. Her lips softly parted in keen anticipation. Her heartbeat accelerated, awakening her entire body with need. But even as his breath mingled with hers, he stopped his forward momentum, his lips a millimeter from hers.

"Open your eyes," he commanded.

Her lids fluttered open, but she couldn't see much beyond the intense green of his gaze.

"What are you waiting for?" she asked.

He brushed his lips briefly across her chin.

"No point in doing this in the daylight if you're not going to watch."

As much as she wanted to fall into a state of blind delirium, she accepted his gauntlet. Her eyes locked with his, and she was only vaguely aware of him curling her hair behind her ear, then trailing his feathery touch down the side of her neck. She was fascinated by the slow slide of his tongue over his lips before he dipped his head and nibbled a ticklish path from her lobe down her chin, which he then tilted so that her face was at just the right angle.

But he still didn't kiss her. Not really. He flicked his tongue across the seam of her lips, applying a quick layer of moisture to her mouth, giving her a brief taste of what was to come. When he broke eye contact, it was only to gaze hungrily at her lips. He was savoring the moment—drawing it out, torturing her so that she had no choice but to grab the sides of his face and finish the job in one mad rush.

The conflagration was instantaneous. Every moment she'd spent alone over the past year collided with the potent memories of their affair, combining into an explosion of sensations that were familiar and exciting and intoxicating and hot. Their tongues danced, explored, pleasured. Her bones dissolved. Her muscles and skin liquefied until she was a pool of nerve endings across the cushions of her couch. Though she'd dragged him down with her, he leveraged his body so that he didn't press against her.

"Whoa," he said.

"What?" she asked, confused. "Why?"

"Just a kiss, Abby."

She shook her head, trying to clear her brain of hormonal overload long enough to comprehend what had happened. A kiss had been all she wanted, so what had gone wrong?

"We've never shared just a kiss."

"Maybe it's time we try," he suggested.

She swallowed deeply, realizing this was going to be a lot harder than she thought. Not just the single kiss, but all of it. Sharing space with Danny. Sharing her home. Sharing her soul enough for him to understand why she'd do anything to save her family from the humiliation of the past, both hers and her grandmother's—but not enough that he'd think they could have something together once this operation was complete.

She opened her mouth to make the perimeters clear, but he lowered his head again and took advantage of her hesitation. In slow, torturous increments, he relaxed his arms so that his body covered hers with the sensation of a silk sheet and the weight of a hot-bodied man. Despite the hard pressure of his sex against her hip, her awareness was caught up in the way his tongue slid across hers, swirling in sweet, sensuous circles. His lips pressed against hers with just enough suction to steal the steady cadence of her breathing.

The kiss lasted for an hour, or maybe a minute or two. No matter the passage of time, when he pulled away, she couldn't speak.

"I kiss better when I'm awake, don't you think?"

She hummed her agreement, still too dizzy to speak.

When he eased off her, she swallowed the whimper of disappointment. Her entire body vibrated, as if she'd just worked out at the gym after months of bed rest.

Since Marshall's death, she'd put herself in confinement, first out of genuine grief, but lately, more out of her fears about what people would think if she smiled too much, went out too often, involved herself in any kind of social activity beyond quiet dinners with her friends or charity events hosted by her family. But lately, she'd felt restless and confined—the same two emotions that had weakened her to Danny's charms five years ago.

Now, however, she was going in with her eyes wide-open. He hadn't come to steal from her this time—at least, not without her being fully aware of what he might try to take.

"So, let's talk about this painting," he suggested.

She had to blink a couple of times to clear her head, then accepted the hand he offered to help her sit up.

"Now?" she asked.

"No time like the present. Besides, if we don't start talking business, I'm going to get down to business, if you know what I mean."

"And that's a bad thing?"

His eyes flared with consternation. "We're taking it slow this time."

She nodded as if in agreement and then went to her desk to retrieve the file she'd collected on her painting. But when she sat beside him again, she skewered him with an indignant look.

"Why?"

"Why what?"

"Why are we taking it slow? I mean, you're only going to be here for a week, tops. If we can't get my painting back before the guy makes it public, then our plan is dead in the water and you have no reason to stay."

He slid the file in front of him and started pawing through the documents. "I might have a reason to stay."

"Like?"

"You."

"Me?"

He groaned, probably because she was being purposefully dense. She knew what he meant—or at least, she thought she knew—but she couldn't really wrap her mind around believing it.

"Do you know what happened to me when you threw me out of your bedroom the night before your wedding?" he asked.

He sounded angry, but somehow, his frustration did not seem focused on her.

"I have no idea."

"I went to Mexico," he said, his tone making it clear that he hated Mexico.

"I'm...sorry?" she tried, not exactly certain what she was supposed to say.

"Yeah, so was I. A sorry mess. For a whole month, I survived on tequila and tortillas. I felt like crap for what I'd done to you, Abby, but even worse than that, I felt like I'd let myself down."

"I don't understand."

From what she'd found out in the week between his stealing her painting and his reappearance on the eve of her wedding to Marshall, David Brandon, aka Danny Burnett, had established himself as one of the foremost art thieves in the country. His name was listed on several government-agency watch lists, as well as Interpol. Complaints against him came from many of the same people she dealt with in the art world—gallery owners, private collectors, museum curators. Seducing her so he could get his hands on an undiscovered painting by an increasingly popular artist, Bastien Pierre-Louis, had been a strategy he must have used before. So while she could understand how he'd let her down, for him, it had been business as usual.

He shoved the file away and turned aside, cursing quietly, though it was loud enough for her to make out the word.

"I shouldn't have gotten personally involved with you, Abby. I never had before and I never have since."

"But I wasn't the first woman you seduced in order to steal something," she guessed.

Danny shook his head, wincing at the depths of her low opinion of him. Yes, he'd enjoyed a few brief affairs during some of his jobs. A spark of attraction had led to the gathering of important information like security procedures, secret hiding places or, as in Abby's case, safe combination numbers. But he'd never gone out of his way to seduce the information out of a woman. He'd never immersed himself in learning everything about a woman's past, habits, interests and vulnerabilities in order to exploit her.

But the minute he'd first seen Abby, he'd known that's what he had to do. Not because it was the only way to get the painting, which rarely—if ever—left the family vault. He had a million different ways to infiltrate security systems that didn't include seducing the woman with the combination. But with Abby, he hadn't been able to resist.

Though moneyed and privileged, she possessed a kind of innocent naïveté that arrested his attention, but he knew enough about women to spot the type who were

keeping their true passions under wraps. Maybe it was
the way she lingered in the sections of the museum that
housed the more evocative sculptures—maybe it was the
way she spoke in whispers to her friends while they admired paintings that ventured near to erotic. Whatever
it was, he'd needed to know more about her.

So he'd learned. And in that learning, he'd fallen in
love.

Or at least, that's what he'd called it at the time. After
pining for her for six full months in Mexico, though, he
hadn't been so sure. From what he'd heard about love, it
required two people to share things like trust and honesty. He'd done neither with her then—but he was ready
to do it now.

He couldn't help but glance down at the ring and
wonder.

"I didn't make it common practice to get so closely
involved with my marks," he said, shifting so that his
hand was out of sight. "In fact, in my business, it usually pays to stay in the background and do reconnaissance without interacting with anyone. That way, no
one remembers you well enough to describe you to the
police."

"I could have described you very vividly," she mused,
her voice deepening to throaty levels that scraped
against his skin like fine-grade sandpaper.

"More vividly than you know," he said, trying to
ignore her perfume, which was suddenly invading his
space with alluring hints of vanilla and spice. "You
knew things about me I'd never told anyone."

She snickered. "I didn't know anything about you! I
knew about David Brandon, but he wasn't even real."

He shrugged. "He wasn't entirely made up. A good
lie is one that's based on truth."

Her expression turned curious. "What was the truth, then? You told me that you were a military brat who traveled all over the world. Was that true?"

"I did travel a lot, but mostly because my mother was a junkie who had a thing for long-road truckers."

"How old were you when you ended up in foster care?" she asked.

He arched a brow.

"I told you I'd done my own research, Danny. But I'd like to hear about it from you."

Danny chuckled mirthlessly. He didn't like to talk about his childhood. Few foster kids did. Living the life of an unwanted brat shuttled through a cold and broken system had hardened just about every child it touched. But Danny had, eventually, found a situation he could manipulate, if not thrive in. The Burnetts had been far from perfect, but they'd, at the very least, given him a trade and a sister in their daughter, Lucy.

"I don't remember much about the first years. I never stayed anywhere longer than six months because I had a habit of taking things that didn't belong to me and trading them in school or on the street for stuff I needed. Then when I was around twelve, I ended up in the Burnett household."

"And it was different?"

"Not really, except for one thing. Lucy. She was their only biological child amid a houseful of ever-changing fosters. She and I—I don't know—connected, I guess. We were best friends. Still are, which is convenient since she's about to marry my brother."

"Which brother?"

"Alejandro," he affirmed. "After I was framed for the attack on the security guard and arrested, a hired thug named Jimmy the Rim paid me a visit in jail and offered me a trade—my continued good health for this ring. Trouble was, I didn't know where the ring was. Ramon, my biological father, had owned it, but he was dead. Lucy…" Here, Danny decided to alter the facts. He could share his own secrets with Abby, but Lucy's private life wasn't his to reveal. "Well, let's just say she went to Alejandro to find out about the ring, and in the process, they fell for each other hard."

"And the person who wanted the ring?"

"Jimmy got pinched for attacking Alex and Lucy, but wouldn't give up who hired him. Alex's lawyer got the charges against me dropped and Michael kept the ring, just to make sure it was safe. Then, last night, he gave it to me."

"And you don't think the person who wanted the ring badly enough to set you up for attempted murder is going to try again to get it?"

He shrugged. "No one knows I have it. Michael's off the grid and Alex is on his way to Spain. The only person who knows I'm here is Lucy."

Abby smiled. "So you did call someone in your family to tell them where you are."

He matched her grin with one of his own. "I'm not inhuman, Abby. I fell into a life of crime for survival, and I'll admit, excitement. Then, from Lucy's dad, who is currently serving time for grand theft, I learned how not to get caught, and how to manage my money so that I've got something left when I decide to quit."

"But it's wrong," Abby said.

"It's not that simple."

She opened her mouth to argue, then closed it and frowned. "No, I guess nothing is ever that simple."

She slid her hand onto his knee. Her touch lacked any sexual intent, but it was intimate all the same.

Danny stood and stalked to the other side of the room. The window gleamed with a clear and crisp view of the city, along with a far-off glimmer of Lake Michigan. He had a sudden urge to get outside. Maybe walk. Explore the stunning Chicago architecture amid streets that burst with the gold and reds of autumn-topped trees.

"Didn't you say we had some shopping to do?" he asked. "I mean, I like your friend's taste in clothes, but I'm going to need to diversify my wardrobe."

"Shouldn't we talk about the painting first?" she said, lifting up the file folder from the table.

He marched across the room, took the folder in one hand and reached for hers with the other. "Business can wait a couple of hours. I have a sudden need to get out of here and I know you don't want to let me out of your sight."

She let him take her hand, and when he pulled her up, she shifted her weight a little so that she accidentally-on-purpose slammed against his chest.

"Sure you want to go out?"

Her tone was suggestive, but something in her eyes clued him in that there was more to her reluctance to leave than desire.

"Yes, I'm sure."

She chewed on her bottom lip. "We can shop online and call a few stores that will deliver. I do it all the time."

"Maybe that's your problem," he assessed.

"Who said I had a problem? Other than wanting to get my painting back?"

He shrugged. "No one. But you do."

She grimaced and pulled away. He supposed they should come up with a cover story before they left the apartment, one that would fit easily into whatever ruse they might construct later in their bid to retrieve her painting. But he'd masterminded enough criminal plans in his lifetime to know Abby wasn't worried about how going out would affect theirs. She was worried what people would think about a recently widowed woman like her being seen outside with a guy like him.

When she spun toward him, her expression was so small, so sad, he thought he felt something crack in the middle of his chest.

"I haven't been out with anyone, any man, since Marshall."

He put on his best reassuring grin. "It's not a date, Abby. It's a shopping spree."

"And how will people know that?"

He put up his hand, forcing her to stop objecting while he took a minute to think.

An idea popped immediately into his mind, but he groaned at the drastic nature of it. Still, it would work.

He took her hand and hurried her into her bedroom, swinging her past the bed and into the dressing area. He stopped in front of the mirror and with a silent gesture forced her to stay put. He'd rummaged through her things enough to know where he could find what he needed— an old pair of her glasses, a chic scarf, and hair gel.

While he used the three items to transform himself, she stood behind him, trying to hide her giggles behind her hand. He tucked the sweater into his jeans and borrowed a belt he could barely fit around his middle to shore up the look. By the time he turned around, the perfect picture of the quintessential gay best friend, she nearly collapsed in a fit of laughter.

"Now do you feel safe being seen in public with me?"

She managed a nod—which he figured was probably the best he could get.

9

NORMAL.

The entire afternoon had been normal.

And that, in and of itself, had been the weirdest thing of all.

Abby had envisioned quite a few fantasies about Danny when she first decided to track him down, but none of them had included strolling hand in hand down Michigan Avenue, mingling with tourists while they shopped for his wardrobe, purchasing, among other things, pants, sweaters, a blazer, a coat, a fitted suit and a tuxedo she thought she might have torn off him just outside the dressing room of the men's department if he wasn't pretending to be gay. With a promise to have the tailored garments delivered to her apartment in the next day or two, they moved on to shopping for her, something he insisted they do, even though she had more than enough clothes in her closet.

He played up his flamboyant persona to the hilt, cooing over outfits in the windows at Nordstrom's and conspiring with the saleswomen until she'd tried on a sexy emerald-green wrap dress with high-heeled Louboutin's and lingerie by La Perla. The experience had been freeing and she realized that she hadn't really bought anything new since before the funeral. Maybe a pair of sneakers for the walking tours she gave or yoga pants or T-shirts she could wear to the gym that didn't have holes, but otherwise, she'd eschewed all retail therapy.

What a mistake.

She spun around on the raised dais in front of the three-way mirror, feeling sexier than she had in years.

Last night's little black dress, which she'd bought years ago but had never worn, had been short and revealing—seductive in an obvious way. This dress, with its slim lines and clingy fabric that flared at her backside into a kicky skirt that barely kissed the top of her knees, was classier but still enticing.

She turned to Danny, seated in a cushioned lounge chair behind her. While the saleswomen had been in the room, he'd played up his effeminate persona to the hilt. Now that they'd scampered off to help other customers, the look in his eyes had turned purely predatory.

"What do you think?" she asked, glancing out of the change room to the main floor. They weren't alone— and it was a good thing. Judging by his expression, if they hadn't been surrounded by shoppers, he'd have got up out of that chair and showed her exactly what he thought of the dress by ripping it off her.

"I think you should wear that when we go to the party."

"What party?"

"The one where the collector plans to show your painting," he replied.

She stepped off the dais, surprised. "You read the file?"

"I glanced through it while you were feeding the cats," he said.

"I can't wear this. His event is a masquerade. I'll need a costume."

"So buy a mask. Trust me, if you wear this, he'll hand over the painting without argument."

Again, his dark green eyes turned feral. He untucked his sweater, tore the fussy scarf from his neck and with a move that would have made Superman proud, whipped off her old glasses and tossed them on the chair as he stood. Even with the metrosexual spiky hair, Danny transformed from fop to fine in the span of a heartbeat—even one beating as rapidly as hers.

He slid his hands onto her hips, swiveling her toward the mirror and guiding her back onto the foot-high dais. To the world beyond the dressing room, he was simply inspecting the fit of the dress on her body, maybe testing out the texture and feel of the fabric. But close-up, Abby could feel his body hardening against hers.

The muscles in his arms tensed. His chest constricted underneath the soft sweater. His face hardened into a mask that betrayed none of his lust—except in his eyes.

God, his eyes gave him away.

"On second thought," he said, stepping up behind her on the raised platform, "maybe you'd better not wear this dress. I'll never be able to concentrate on anything but you."

"That would be bad," she said, breathless as he ran his hand up the curve of her waist. She shifted nearer, needing to feel him pressed even closer than he was. Of course, what she really needed she couldn't get while they were playing dress up in a department store. They needed to return to her apartment, hole up in her bedroom and break the sexual tension spiking between them by surrendering to it. The sooner the better.

She turned to tell him so when the saleswoman who'd shuttled the undergarments from the lingerie department popped in to ask how they were doing.

Danny hopped down from the dais, throwing himself back into character so quickly, she blinked in amazement. Before the woman had a chance to register what might have been going on between them, he'd put his glasses and scarf back on and scooted her out of the room with overblown demands for a second set of bras and panties and another pair of shoes.

Despite how much Abby had enjoyed the fun and folly of shopping, she was done playing mannequin. Suddenly, the only thing she could think about was taking her clothes off.

At the doorway, Danny turned to her, his hands braced on the jamb. "Ready to blow this popsicle stand?"

"Do you want to get some lunch?" she asked, knowing she was being cruel. To both of them.

His mouth tipped up in a wicked grin. "Oh, we have appetites to satiate, love, but we won't be doing it in a restaurant."

A thrill shot through her. She took her time unfastening the zipper that ran along her side, watching the heat rise in his face until she thought he might combust right out of his skin. As it was, his knuckles whitened as he gripped the doorjamb. It was taking every ounce of his control to remain on the other side of the small room instead of joining her behind the curtain. Wouldn't that shock the poor saleswoman when she came in to bring her another set of undies?

Abby changed quickly and waited, her foot tapping, while the saleswomen rang up her purchases and wrapped them in thin layers of tissue before placing them into handled bags stamped with the store logo. Her impatience grew when Danny directed the cabbie to stop outside a bistro a couple of blocks from her apartment and actually made her wait while they filled his order for lunch. They walked the rest of the way, packages swinging from their arms while hunger spread to every cell in her body.

Just before they crossed in front of her building and her doorman jumped into action to help them with their load, Abby was struck again by how normal yet extraordinary the moment was. They'd gone shopping, for Pete's sake. But somehow, Danny had elevated the experience so that for a couple of hours, she'd forgotten about her grief, her regrets, her self-imposed determination to do nothing that would embarrass her friends or her family.

For one brief afternoon, she'd just been Abby.

Abby, who liked to laugh.

Abby, who liked to shop.

Abby, who liked to look beautiful and sexy.

And now, Abby, who liked sex.

The doorman accompanied them upstairs. Danny kept up his act so that the man hardly looked in his direction. It was funny, and not a little sad, how heterosexual men avoided direct eye contact with guys who played for the other team. But in this case, it served them well. If he were asked, the only thing the doorman would remember about the guy with Abby was that he was gay. He wouldn't remember his hair, his height, his eye color or his build. Even when Danny was as "out there" as a guy could be, he'd ensured that people who might be asked to identify him by the police wouldn't recall what he looked like.

Too bad his strategy wouldn't work on Abby. She'd tried forgetting him. Safe within the confines of a happy marriage, she'd thought she had. But without that wall of protection around her, the memories of their affair saturated every fiber of her body and soul. She could set aside the betrayal and the lies, but not the attraction. It was too powerful.

Abby locked the door behind the doorman, then turned to find Danny staring at her from the archway that separated the living room from the bedrooms. He'd torn off the scarf and glasses and removed his sweater and untucked his T-shirt so that he looked every inch the kind of man a woman wanted to devour. With each step she took toward him, her mouth watered. Pearls of sweat beaded between her breasts. Danny held out his hand, daylight streaming through the windows.

With a sigh, she reached out and placed her spirit in his care.

Wordlessly, he led her to her bedroom and shut the door behind them, though she couldn't imagine why, except to keep out the cats. With a combination of need and restraint, he speared his hand through her hair and kissed her cheek.

"I'm just going to lower the blinds," he explained. "I want you in the light, Abby. But I don't want to share you with the neighbors."

She grinned, then used the time it took him to adjust her windows to dash into the bathroom and freshen up. When she came out, he'd placed a couple of condoms on the bedside table. He'd clearly stocked up on the essentials when they'd gone to the pharmacy for shaving cream and razor blades that weren't made of pink plastic.

But the protection was forgotten when she sidled up to him. He braced his hands on her hips and again placed a soft kiss on her cheek. The act was neither chaste nor friendly. It was a promise to take things slow—to make this count.

He kissed a path from her cheek to her temples and forehead, then down to the tip of her nose. His hands tangled in her hair, massaging her scalp until she fell into a hypnotic state between relaxation and desire. When he finally pressed his lips against hers, he stepped fully into the kiss so that their bodies were flush, curve to curve, tongue-in-groove, interlocking puzzle pieces that formed a picture of sensual perfection. With a tentative tongue, he tasted her, never allowing her too much pleasure or too much satisfaction. This was a tease. An appetizer. A precursor for pleasures yet to come.

"Are you sure you want this?" he asked, his breath hot against her neck while he nuzzled her ear.

"Yes."

"You won't regret making love to me this time?"

"I didn't regret it last time," she confessed.

This stunned him. He leaned back, not breaking their body contact, but giving him room to examine her face and see the honesty there.

She'd never said this out loud—she'd never had the chance. But it was true.

"But because of me, you lost your painting. You nearly lost your fiancé."

"That I regret," she admitted. "But we're going to get the painting back and Marshall didn't leave me. I had a four-year marriage to a wonderful man and memories of him that I'll cherish forever. But if I was still really beating myself up about you, Danny, I never would have come to find you in New Orleans. I know that now."

His eyes darkened and she watched his Adam's apple

bob while his lips, a thin line, quaked. "I didn't destroy you."

She shook her head, her chest tight with emotion.

"No, you didn't. I think, in the end, you made me stronger. Strong enough to know what I want now. And that's you."

He caressed her cheek. "Then you're going to have me."

This time, his kiss had a little more power, but he still held back. Her nerve endings prickled with delight—he was going to make this last. He held her face steady while he thoroughly explored and pleasured her mouth, then nibbled her neck until she tossed her head back in complete surrender to his minimalist assault.

She was hardly aware as he worked the buttons of her blouse. His fingers danced down her midriff, magical and quick. The material fell away from her body like a silken cloud. Her skirt followed suit. She forced herself out of the pleasured trance long enough to grab the hem of his T-shirt and drag it up and over his head.

They still stood beside her bed, half-undressed and fully exposed to the light of the late-afternoon sun. She unbuckled his jeans, but he took control of kicking off his shoes and sliding the denim down his body. Once he was as exposed as she was, he took her hands in his and eased her onto the bed.

He positioned himself beside her, leaning on his elbow so he could devour her with his eyes. He ran his hand from her temple to her neck to her shoulder, then across her collarbone where he fingered the beauty mark in the center of her throat. He leaned forward and kissed the dark imperfection.

"I love this spot," he murmured, running his tongue in tight, tiny circles around the mole, another gift she'd received from her grandmother, who had exactly the same mark in exactly the same spot.

"My grandmother called it her dot of desire," she said with a laugh. "I never really knew what it meant, but my father used to shush her whenever she said it."

"It draws a man's eye to your throat, which is a highly underrated erogenous zone," he said, continuing to bathe her neck in suckling kisses.

She moved to touch him, but he stayed her hand. "Keep still. I've waited a long time for this and I'm going to take my time."

"So I'm just supposed to lie here and think of England?"

He chuckled, then did something with his mouth on her pulse point that knocked any thoughts of Britain out of her mind.

"No way, baby. I want you thinking about where you want me to taste you next. Show me where you want me, Abby, and I'm there."

The challenge was so simple, and yet, so thrilling. She smiled, then pointed first to her lips. She missed his kiss. She missed his flavors. She missed the pressure of his hot mouth and thick tongue. She ran her hand over his jaw, loving the feel of his chin, so square and strong, as it undulated with his mouth.

"Where next?"

The choices were endless. He wanted to take this slow, and as foreign as this concept was to the two of them, she trusted that he had the right idea. She touched a spot between her collarbone and her breast, just above her beating heart.

He smiled, then attended to the spot, skimming his tongue across the lace of her bra, which she suddenly wished she'd removed. As if he'd read her mind, he slid his hand beneath her back. She arched her spine, and with a flick, the tension broke. Her breasts, full and heavy with want, spilled out of the cups so that when she met his gaze and pointed to her nipples, her vision was blurred.

He slid his finger underneath the strap on her left shoulder and slowly dragged it off her arm, making sure that the lace still covered her. He did the same on the right. The lingerie slipped, revealing the breast nearest to his mouth—the one he took first. The sensation was exquisite and tight, a concentrated spire of need that drilled straight through her, burrowing into her body and hollowing out the space between her legs, preparing for his sex to join with hers.

As he worked his magic, he tossed her bra aside, then pinched her other nipple with sweet pressure, rolling the nub between his fingers just enough to create a swirling whirlpool of need that stopped her breath halfway up her throat.

Desperate, she touched the tip of the nipple he held and he shifted, throwing his leg over hers before doing precisely what she asked.

"So tight and sweet," he said once he'd dragged his tongue over the sensitive bit of flesh. "I could taste you for hours. I could make you come just from this."

Danny never made promises he couldn't keep. Her sex throbbed as blood rushed and swelled to the center of her need. She could feel the orgasm at the edge of her awareness, lingering like a long-awaited promise— a need too long unfulfilled. But Danny wasn't in any hurry to bring her to the edge. He was taking his time, relearning her body, regaining her trust by allowing her to choose where he touched her, where he kissed her, and when. She relished the power, and instead pointed to the area just above her hip.

The game lasted for what felt like hours. From her hip, she led him to her belly button. From there, she deviated from the downward path and brought him back up to the curve just underneath her breasts, though he cheated once or twice with quick swipes across her nipples, just to remind her of her needs. She bent her leg up and indicated the back of her knee, which was a tactical error if she meant to slow down the progression of his exploration. He flipped her over onto her stomach and took his sweet time exploring the underappreciated crevice, all while he ran one teasing finger along the edge of her panty.

She grabbed a pillow and tugged it underneath her. Her bare breasts scraped against the material and her mind was lost in the possibilities of where she should direct him next. She settled on the small of her back and with a groan he was there. She could feel his hands, tense and rigid, scrunching the material of her panties. He wanted to drag them off, but was waiting for her invitation, which she gave by lifting her bottom. With that, she was naked, laid bare to him in ways she never had been before.

He groaned. "God, you're so perfect."

She craned her neck to see him straddled over her legs, his briefs barely covering his erection, his hands hovering over her ass as if he didn't know what part of her to touch next. She wriggled under the weight of his hungry stare.

"Not perfect," she said, catching his gaze with hers.

He arched a brow. "Don't argue with me. I know a masterpiece when I see one."

She relaxed into the pillows. He massaged and

kneaded, kissed and caressed until she imagined her backside was suddenly on par with Kim Kardashian's or J.Lo's. It didn't matter how round it was or wasn't—it only mattered that he loved every inch of her skin and awakened every dormant nerve ending until she thought she might explode. She was done with this game. She wanted him inside her. And she wanted him now.

She drew her knees up beneath her.

"God, Abby, don't," he begged, his voice twisted with restraint even as he buoyed her backside with his hands.

She grabbed a second pillow and pulled it underneath her. "You know you want me, Danny. I'm showing you how I want you."

She tossed another look over her shoulder and witnessed the conflict raging through his body. His sex was so thick and elongated, the head peeked from his waistband. They'd done it in this position before—more than once. He'd introduced the sensations of this animalistic coupling to her and she couldn't help but want it again.

She grabbed his hand and slid it between her legs, where he could feel the slick heat of her sex. He smoothed his fingers around her labia, found her clit and pressed. She cried out in pleasure, and with that sound, he stopped fighting her. He left the bed long enough to remove his briefs and don the condom.

Her thighs quaked. When he rubbed the tip of his lubricated cock against her, she cried out in anticipatory pleasure. He took his sweet time easing inside. An inch. Maybe less. Sensations shot through her body, weakening her muscles until she thought she might melt. She drew her elbows in tight, bracing herself for the next wash of pleasure.

He didn't make her wait. He grabbed her hips, bracing her for the full length of him. With one swift thrust, he slid deep into her sex, stretching her, filling her. Dizzy, she buried her face in the pillows and relinquished the last of her control.

He pumped into her with long, slow strokes that dragged the pleasure out with infinitesimal delight. Bracing her hip with one hand, he ran the other up her spine, all the time telling her how beautiful she was, how hot and wet and needful. Soon, his words became unintelligible—either because he'd lost his ability to speak or because she'd abandoned all need to hear him. She just wanted to feel him, inside her, in and out, compounding her pleasure when the last of his control broke and the tempo flew into madness.

Her orgasm didn't come in an explosion, but in a sudden awareness that she'd been in the middle of it all along—as if the minute he touched his lips to her throat, she'd started to come, and now this was the culmination of that long, drawn-out road to release. She buried her face in the cushions, her scream muffled when he finally stiffened and ground out a groan that meant he'd reached his breaking point. She collapsed and he came down with her, breaking their contact even as his body folded over hers like a warm blanket on the coldest day of the year.

It took a while before she had enough air in her lungs to breathe. In the meantime, Danny had twisted the comforter on her bed so it covered most of their sweaty bodies. She tugged the pillows out from under her and tossed them to the floor.

"That was unexpected," he said.

She rolled over to face him. "Disappointed?"

He rubbed his face, which was flushed and wet with sweat. "With you? Never. You just surprised me."

"I guess you thought marriage made me less adventurous in the sex department?"

"Maybe," he confessed.

She snuggled into his arms, which seemed to take him aback. She smiled. In their previous affair, she never got the impression that she surprised him. Now, she seemed to be shocking him left, right and center. "Sex with Marshall was great, Danny. I think, after our affair, he stopped treating me like a china doll. So I've had two fabulous lovers in my lifetime, and thanks to both of you, I love sex. I missed it. And more importantly in this moment, I missed it with you."

10

THE SUDDEN NEED TO disappear seized Danny with such inescapable power, his body started to shake. He knew it was wrong. He knew it was cowardly. But he couldn't stop himself from kissing Abby briefly and then excusing himself to the bathroom.

He disposed of the condom and then, stalking the small space from corner to corner, turned up the shower to full blast and stepped inside before the water was even hot. The iciness sluiced over him and the shaking intensified—not from the frigid temperature, but from her confession.

She'd missed him.

For five years, he'd convinced himself that she probably hadn't given him a second thought unless it was to curse the minute he'd come into her life and nearly wrecked her future. He'd spent nearly six months—six months!—wallowing in his own guilt, regrets and despair. When he'd first taken the job to steal her painting, he never conceived of how quickly and powerfully a man could fall in love.

He had no real experience with the emotion. Yes, he

loved Lucy, but like a sister. His loyalty to her was a reflection of her unwavering devotion to him.

In the beginning, Danny had thought his connection to Abby was the same—not real, but a reflection. He'd created David Brandon to be her dream man, so she couldn't help but fall for him. And once she did, he'd simply gotten caught up in her fantasy and loved her back.

But after she'd refused to run off with him, he realized the truth. His feelings didn't fade. His pain became physical and only copious amounts of booze had dulled his agony. He'd spent six months wallowing in the mess he'd made of his life, when in truth, the only mess he'd made had been in his heart. While she'd loved a man who didn't really exist, he'd fallen hard for the real Abigail Albertini, the one who now, despite knowing the full truth of what a bastard he was, had just made love to him with complete and total trust and intimacy.

None of which he deserved.

She knocked on the door just as the shower turned scalding. He turned down the temperature and braced his hands on the glass tiles, but didn't respond.

"Danny?"

She opened the door.

"Yeah," he said, trying to sound unaffected, casual, cool, when in fact, he felt as if he'd swallowed a writhing mass of poisonous snakes.

"Want company?"

Hell, no.

He leaned around the opening and forced a smile. "I was going to make it quick, but how can I say no to you?"

She'd wrapped herself in a plush pink robe. Her dark hair was a lush tangle and her apple cheeks glowed with

spots of color that matched her wrap. She looked well-
loved, but worried.

Well loved because of him. Worried because of him.

"It's a simple word, *no*. One syllable. I won't be hurt
if you say it."

He groaned. She was too good for him. He'd run and
she knew it. But she still came to check on him and he
had no doubt that she was truly willing to give him space
if that's what he wanted.

But hadn't he had enough space in his lifetime?
Hadn't his life been about nothing but space? He supposed he might have been close to his mother while
in the womb, but in life, she'd chosen a relationship
with drugs over one with him. He'd never known his
father, and once they'd finally met, Danny had been
too hardened and too angry to let him in. Even with
Lucy, he'd established boundaries. To keep her safe from
prosecution in case one of their deals went bad, they
communicated sporadically and under false names and
appearances. The only person who seemed determined
to be with him, whether he wanted it or not, was Abby.

And dammit, he wanted it.

He held out his hand to her, the Murrieta ring spar-
kling on his finger. The stupid thing was supposed to
influence the wearer, wasn't it? Make him more like the
first man who'd worn it, drawing from him the qualities
that made a man a hero? Well, Danny was no hero. He
never would be. But he felt more like a man than ever
before in his life. His emotions were no longer buried
deep beneath layers of fear and resentment. Abby had
drawn them to the surface, where he had to deal with
them, like it or not.

As her robe dropped away, Danny's body reacted.
When she took his hand and allowed him to lead her into

the spacious shower stall, all thoughts of regrets steamed out of his skin. She braced her hands on his cheeks and kissed him softly, but thoroughly, then pulled away.

"I freaked you out," she said.

"What? No," he argued, but gave up quickly. He couldn't lie to Abby. Not again. Not anymore. Not even about this. "Yeah, you did. I didn't expect you to trust me that way."

"I don't think I expected it, either. Trusting you means trusting myself, and that's something I haven't done in a long time. Maybe ever."

"How could you when the last time you did, your life nearly fell apart?"

"But it didn't," she said, kissing his wet shoulder.

"I realize that now. I kept thinking that deep down, you still hated me. That you'd always hate me."

She shook her head, and though he wanted more than life itself to blame it on the shower, her eyes were wide with moisture. "I never hated you, Danny. I was angry. I was devastated. But I wanted to believe that somewhere deep down, you really did care about me. A little."

"More than a little," he said. "I cared more than I should have."

"But you still took the painting," she said.

"I had a job to do," he explained. "I'd already taken the payment. But I don't think that's why I went through with the job. I wanted to prove to myself that I didn't love you as much as I thought I did. I was wrong. I did love you."

"Do you even know what that means?" she asked, running her hands over his shoulders and down his arms.

"No," he admitted, his muscles relaxing under the

hot, beating water and her magical, hot hands. "But I'm learning."

"Me, too," she said.

Their kiss, hot and wet as the water showering down on them, was neither measured nor wild. It was somewhere in between an expression of desire and a sign of love. Danny didn't fool himself. Even if he did figure out that he was truly, madly and deeply in love with Abby, their relationship couldn't go beyond these walls. She had a life, a family, friends and associates who would never accept their relationship. And they shouldn't. She needed a man who could fit into every part of her existence and buoy her up, support her, make her better than she could be alone.

He wasn't that guy—at least, he couldn't be for the long haul. He'd fill that role the best as he could for now, but once he retrieved her painting and put the matter to rest, he needed to move on.

And yet, for now, he was going to take this time with her as a treasure more precious than anything he'd ever stolen. He would love her as much as he could and accept whatever love she offered him in return. But she needed to know—she needed to understand, up front—that he couldn't stay.

"Abby, this thing between us," he said, trying to find the right words while she blanketed his chest in kisses. "It can't last. You know that, right?"

She hummed her agreement, her mouth encircling his nipple while her tongue flicked crazy eights across his sensitive skin.

He grabbed her by the shoulders and forced her to look up. "Abby? When this is done, I'm leaving. Tell me you understand."

"I understand," she said, then pushed him so that he

slammed against the tile beneath the showerhead. "Now shut up and let me have my way with you before I go crazy."

He laughed, then readjusted the fixture overhead so she didn't drown in the wash of water falling from above. Though the water was hot, the stall was cold. The contrasting sensations threw his brain into overload, especially when Abby slid down to her knees.

She was bold, his Abby. She was fearless and sexy and cruel. She licked his flesh as if he was a sweet lollipop, lapping up the water dripping down his body and humming her lips against his skin until he thought he'd go insane. She rimmed her fingers around his length and stroked hard and long, coaxing his erection to full capacity, teasing the tip with her tongue but not taking him into her mouth until he tangled his hands into her wet hair and said, "Please."

The suction was madness. Her tempo was a gift. She continued to mouth him as if he were the most delicious treat she'd ever tasted, and even above the sound of the shower, he could hear her moaning with pleasure as if sucking him was getting her off as much as it was him. Maybe it was. He couldn't concentrate enough to tell. Not with pressure building. Not with the blood rushing down, filling his balls until they were heavy and hot. She cupped them and squeezed harder, swallowed him deeper. He couldn't help moving with her, groaning with need, begging her to finish what she'd started, to take it all the way and leave nothing behind.

When he came, the echo of his pleasure crashed against the tile walls. The shower water was starting to cool, even as Abby tilted her face to the water, then kissed a cooled path up his body.

"You're amazing," he said, dousing her face in kisses.

"No, I'm horny," she replied.

He turned off the water and reached out of the shower stall to reclaim her abandoned robe. "Then by all means, let me take care of that."

ABBY OPENED HER EYES around midnight, blinking several times before her night vision made out the mass of twisted sheets on her bed. She dragged her hands through her hair, still damp from the shower, and wondered if her bedroom had ever been such a disaster area. The comforter had long ago slipped to the floor. Pillows were strewn everywhere. Half-empty wineglasses and takeout containers covered the surface of her dresser and bedside table.

And her chair.

Oh, her chair.

Last night, she'd curled into the soft cushions to prevent her from taking advantage of Danny's erotic dreams and making love to him before he had a chance to realize the act was real. But tonight, he'd spun the chair toward the window so he could take her from his lap, her arms braced on the window sill, his cock sliding in and out of her in a sweet, slow rhythm that had provided her longest and most delicious orgasm of the night. Through the reflection in the glass, she'd watched him pluck her nipples and flick her clit until she'd come like a raging wild woman. And she'd watched, fascinated, wondering if anyone outside could see her, if anyone outside would understand the significance of the act.

This wasn't just sex. Maybe with Danny, it never had been. Watching herself ride him had been deliciously wicked and painfully poignant at the same time. With Danny, she was a mad, sexual adventuress with no boundaries, no inhibitions, no shame. With Danny, she was the woman she always wanted to be—the woman who could never exist with anyone else but him.

Since Marshall's death, she'd been searching for her true self. The need to retrieve her painting and, by default, contact Danny again had been just another trek in her own inner exploration. And he hadn't disappointed her.

But this time, she wasn't under his spell. She wasn't running from a future she feared or exploring sensual experiences she was certain she'd never get with any other man. She was, with eyes wide-open, having an affair with a man who'd once fallen in love with her, despite his best efforts not to.

Her body ached in the most delicious places. The musky scent of sex and sweat acted like an aphrodisiac, and even though she knew she might not be able to walk in the morning if they made love again, she couldn't help wondering where he'd gone as his side of the bed was empty.

"Hey."

She rolled over, her body drawn to his husky voice. He stood in the doorway dressed in a pair of sweatpants with Lady cuddled in his arms.

"Oh, crap," she said, sitting up. "The cats. I haven't—"

"I fed them," he reassured. "Might be a good thing they were hungry. Black Jack didn't hiss at me for once."

She relaxed into the covers. "They're getting used to you."

He padded to the bed and dropped the cat onto the mattress. The tortoiseshell feline pounced onto the sheet and batted the folds and tents as if mysterious prey existed underneath. Abby laughed as Danny sat down on the edge of the bed and caressed her cheek.

"No one around here should bother getting used to me," he said. "I won't be here that long."

Unable to deal with that reality just now, Abby leaned into his hand. "Then how about if we all just enjoy you while we have you?"

Danny chuckled, but something in the sound made her look up. His eyes, so brilliant green, seemed—for a split second—sad. But he erased the expression the instant he realized she was watching. He drew his hand back, but she caught it and turned his palm so she could better see the ring that he'd inherited from his father.

"Tell me more about this," she said, reaching across to turn on the decorative lamp on her bed table, which was more for show than light. But the 10-watt bulb illuminated the center stone enough for her to see a scratch in the shape of a Z. "What does the Z mean, or was the mark accidental?"

He allowed her to turn his hand and examine the ring from all sides. It was old, that was for sure. The gold had worn thin on the inside and showed signs of repair. The center emerald, though marred, still sparkled a green nearly as brilliant as Danny's eyes. The black opals on either side, however, flashed with brilliant turquoise and tiny flecks of gold. Her area of expertise was not jewelry, but she'd seen enough to know this was an exquisite piece of workmanship.

"Not accidental, no. It's the mark of my ancestor, Joaquin Murrieta. My great, great, great, great—" he counted on his fingers, then added one more "—great grandfather."

"Neither Joaquin nor Murrieta is spelled with a Z."

"Apparently, it came from a nickname. He was a sort of, um, bandit. A famous one. A couple of books and movies were based on his life."

Abby sat up and yanked the hand that had been responsible for so much pleasure over the past twenty-four hours closer to the light. "Wait, you're telling me you're related to Zorro?"

"Zorro is a fictional character, but yeah, that's what my brothers tell me."

A thrill chased up her spine and she couldn't help but envision Danny dressed all in black, with a slim mask and voluminous cape, a finely honed sword at his side and whip coiled in his belt. The image was highly erotic—though everything about Danny was erotic at the moment.

"That's really cool," she said, sounding sixteen and not caring. That's how old she'd been when Antonio Banderas swashed his buckle across movie screens in the role of the notorious rogue. She'd watched the movie as many times as teenagers today swooned over *Twilight*.

And though she'd been drawn in by Banderas's sultry good looks, she'd also totally connected with the female lead, Elena, played by Catherine Zeta-Jones. The good girl. So prim. So proper. So torn between the upstanding Don Alejandro and the wanted man he became when he donned the mask.

Danny, however, didn't share her enthusiasm. He shrugged noncommittally. "*Cool* is not the word I'd pick."

"What, then? I mean, this ring is over a hundred years old and belonged to a guy who is notorious and mysterious. Books and television shows and movies have been made about him. He was California's Robin Hood."

"But was he? What part of his story was real and what was just romanticized bullshit that sold a lot of movie tickets?

She could see this was more than mere speculation for him. This was his family legacy.

"Does it matter? What's left now is a powerful legend."

"And this," he said, taking his hand back and examining the ring as if it was the first time he'd really looked at it. "If not for this hunk of metal and stones, I might not have gotten arrested or reconnected with my brothers or put Lucy's life in danger."

"If you hadn't gotten arrested, I never would have found you."

She drew his hand back to her and kissed the center stone, genuinely thankful that it had fallen into his possession, no matter the circumstances or the consequences. He was here with her now, openly grappling with who he was in relation to his brothers, his family, the world and her. She didn't have any answers for him, but she wasn't afraid to confront the questions anymore. Not for herself.

And not for him.

Leaving the ring, she kissed his knuckles, then turned his hand so she could swirl intimate circles in his palm with her tongue. Though her body had not yet fully recovered, she couldn't help wanting him again, especially now that she knew he was a direct descendent of one of the world's most legendary lovers.

"The history of the ring says it, um, bestows certain gifts on the wearer," he said, his confession clearly reluctant.

"Really? Like what?"

"It's supposed to boost a guy's need for risk and danger."

She laughed. "I think you already have that part covered."

"It's also supposed to increase the wearer's appeal to women."

At this, she guffawed. "You've never needed a ring for that, though things have been more intense this time around."

He scowled until she calmed her laughter to a quiet giggle.

"What's the third thing?" she asked.

"How do you know there's a third thing?"

She rolled her eyes. "There's always a third thing in legends and curses and spells."

He frowned. There was a third thing—one he was clearly reluctant to admit.

"When a Murrieta descendant wears the ring, he's supposed to have a heightened sense of right and wrong and a strong urge to fight for justice, rather than personal gain."

She smiled at him. "So you think the ring is the only reason you agreed to come back to Chicago with me? To help me recover what you took?"

"The thought occurred to me."

She shook her head, then tugged him onto the bed and climbed, naked and needful, onto his lap. "Does it really matter why you came? Because it doesn't to me. All I know is that while you're here, I'm going to take advantage of you in every possible way."

He slid his hands down her back and underneath her bottom so he could tug her against his growing erection.

"Promise?" he asked.

"Oh, yeah," she agreed. "And I don't make promises that I can't keep."

11

TO MAKE SURE THEY DIDN'T get distracted, Danny got out of bed before Abby to shower and dress in the guest room. He wasn't one to complain about nonstop sex, but he'd come here for a reason and it wasn't to connect to her so deeply that he wouldn't be able to break away when the thing was through.

After he'd gone into the kitchen to find sustenance, he heard her stir. He half expected—and half wanted—her to appear in the living room wrapped up in a sheet, mussed from the night's loving, and ready to go again, this time on the kitchen counter. But when she finally emerged from her room, she wore a pair of slim gray pants and loose tunic sweater that slipped sensually off her shoulders, but otherwise kept her relatively covered. With her face scrubbed and her hair pulled back in a flouncy ponytail, she looked fresh and well loved.

Just like a woman should.

"You made breakfast?" she said, pointing to the plate of scrambled eggs and bacon he put in front of her.

"My specialty."

She slid onto the bar stool and immediately picked up a fork. "I hope you're good, because I'm starving."

"I believe you said that at some point last night," he teased.

She scooped a large bite of cheesy eggs onto her fork. "I'd never doubt your sexual prowess, but your cooking is a different matter."

"We both had quite the workout last night."

She hummed her agreement while she chewed and swallowed. "I have aches in muscles I'd forgotten I had. I might need a massage later."

He rubbed his hands together. "I'm a little out of practice, but I can probably oblige."

"I meant from my masseuse," she said with a wink.

"Even on an off day, I'm better than Svetlana."

She crunched through a strip of bacon, extra crisp, the way he knew she liked it.

"You remember her name?"

"I remember a lot of things about you, Abby, including how much you hate to eat food when it's cold. Eat, and then we'll talk."

She dug in and they spent the meal in relative silence, chatting mostly to the cats, who were circling underneath the table in search of scraps. While she cleared the dishes into the dishwasher and tossed puff balls for the cats to chase, he pulled out the file on her painting and booted up her laptop. With Lucy on her way out of the country, Danny had to depend on his own research skills to come up with a plan for breaking into the collector's house before he unveiled the painting to the general public.

He pulled out the invitation that Abby had received to the masquerade and typed the name of the collector, Harris Liebe, into the search engine. He came up with several references in art newsletters and blogs about the upcoming event, along with loads of speculation about the subject of the nude, but little else. Most of the links went to Harris Liebermann, a chain of art galleries to which this Liebe guy seemed to have no connection.

"Not finding much?" She joined him in the living room, where he'd set up shop on the couch. She placed a fresh cup of coffee for him on the table beside the computer while she sipped her own. "I didn't."

"No, nothing. What did your sources tell you?"

"He's a foreign speculator of some sort. Made a lot of money investing in war-torn Middle Eastern countries—very hush-hush. He supposedly inherited a load of art from a relative and just started expanding the collection a few years ago, which is why no one knows him."

"And how did he get ahold of your work?"

She shrugged. "I don't even know for sure that the painting he has is mine. But my private investigator in New York has really great contacts on the black market. He's 99.9% sure the painting is mine. But you'll know it when you see it."

Would he? Danny had stolen the painting, but he hadn't spent a lot of time studying it. It had, after all, been a nude of her grandmother.

"Let's hope. This art blog has a couple of posts speculating about which Pierre-Louis painting he might have and what young socialite the artist enticed to take off her clothes. That seems to have been his specialty."

She nodded. "He even kept a journal that details most of the women he painted, particularly the nudes. I managed to get a look at it a couple of months ago. It's housed at a library where a friend of a friend is on the board of directors. My painting is mentioned, but the model, surprisingly, isn't named."

"If that's the case, why are you so worried? If he can't

identify the subject, then your family will be kept out of it."

"It won't take much detective work to connect the painting to the Albertinis. My grandmother—well, she had a reputation. A deserved one. She was a great woman, but she had her appetites, so to speak. The family tried to cover it all up, but society pages in the thirties were just as bad as the tabloids today."

"And you really care about this?"

In the past twenty-four hours, he'd watched Abby transform into an entirely different woman from the uncertain, wounded girl who'd played dress up in the New Orleans casino and enticed him away in her private jet. She was bolder, more confident, more comfortable in her own skin. He doubted she'd pass up a chance to pose for a nude painting herself if given the chance. In fact, after last night, he'd bet money that if the guy with the brush was attractive enough, she'd have an affair with him just because she could.

But then, his experiences had been limited to the privacy of her home. Out in the world, in public, where her actions would affect the people she loved and respected, she'd likely hold tight to her good-girl persona if it killed her.

"My father would care," she explained. "He'd be humiliated to have all this dug up again. Viviani Goletti—his mother—was married when she had the affair with Bastien. And if the truth about our affair gets out, too? It'll kill him."

"A bad reputation never killed anyone. I mean, your grandmother lived into her eighties, right? And I have no doubt your father would stand beside you, no matter what gets out about us. Isn't that what fathers are supposed to do?"

He had no experience of his own on this point, but from what he knew about Ramon, his past had been fairly shady. The natural instinct to work on the wrong side of the law had come to Danny genetically, as well as through his exposure to his adopted family. He came from a long line of people who made mistake after mistake.

Abby's family, on the other hand, seemed to treat questionable decisions with much more fear and loathing.

She picked up the engraved invitation to the masquerade and unveiling at Harris Liebe's home. "I don't want to risk hurting my family, Danny. My father's childhood was pretty rotten sometimes, thanks to what people whispered about his mother. He says now it made him stronger, but he still doesn't want it all brought up again. And when I had to tell him about you, about what I'd done..." She shook her head, as if she couldn't stand to let the memory form in her mind. "It won't take long for the right people to connect the dots. Our affair could be exposed and then Marshall's memory will be dragged through the mud, too. It will be so much easier if we just get our hands on the painting first and make it disappear."

Danny decided not to argue. She wanted the painting back, no matter her reasons, and he needed to get it for her. Once he did, he could close this chapter of his life with a definitive thud. He knew she forgave him—she never would have made love to him the way she had if she hadn't emotionally healed. But until the painting was back in her possession and her family legacy restored, he wouldn't be able to put this part of his life behind him.

He glanced down at the ring. Before his arrest, he

never would have let his brothers into his life. But since he had, he was starting to understand the importance of having pride in where he came from, in what he'd leave behind when his time on this earth was over. When he left Abby behind, the least he could do was leave her with more than she had when they'd first met.

"I need to get into Harris Liebe's place. Scope out the lay of the land."

She smiled and yanked out another slip of paper. "This is the catering company that will be doing the masquerade. My friend Erica uses them all the time for her events and they owe her a favor. They have people coming in and out for days prior to a party like this. I'll have her tell them we're throwing a similar shindig and so we're coming along to see how they operate."

He shook his head. "We? No way. I don't want you anywhere near this."

"Without me, there is no *this!*"

That much was true, but other than having Lucy to fence the items he stole, Danny worked alone. And he certainly wasn't going to make an exception for a socialite with no thievery experience. She wasn't even a good liar.

"As remote as it is, there's always a chance that I'll be caught," Danny said. "If that happens, I don't want you connected to me in any way. Talk about embarrassing your family."

Danny flattened his hand over her mouth.

"It's either my way or no way on this, Abby. Nonnegotiable."

She scowled, but nodded her assent.

"Good," he said, removing his hand. "I'll case the place, then figure out the best time to break in prior to the party. But there are other plans to be made. For instance, once I have the painting, what do you want me to do with it? You'll want it out of Chicago in a hurry, at least until the heat dies down. If this Liebe guy knows about your original ownership, you're going to be the first person the police question."

"If he reports the theft," she reasoned. "He might not, since it was originally stolen, right?"

"But he might. You know, I could pose as a private collector and try to buy the thing back before the auction."

She shook her head. "I made discreet inquiries about a private purchase the minute I found out what he intended to do. He insists on an auction. But you're right. I'll need a place to stash the painting until I can bring it home. And I have an idea about that."

She flipped to the bottom of the file and retrieved a glossy catalogue emblazoned with the header *El Dorado Auctions*. "When I was researching you, I learned about your brothers liquidating the inventory of your father's auction house. If they haven't sold the building yet, I was thinking maybe we could stash the painting in their vaults."

Danny grimaced. The last thing he wanted to do was involve his brothers in another one of his messes. But at last count, Michael owed him for helping save Claire from a serial rapist. Since Michael had inherited the property in San Francisco and Danny knew from Lucy that the vaults there were formidable, this wasn't a bad plan.

"I don't know what the security is like there now that the building is unoccupied. The painting could get stolen again."

"Do you have another idea?"

Danny thought about it, but this wasn't his area of

expertise. Taking paintings was what he did—moving the merchandise underground was Lucy's forte. "No, but I know someone who might be able to advise us. We'll worry about that later."

They spent the rest of the morning working through every possible scenario, then Abby called her friend Erica and arranged for her to meet them later in the afternoon. Danny had hoped to avoid this—for Abby's sake—but there was no getting around it. Erica wasn't getting Danny into Liebe's place unless she vetted him first.

An hour or two after lunch, Erica showed up. She looked a little like Abby, but in miniature. She was no taller than five foot three, though in four-inch heels and with steely gray eyes that missed nothing, she compensated for her stature with her attitude. Abby made small talk for a few minutes, then after a pointed suggestion from her friend, decided to take a stroll downstairs to get her mail.

Erica waited until she heard the elevator ding in the hall before she turned her frown on him. "Okay, who are you, really?"

"I'm a friend of Abby's."

"Abby and I went to high school together. We went to college together. Our families go way back, so the only friends of hers that I don't know are either reclusive art collectors or people she's purposefully kept hidden from me. Which one are you?"

He knew from her tone that she already had her answer.

"Shouldn't you be having this conversation with Abby?" he asked.

"Yes, but I'm waiting for her to open up on her own terms. But before I help you get into some guy's house,

I want to hear the story from you. You're the guy she messed around with before her wedding, aren't you?"

"I thought you didn't know."

"I'm not supposed to know," Erica said, her fingers lacing in her lap. "But Marshall told me. He was a wreck after Abby confessed. He played it cool with her because he didn't want to lose her, but until he showed up at the altar, I wasn't sure if he was going to go through with the wedding. He came to me and asked what I knew about you. It helped that I knew nothing."

"So to him, it wasn't a great conspiracy, just a mistake she made."

"Exactly," she verified. "But are you still a mistake? Because Abby's been through a lot. She's lonely and she's vulnerable. I can't be a good friend and sit back and let you rip apart what's left of her."

"She's stronger than you think."

"Maybe, but that doesn't mean she deserves to get hurt."

"I'm not here to hurt her. I'm here to help her. That painting means a lot to her, and if I can get it back, then that's what I'm going to do. I owe it to her. I owe her more, but this seems to be the only thing she really wants."

Erica stood and strode across the plush carpet with amazing assuredness, considering the height of her shoes. Black Jack, who'd been stingy with his affection to Danny, sidled up to her immediately and she lifted the hefty cat into her arms with a grunt, petted him for a few minutes, then deposited him on the scratching tree by the window and turned to spear Danny with what he guessed was her most intense glare.

"Do you plan to stick around Chicago once you get the painting for Abby?"

He leaned back and spread his arms wide on the back of the couch. "Not a chance."

She pursed her lips, which confused him. He would have bet big money that she wanted him out of town as soon as possible.

"And Abby's okay with that?"

He chuckled, understanding. Erica didn't want him around, but she'd put up with him if that's what it took to keep her friend happy.

"She knows who I am. Probably better than I know myself."

Erica made a final pass from one end of the room to the other, then slipped her hand into her pocket and took out a business card. "This is the woman who is catering the event. I've already called and told her that Scott Ripley was interested in doing a walk-through with her, as he's planning to host a huge fundraiser for a motorcycle club he belongs to, one of those groups where weekend warriors raise funds for charity by biking through big cities in their best polished leathers."

Danny took the card, impressed by the woman's storytelling skills. Unlike Abby, Erica Holt seemed to have a better handle on crafting plausible lies.

"Scott Ripley. Weekend warrior. Got it. Who is he?"

"Who is who?" she asked.

"This Ripley guy. You didn't just make him up."

She cleared her throat and he suddenly saw the uptight, laced-up part of her personality that matched so well with Abby's. "A guy I used to know. First name I thought of."

He smirked. "Wonder why that is."

"Don't," she warned. "Don't wonder anything about me. Just get in, get Abby's painting back for her and get out. I don't ordinarily condone thievery—"

"But since it was stolen in the first place, you're willing to look in the other direction this one time."

"I'd look in the other direction for Abby a thousand times if it meant she got what she deserved. And she deserves happiness. You agree with me on that, right?"

"Completely."

"Good."

And with that, she left. She must have met Abby in the hall, because he heard them talking for a few minutes before Abby came back into the apartment holding what looked like more than one day's worth of catalogs, bills and invitations. She wasn't smiling.

"She loved me, didn't she?" he asked.

"Hardly," she replied. "But she's helping us and that's all that matters. She'd do anything for me."

He nodded. "So would I, Abby. So would I."

12

ABBY HATED WAITING.

Unable to deal with anyone invading her space while Danny was staying with her, she'd cancelled her housekeeper and expended her nervous energy dusting the furniture, emptying her dishwasher and trying to capture as much cat hair as possible with her broom and vacuum cleaner. He'd been gone for hours. First he'd borrowed her car, taking it into an area of the city she'd never once gone to while he constructed the disguise he needed to be Scott Ripley, a name that had shocked Abby to her core. Then he'd gone to his meeting with the caterer. He'd called her in between, but she was still a bundle of live wires. What if he got caught? What if he had the opportunity to take the painting during reconnaissance? Because once he had her grandmother's portrait, he'd have no other reason to stay in Chicago.

And she wasn't ready for him to leave.

She also wasn't ready to deal with why that was.

Instead, she focused on sweeping her balcony, and wondering why—of all the names Erica could have picked for Danny's cover—she'd gone with Scott Ripley.

The name wasn't made-up. It belonged to a guy that

Abby had gone to high school with, though he'd been a year younger, just like Erica. He must have recently responded to the invitation to their class reunion, because otherwise, Abby couldn't think of why he'd be on Erica's mind.

Just about every girl in the school had crushed on the infamous bad boy at one point or another, but Abby didn't remember Erica every mentioning him. They'd probably gossiped about which girl he'd made out with in the stairwell in the north building or what act of vandalism he'd been blamed for that week, but otherwise, she couldn't recall him ever coming up in conversation. Especially not since graduation.

Erica hadn't said anything about him coming to the reunion, but Abby supposed her best friend didn't tell her everything. And vice versa. Abby still hadn't told Erica the whole truth about Danny. They were both keeping secrets, something Abby vowed to rectify as soon as this mess was over.

Mess. Was that really how she'd categorize what was happening? So far, everything had moved along with smooth precision. She'd found Danny, a man who prided himself on being impossible to find. She'd convinced him to come back with her to Chicago and had even let down her guard long enough to explore the last vestiges of their powerful attraction. Now, they were on a narrow course to retrieve her painting and put that painful chapter of her life to rest.

So why wasn't she happy?

She was storing her broom in the closet by the front door when she heard the doorknob rattle. She tore open the door, ready to jump into Danny's arms, but she gasped at the sight of the man standing there. Blond hair, dark brown eyes, impeccable suit—he wasn't Danny.

Or was he?

He grinned, giving himself away.

"Convincing, yes?"

She launched herself against his chest. "You've been gone forever!"

"Hey, hey," he said, moving her inside the apartment and shutting the door behind her. "I hoped you'd miss me, but I was only on a fact-finding mission. You knew it might take all day."

She walked in a tight circle around him, her hands shaking and her chest so tight, she feared her ribs might crack. "Did you see the painting? Is it mine? Do you think you can get it without getting caught?"

"Calm down," he said, taking her by the elbow and leading her into the living room. Once there, he sat, then tugged her down onto his lap and kissed her. The minute his tongue tangled with hers, the flow of her adrenaline rush shifted. Worry and panic turned to relief, and then lust. He inched his fingers underneath the edge of her T-shirt, humming his appreciation when he realized she wasn't wearing a bra. He leaned her back against the couch, pulled up the shirt and was sucking her nipples like a starving man when she realized he hadn't answered a single one of her questions.

"Danny? You have to…tell me…what happened."

He tweaked her nipple hard, sending a white-hot shard of need directly to her sex, which creamed in instant response. God, he owned her. Every inch of her skin was primed to his touch, prickling in anticipation of the pleasure he seemed determined to give.

"My reward first," he murmured against her skin.

She tore her clothes away, but he only removed his jacket. She didn't care that she was coated in a thin layer of dust from all her housework—she only cared about the hungry look in his eyes as he took her breasts in his mouth again, then slid his hand downward until his fingers met the wet and needful flesh between her legs.

"Oh, God," she groaned.

Was it really this easy to get her off? How did he know just how to touch her? Just how to play her like a finely tuned instrument until she was singing with need.

"Oh, yeah, baby," he crooned. "You're so hot. So tight."

He slipped a second finger inside her, curling his thumb against her swollen clit as his mouth crashed against hers. She tore her fingers through his hair, surprised at the stiff texture. But the increased tempo of his hand brought every wayward thought into sharp focus. She could think of nothing but taking the pleasure he offered. Nothing but need. Nothing but…

She tossed her head from side to side, arching into him, pumping her pelvis wildly against his generous hand. The waves of release crashed through her and he held her, kissing her, crooning to her in words she couldn't process, until her powerful orgasm subsided.

He brushed a dozen sweet kisses across her temples and cheeks.

"Now, that's the way a man likes to be welcomed home," he said.

"You're wicked," she chastised, the heat in her body settling into her cheeks.

"But in a good way," he corrected.

She licked her lips. "In a very good way."

He leaned over the edge of the couch and retrieved her clothes. "I never realized reconnaissance missions made me so horny. Must have been because you were waiting for me."

"You're full of yourself right now, aren't you?"

His grin was such a potent combination of confidence and satisfaction that she thought it was a sin to behold it.

"I am, I really am. I found the painting. Saw it in the man's study. It's the one I took, I'm certain. And getting it back is going to be a snap."

While she put her clothes back on, Danny filled her in on all the details. The man's house had decent security, but nothing he hadn't seen before. The biggest challenge would be disabling the security cameras in a way that would allow him time to retrieve the painting before any guards intercepted him.

"This isn't a high-tech museum or bank vault, both of which I've breached. I mean, let's be honest, the painting is valuable, but he's not going to spend more than its worth to protect it. The house is a rental, and according to the housekeeper, he hasn't been there very long. This is going to be a breeze. By tomorrow, the painting will be yours."

Her hands froze as she retied the strings on her yoga pants. "Tomorrow?"

He unknotted his tie, then folded it over the edge of the couch and spread his arms out and relaxed, looking every inch the triumphant king of the world. "The man of the house left his calendar open on his laptop. He's going to be out tomorrow night. And I'm going to get you back your painting."

Abby forced herself to smile. This was supposed to be good news. She was supposed to be overjoyed that Danny's initial exploration of Liebe's house had resulted in verification that Liebe had her painting, and that her seasoned thief of a lover saw no major obstacles to retrieving it. But all she could think about was the fact that in a little over twenty-four hours, Danny would be leaving her, possibly for good.

STRIPPED DOWN TO HIS boxer-briefs, Danny adjusted the shades in the guest room to mute the sunlight from outside. He moved a chair and end table into a corner, then turned up the volume on the clock radio beside the bed, which he'd tuned to play white noise. The room was awash in sounds of the ocean, and when he closed his eyes and breathed in deeply, he could practically smell the salty sea air.

Abby had made some excuse about having errands to run, so he'd left her to it. He preferred to prep for a job alone. He'd managed to keep his mind on his work while in Liebe's house, but the minute he'd seen Abby in the doorway wearing dusty clothes and sweating a little from what looked like housework, his brain had turned from felony to fantasy in a heartbeat. But he hadn't wanted to take her—he'd just wanted to make her come. He'd wanted to taste her skin, wanted to taste her delicious breasts and feel the convulsions of her orgasm at his hands. The whole thing left him hard as a rock, but the pain was good.

And he was going to have to get used to it.

Part of him was disappointed that the operation was going to be so easy, not that he'd expected much of a challenge. The painting was valuable, but not priceless. It was a curiosity, really, worth little to anyone but specialized art deco collectors and speculators trading on Pierre-Louis's increasing popularity. He was an *artiste du jour* whose importance mattered more to Abby than to the art world at large.

Abby, whom he would soon abandon.

He'd already arranged for his transportation. He'd

used cash from an offshore account to buy a nondescript Honda Civic he'd parked in a lot he could access easily from Liebe's rented home. He'd scoped out the security cameras at nearby businesses and had put together a route that would allow for a quick and unnoticed escape. He'd set the clothes he needed aside and had packed a go-bag that would ensure he could change his looks several times between here and Detroit, where he'd ditch the car, alter his appearance and then board a train to another destination, likely Las Vegas. He had a safe place to hide out there, and once the coast was clear, he'd move on to San Francisco, where he'd deposit the painting in his father's old vault and then take off for parts unknown.

He'd already called Michael to make the arrangements. He'd been vague about his reasons, but his brother owed him, so he didn't ask a lot of questions. Danny figured that in the end, Michael didn't want to know what was going on. He didn't even ask if what Danny was doing was legal, though since he'd quit the FBI, maybe he no longer cared. Or maybe he did care—just more about Danny and his problems than about the law.

Danny mulled this over while he stretched. Normally before a job, he'd spend weeks training, but he had only about twenty-four hours to make sure his reflexes were at peak capacity. He'd studied countless techniques for honing his control over his musculature, speed and strength, from Ashtanga yoga to gymnastics to tai chi chuan. Ordinarily, he didn't go to bed at night or shower in the morning until after he'd gone through several rounds of one of them. But for the past few days, he'd opted instead to start and end his day making love with Abby.

He did his best to erase her from his brain, concentrating instead on the burn and pull of his muscles as he worked through repetitive motions that pushed his body to the limit. He twisted, contorted, lifted and split until he was dripping with sweat. He ended the workout only when his body was shaking so hard he could no longer stand. He relaxed facedown onto the carpet in a heap, promising he'd give himself only a short breather before he treated his battered body to an ice-cold shower.

"You look like you could use a rubdown."

Unable to move his arms and legs just yet, Danny turned his face. Abby had slipped into the room unnoticed. Wearing a snug sports bra and shorts folded down across her hips so that they hinted at the sensual triangular shape of her pelvis, she sipped from a water bottle and looked as if she'd just gotten back from a workout of her own. Her hair, pulled up in a haphazard ponytail, dripped with sweat, and even in the darkening orange glow of the coming sunset, he could see the flushed pink of her skin.

He shoved his hands underneath him to push upward, but she stopped him.

"No, I'm serious. I've learned a lot from Svetlana."

He did as she asked, relaxing into the towel he'd spread across the floor. "Not too much, I hope. I'm pretty sure she plays for the home team, if you know what I mean."

Abby laughed as she disappeared into the guest bathroom and emerged with a couple of clean towels, one of which she took her time dousing with the icy water in her bottle. "She actually switch-hits, but I think it makes her aware of what feels good. Want me to show you?"

Danny instantly acquiesced, grabbing one of the rolled-up towels and wrapping his arms around it for comfort. His time with Abby was slipping away, and though he was painfully aware that each time he made love to her, he was leaving her with a part of his soul he'd never get back, he couldn't resist.

She used the cool towel to wipe the sweat first from the back of his neck, then across his shoulders and down his spine, the temperature warming as she washed the salty slickness of his sweat off his skin. She then tossed the towel aside, straddled him and dug straight into the muscles in his shoulder blades.

She was right. She was good. He'd expected the massage to be more sensual than deep-tissue, but she hit all the right spots with the perfect amount of pressure. Her fingers dug into his tight sinews and worked out the last of the knots he hadn't broken free with his workout. After about fifteen minutes of pure heaven, he groaned and released the last bit of tension in his body. If she wanted him to move, she was going to have to get a spatula.

"I told you I was good," she said.

He grunted his response. She laughed and, climbing off him, slid her hands beneath his side and flipped him over. He threw his arms out to the side, completely at her mercy.

"I can't move," he muttered.

She waggled her eyebrows. "Good. You stay right where you are."

She dragged her bra over her head and then, standing over him, shimmied out of her shorts. Though he was utterly spent, a mass of melted muscle and bone splayed across the floor, one part of him surged and she zeroed in on it immediately. She dragged his shorts off his body, then kissed a hot path up his foot, over his ankle, knees and thighs. She spared his dick a short flick of her tongue, then blazed the rest of her trail up his abdomen, chest, neck and chin. She covered him like an undulating blanket, and he imagined that if not for her obvious intention to take advantage of his weakened state, he could drift into the most solid sleep of his entire life.

But she wasn't going to have any of that. She straddled him again, this time facing forward, her slick sex sliding over his. He moved to touch her, but she slammed his hands back down on either side of him.

"Oh, no," she chastised. "You don't need to move. You've been working so hard. First, checking out the house and then honing this delicious body of yours into shape. You've done enough. I can take care of things from this point."

And man, did she ever.

His eyes drifted shut, his senses in a kind of delirious overload that only allowed him to alternately register the feel of her hands on his chest or her lips skimming across his shoulder, down his pec, then latching on to his nipple. The pressure of her body on his shifted when she reached over to retrieve her water bottle, then suddenly, she leaned up to his ear and asked if he was thirsty.

He replied by opening his mouth. She squirted the cold water between his lips, then aimed the stream across his chest so she could lap up what didn't drip away. The entire time, she pressed his erection between her legs, the slick pressure driving him mad with want.

She disappeared again for a minute, causing his eyes to pop open. She'd brought a condom with her, and she made quick work of removing it from its packaging and rolling it over him. She hummed as her hands, enhanced by lubrication, slid over the slick casing.

"Oh, this is good," she said.

She mounted him, manipulating her body to the perfect angle so that he could slide straight into her without having to move. When she sat up, she locked her gaze with his, her hands splayed in front of her, her fingers shiny from the lube that had spread to her palms.

His gaze locked with hers and she seemed to read his mind. With intricate care, she smeared her fingers over her nipples, which grew hard and long. She crooned her pleasure to him, moving with exquisite slowness up and down his body.

Danny couldn't look away, mesmerized by the way she used him to fulfill her own selfish needs. She pleasured her breasts, writhing over him, until he saw the beginnings of her orgasm tease the edges of her consciousness. At this point, he'd recovered enough to play his part, but he resisted.

This was the purest art he'd ever seen—and the thought of stealing it from her was a crime in itself. He did nothing more than shift his hips to maximize the tilt of his body into hers. She grabbed hold of his chest hair, alternately tugging hard and then bending forward to kiss away the pain. In the end, she braced her hands on the shoulders she'd massaged into submission and pumped until he could feel his own release building to an inevitable end.

They came together. She was wild with movement; he was utterly still. Danny squeezed his eyes shut so tightly, moisture leaked from the edges, spilling into the sweat on his temple. This was pure, raw sex. This was unconstrained pleasure. This was trust and need and selfless selfishness unlike anything he'd ever dreamed imaginable.

Then she collapsed against him, spent and satisfied, and reality drove into his heart like a spike.

He had to let her go.

Not only had it been their deal, but it was the right thing to do. Her family was desperately important to her—as his was beginning to be. He couldn't ask her to give her life up for him, and under no fantasy scenario could he imagine that he'd ever fit into her world. He was a thief. A liar. A con man. She needed to take this rare and beautiful passion and share it with a man who could match her honesty and integrity point for point.

He wasn't that man. He could never be that man... though as he drew his palm up her back, curved over him in a cradle of naked vulnerability, he couldn't help but splay his hand so he could see his father's ring and wish, for the first time since the damned thing got stuck on his hand, that the transformative magic of the bandit's legacy truly worked.

13

ABBY SWIRLED HER FINGER around the rim of her wineglass. The light from the votive candle on the restaurant table sparkled through the deep red, creating a spectrum of color across the white tablecloth. Her mind drifted to Picasso's rose period, so less famous than the blue. She had a theory about why—he'd used red to portray cheerfulness. Not passion. Not love. Not heartbreak.

That's what red meant. Leave it to a man to not understand.

"Hey, you okay?"

Erica, who'd slipped away from their table to take a phone call from her office, drew her napkin across her lap and then scooted forward in her chair. "You look like you're about to fall apart."

"Do I?"

Wisely, her friend took the wineglass away from her. She'd already had more than her usual and perhaps it was the alcohol spurring the melancholy mood. She'd arranged to have dinner out with Erica not only because Danny insisted it would establish an alibi for her in case he was caught at Liebe's house, but because she couldn't bear the thought of hiding in her apartment, pacing the rooms and worrying herself into madness while he perpetrated a crime on her behalf. What the hell had she been thinking?

"Okay, that's it," Erica declared. "I'm done with this secretive shit. You need to talk, Abby. And I'm here to listen. I'm not going to judge you."

Abby wished this was true, but how could it be when she was so harshly judging herself?

"You don't need my drama, E," she replied.

"Right, because I have so much of my own? Come on, Abs. If nothing else, I could use the entertainment."

Abby chuckled. She wanted to talk to Erica. She trusted her to keep her secret, but the thought of destroying her friend's respect for her held her hostage to silence. So many of her relationships had been inalienably altered by her bad choices. Could she risk her friendship with Erica, too?

"Trust me, you never would have gotten yourself into this kind of mess," Abby said.

"Right, because Erica Holt would never do anything stupid or unwise or potentially embarrassing to everyone she loves."

"Exactly." She locked eyes with her friend and tried to gauge if the mocking sound in her voice was from sarcasm or frustration. Or both.

"I lost my virginity to Scott Ripley," Erica announced.

Abby slapped the table so loudly, people at nearby tables turned to look. "You did not!"

Erica held her indignant stare for a minute, then buckled. "No, I didn't. But dammit, I wanted to."

"Scott Ripley? Really? Is that why you picked his name for Danny to use? After all these years?"

Erica took Abby's glass of wine and drank half the

Zinfandel down in one gulp. "He sent in his RSVP to the reunion this summer."

Though Abby hadn't known Scott, she knew his uncle's family. She'd helped his aunt authenticate a cache of Picasso sketches she'd bought at an auction. Out of politeness, she'd asked about her nephew, but the woman had been tight-lipped. From what she'd remembered, he'd left town on his motorcycle the night of graduation and hadn't been anywhere near Chicago since.

"I'm surprised he's coming back to town," Abby said.

"Tell me about it. It's bad enough that I could have gotten my cherry popped by a guy who knew what he was doing rather than with Will Jensen, who took about three tries to get it right. Now I'm going to have to face Rip again with no boyfriend or husband. I don't even have a scandalous divorce to brag about!"

"You have three broken engagements," Abby pointed out, never imagining that she'd use that fact to sound encouraging.

Erica was not swayed. "He's probably married to some hot supermodel."

"Or a stripper," Abby ventured, trying to find some bright side for her friend to hold on to. Scott Ripley had not seemed like the type to settle down, much less with a woman as educated and accomplished as her friend—her obviously lonely, filled-with-regret friend. Where was the justice in this? Women like Erica acted precisely the way society expected them to, so why had she ended up so sad?

"Maybe I should have married Will or Brent or Stephen."

"And ended up divorced? You didn't love any of them, E. If you had, you would have married them."

"Divorced is better than not being married at all."

"Do you really think that?" she challenged. Though neither of them had ever been divorced, they had a ton of friends and acquaintances who had—and she wouldn't have wished that pain on anyone, especially a friend.

"No, I don't. But I guess I've reached the point in my life where I need a change. The reunion, the possibility of seeing all those people again. It makes you take a hard look at your life. And I don't like what I'm seeing."

Abby shifted in her seat, glad to have Erica's neuroses to explore rather than her own. She'd never really understood why Erica had attracted such great guys, but then to a one, rejected them all. It was never a mean rejection. It was never even particularly dramatic. Just one by one, her relationships fell by the wayside. They hadn't "felt right." Abby had never completely understood what that meant—but now she had an inkling of an idea.

Erica had been looking for someone exciting. Someone forbidden. Someone who would trip her heartbeat into maximum overdrive.

Someone like Danny.

"You'll find the right guy someday," Abby assured her. "But I don't think it will be Scott Ripley any more than my knight in shining armor will be—"

"Danny Burnett?"

"He's just a friend."

"Stop lying, Abby. He's not just a friend. He's your lover. God, just own it already."

"Excuse me?"

Erica leaned forward and whispered, but her words were no less passionate for the decreased volume. "I know who he is, Abby. I know what happened between the two of you five years ago. I've been waiting for you to tell me yourself, but maybe you're too embarrassed or maybe you think I won't want to be your friend anymore, but the fact is, I'm jealous as hell that you did something so outrageous and lived to tell the tale."

Abby took her wine back. "He told you?"

"Danny? No, he denied it, too. He might be a thief and a liar, but he's got your back." Erica chewed on her bottom lip before she said, "Marshall told me."

Abby finished off her Zinfandel and then directed the waiter to bring them another bottle.

"He—"

Abby closed her eyes, remembering again how devastated Marshall had been when she'd confessed her betrayal to him. He'd been so quiet. So still. She'd wanted him to rage, yell, scream and curse, but he'd done nothing but get out of his chair, kiss her sweetly on the cheek and ask for time to think.

Then he'd left. For hours, she'd cried her eyes out, convinced he'd never come back and never forgive her. But he had. The next morning, he'd snuck into her room, curled up beside her in bed and whispered how deeply he loved her and how desperately he wanted to forgive her and move on. They'd made love that morning with such heat, she'd been convinced he was trying to burn away all of her memories of Danny.

And he'd succeeded.

Marshall had stunned her with his capacity for love and forgiveness, but she'd never dreamed he'd used Erica as his sounding board.

"I don't understand," she confessed. "You knew all this time and you never said anything?"

Erica shrugged. "I was waiting for you to tell me yourself, but I understood why you didn't. You wanted to forget it all, put it behind you. I would have, too. Marshall worshipped you. He dreamed about a future with you since you first met and he didn't want to give it all up because you made a mistake. When I explained to him, really explained to him, what it was like for women like us who never rebelled, never pushed our own limits, sexual or otherwise, but instead bowed to the expectations of everyone around us, he understood. He was one in a million."

Abby nodded her agreement, but still couldn't get beyond the fact that her best friend and her husband had had such an intimate conversation.

"I can't believe you talked about sex with Marshall."

Erica smirked. "Sometimes, I think the conversation was more cathartic for me than it was for him. He was like a brother to me, Abby. And I knew how much you really loved him. And more than that, I knew how much he loved you. If he hadn't worshipped you down to his soul, he would have walked away without ever reaching out to me. So yeah, I pulled out all the stops. I told him the hard truths, and in the end, he decided he wanted to be the only tall, dark and handsome stranger in your life—the man who swept you off your feet and into his bed. And it worked out, right? You had four awesome years together. And now you have a shot at the guy who started it all. It's not a bad run for a good girl who rarely strays out of her comfort zone."

"Out of my comfort zone? That's the understatement of the year. Danny's zone should have its own zip code. He's bad for me."

"How do you figure?"

"He's a—" she lowered her voice "—a thief."

Erica waved her hand dismissively. "Good thing, too, since he's off right now stealing something back that rightfully belongs to you."

"But once he has it, he's leaving. And he won't come back. He doesn't fit here."

"How do you know?"

Abby thought she might lose her mind. Why was her friend being so dense?

"Oh, I don't know, because I can't really see my father opening up his house to a man who steals art for a living."

"Your great-grandfather was a bootlegger," she pointed out.

"No, he wasn't."

Erica snorted. "Yes, he was! Your father's so uptight about his family's history because it lines right up with the likes of Al Capone and Bugsy Moran. He wasn't a mobster, but without his special formula and the money it brought in, his son, your grandfather, wouldn't have had his Harvard education and you might still be living on the South Side rather than Lake Shore. That's why he gets so freaked out about anything that puts the family in a bad light. But that doesn't mean Danny won't grow on him. Don't use your family as an excuse for not seeing Danny for who he really is—a guy that you have a powerful chemical attraction to and a guy who's willing to risk his freedom just to get a stupid painting back."

Abby sat back in her chair, stunned. The information about her family roots was surprising enough, but what Erica had said about Danny hit home even harder. She couldn't deny that her family mattered to her. She'd never consciously thought about seeking their approval. They'd always given it to her, even after she'd lost the painting to a con man. Maybe her deep-rooted need to play the good girl hadn't come from them as much as it had come from herself.

It was, after all, safe. When she followed her strict

code of behavior, she didn't get hurt. The one time she'd strayed, she'd nearly lost everything, including her self-respect.

But what about what she'd gained?

"It's not a stupid painting," she argued, but her voice was as weak as her conviction.

"No, it's the reason he sought you out in the beginning and it's the reason you went looking for him. But it's not why you slept with him again."

"Did he tell you that?"

"I told you, he's got your back. But he didn't need to tell me. You've got that glow, sister-friend. A rare and beautiful glimmer of a woman who has had more than one orgasm in the last twenty-four hours. I'm jealous. But through the pea-green haze of my envy, I'm also happy for you. If Danny turns you on, why can't you see where it could lead?"

Abby frowned. She knew where their relationship would lead—nowhere. Once he got the painting for her, he'd have to disappear. Not only because that was the deal, but because that action would keep him from getting caught by the police or whoever else Harris Liebe might send after her. She'd set up this elaborate scheme to get Danny back in her life, but only temporarily. And now that she maybe wanted their time together to last a little longer, she'd inadvertently arranged for that to be impossible.

"I know where it will lead. To heartbreak and disappointment. I've been through that once. I can't survive it again."

THE SKIN ON THE BACK of Danny's neck prickled with warning. One last lock and he'd be in. An unexpected close call with a trio of musicians setting up in the ballroom one floor down had nearly scrapped the operation, but he'd improvised and had made it up the stairs to the third floor, where the painting was being housed. With party planners, caterers and cleaning staff traipsing through the lower innards of the house, security had been nearly nonexistent. Who'd expect someone to break in when the house was overflowing with people?

Still, something felt off. The lock was the greatest barrier so far, and for someone with less experience than him, it might have been a problem. And yet, this all seemed just a little too easy to be real.

He made short work of the security camera mounted down the hallway—one he'd determined was unmonitored—then disengaged the security alarm with the code he'd swiped from the owner's smartphone when he'd visited the day before. With tools he never traveled without, he dispatched the keyed dead bolt and slipped inside the dark room. He flipped down the slim nightvision goggles he'd picked up in a downtown spy shop and scanned the pitch-black room. The painting was hanging on the opposite wall, farthest from the door, but he wasn't making a move until he was sure the path to his prize was clear.

He saw nothing to indicate anyone else was in the room, but he wasn't yet ready to move. He closed his eyes and listened intently for the hum of unexpected electronics or maybe some breathing beyond his own. His heartbeat thumped loudly, masking any warning signs. But he couldn't wait around all night. His senses were on alert. His best bet was to get the painting and get out as soon as possible. Stealing for money was loads less stressful than stealing for the woman he loved.

He was halfway across the room when he heard it—a whisper of a click that could have been a door opening or the release of a safety on a gun. He froze in place, then with a soundless arc, dived and rolled to the corner. But his countermeasure was useless. The lights flicked on, blinding him. He tore off his goggles, and by the time he'd regained his ability to see, a man stood ten feet away from him, holding a gun.

"Danny Burnett," the older man said genially. "Good to finally see you again."

Danny blinked, and slowly, the man came into focus. His shaggy blond hair, streaked with gray, the goatee and thin, wire-rimmed glasses masked a weathered face whose shape and dimension Danny had seen before, but he couldn't remember where.

Oh, crap. Had he stolen from this guy before?

"You've got one up on me, my friend," Danny said with a grin. He held out his hands as he straightened, wanting the man to see he was unarmed. He hated guns, especially when the barrel of one was trained at the center of his chest.

The man smiled in return, but did not lower his weapon.

"I'm crushed," he said, his frown exaggerated. "You don't recognize me?"

Danny studied the face, though it was hard to tear his gaze away from the gun aimed at him. The man removed his glasses, but it didn't help.

"Sorry," he said, truthfully. If conjuring a name to match the face would keep him from getting shot, he sincerely wished he could.

"Maybe if I pour us some cheap tequila and order up a few Tijuana whores, your memory will be jogged?"

The Tijuana whores jibe got him. When Danny had retreated to Mexico to drown his sorrows after betraying Abby, he'd met a lot of people. For a couple of weeks, he'd hung out with an old California surfer dude who'd had a lot of pesos and didn't mind sharing them with his inebriated new best friend. Though Danny had sworn off women—even the kind you paid for—this guy had sampled just about every pair of feminine lips on the Yucatan peninsula.

If Danny mentally shaved the beard off the guy and ditched the glasses, he could vaguely connect him with the surfer who'd financed his pity party. Danny, whose legs had started to ache from the prolonged half crouch that he'd affected out of surprise, relaxed. This guy might have a gun, but he'd been a former drinking partner. Men like that didn't tend to shoot first and ask questions later.

"That was a fuzzy time in my life," Danny admitted. "I don't know if I ever caught your name back then."

The man smiled. His teeth were so straight and white, Danny figured he'd paid a price equivalent to the cost of Abby's painting just for dental work. But it was the sharp eyes, in contrast to the aging body, that had Danny on alert, his arms slightly spread, hands splayed.

"Whatever name I gave you probably wasn't real anyway," the old man admitted, crossing over to a desk that was set up with several decanters of liquids that ranged from clear to golden to caramelized brown. "At the time, I wanted to know you, but not the other way around."

"And that's different now?"

Danny's gaze darted toward the window. He'd scoped out the building thoroughly and knew that a tall elm reached well beyond the third floor. The branches had been cut about five feet away from the house. For this reason, he'd opted not to use that means to enter the room where the painting was displayed, but it didn't mean he couldn't use it as a possible escape route if he failed to talk his way out of whatever trap he'd fallen into.

Because that's what this was—a trap. The ease of Danny's access had been calculated by the man standing across from him with a gun. He'd gone to a lot of trouble to lure Danny into an isolated room on the third floor.

The question was, why?

"Things have changed drastically in the past five years, Danny. For both of us, I expect. Look at you. You're sober, practicing your trade again. Back in bed with the woman who broke your heart—or did you break hers? I was never sure on that point."

Danny didn't answer. He and Abby had both done a little breaking and a lot of hurting. But it sure as hell wasn't any of this jerk's business.

"And you have brothers!" he went on. "Two of them, each more different from you than the other. One a respected art expert and auction-house owner. The other, a decorated FBI agent. Who would have guessed that the man I met when he was sleeping in sawdust would experience such a series of life changes over such a short period of time? I mean, it all really started to change for you after your father died, didn't it? I can't help but wonder what's behind that sudden alteration of fortunes."

Danny made a quick and nonthreatening gesture toward the gun. "Funny, but I'm not feeling particularly fortunate at the moment."

"Don't worry about this," he said. "I just happen to know how slippery you are. The gun will simply ensure that you stay to hear what I have to say."

"I'm listening," Danny said. "But it would be polite

if you offered me a drink. Maybe a chair. That name I don't remember."

The man nodded, poured a finger of what Danny assumed was Scotch into a glass and held it out to him. He considered rushing the guy and disarming him, but for the moment, it was in his best interests to keep him talking. If this guy had manipulated the situation enough to get him here, he needed to know why.

Clearly, the painting was not the old man's priority. In the few minutes since he'd turned on the lights, he hadn't looked at the portrait once. He'd used it as bait—his true prize was Danny.

Danny grabbed a chair from the massive desk and sat as far away from the mystery man and the gun as he could. He perched on the edge of the leather cushion, but didn't take a drink.

"Comfy?"

"Not particularly. I'd like to take that painting and go. It's not yours. I mean, technically. It belongs to Abigail Albertini, but clearly you know that and used the information to lure me here."

"I did indeed."

"But you still haven't told me your name."

"No, I haven't, but you've broken into my house."

His eyes widened as he waited for Danny to react to his declaration. "So you're Harris Liebe." Since he'd never heard the name before he'd taken this job for Abby, Danny shrugged his shoulders. "Is that supposed to mean something to me?"

Harris narrowed his gaze. "It should, after the years of bad luck your family has brought to mine. It's a name you won't forget, once I tell you the whole sordid tale."

Danny glanced down at his glass. He knew it was smarter to stay clearheaded when dealing with an armed megalomaniac, but the whole situation made him extremely thirsty.

"You do realize you sound like some kind of master villain, right?" he asked. "And if you're casting me in the role of superhero, buddy, you've got the wrong guy."

The man laughed, but had the decency to make the sound a low chuckle rather than a maniacal cackle.

"But you are the descendant of a hero, are you not? That, sir, is why we're here."

14

This was about the ring?

Underneath his gloves, Danny could practically feel the gold band constrict even tighter around his finger. This was what he got for having family ties, for thinking, for even a minute, that having a history that dated back to the 1800s was kind of cool. He'd been better off when he was anonymous, a man with a cache of names at his disposal. Even his "real" name, Daniel Burnett, wasn't entirely legit. He shared no ties with the Burnetts any longer beyond Lucy, who'd stopped being Lucy Burnett months ago.

Danny had been slow to warm up to the idea of being a Murrieta, but learning about his father and his brothers had not been as insignificant as he'd pretended. The idea of having men who shared his blood watching his back appealed to him. He sure as hell could have used both of them right about now.

But they weren't coming to his rescue. Danny would have to talk his way out of what should have been a quick and easy operation to retrieve Abby's painting. But then again, nothing associated with Abby was ever easy, was it?

"I don't know what you're talking about."

The man smirked. "You know about your relationship to Joaquin Murrieta because I told you."

Danny clicked his tongue. "If you expect me to recall anything you said to me in Mexico—"

"Not in Mexico—in your jail cell," he replied. "Of course, I didn't deliver the message myself. Perhaps my associate, Mr. Jimmy the Rim, did not outline the true significance of your family's legacy and how it intertwines with mine. But I imagine that since your release, you and your brothers have talked about it extensively."

"You almost had me railroaded for murder!"

Liebe waved his hand dismissively. "Mr. Rim can be a little enthusiastic with his work. The manufactured evidence against you disappeared because I wanted it to. Despite your family's felonious history, I saw no need to incarcerate you in the long term for a crime you did not commit."

"Wait," Danny said. "Are you talking about all that crap about me being related to some Chilean street thug named…Juan? Or was it…Joaquin? But what the hell does that family legend have to do with my arrest? Or you? Or even more important, that?"

He hooked his thumb at the painting, but Harris didn't follow the direction of his gesture. He focused on Danny, his eyes locked and intense while he tried to figure out if Danny's proclaimed ignorance was real. One thing was for sure—if Harris knew the details of the Murrieta connection to the legendary bandit made famous by books and movies and television shows, then he must have gotten close to someone in the family.

Alex still had mixed feelings about the bandit blood running through his veins. Even Michael, in the middle of an FBI investigation that centered on a madman's obsession with the caped crusader of colonial California, had kept his personal connection on the down-low. So how could this guy possibly know?

Unless...

"You knew Ramon."

Harris grinned. "If you mean your biological father, Ramon Murrieta, then yes. We did business over the years. We shared an interest in the old mission era of California. I was particularly interested in cavalry pieces. My family, you see, played a large role in the protection of the missions and villages in the area. Ramon tracked down quite a few swords and uniforms for me over the years. An interesting man, your father. More than worthy of the legacy left to him by the notorious bandit."

For the first time since Danny had learned about his so-called family history, he wished he knew more about Joaquin than just his somewhat unbelievable connection to the fictional Zorro. It made for a great story, but anyone could have scratched a *Z* into the center of the ring's stone.

It was harder, however, to argue with the documentation Alex had shown him and the journal he'd peeked at while holed up with Michael in New Orleans. Still, he didn't know much about the details. He'd always preferred to live in the moment and leave the historical context of the art he stole to people like Lucy or Alex. But he'd seen enough of the movies to know that in the Zorro milieu, the army officers garrisoned in places like San Diego and San Luis Obispo were, to the masked bandit, the enemy.

Clearly, this guy was following in their footsteps.

"He's dead, you know."

"Ramon? Yes, I attended his funeral. Shame you weren't there."

"Families are complicated," Danny replied coolly. If the guy was trying to play him emotionally, he was barking up the wrong tree. His non-relationship with his father hadn't been an issue for years.

This guy, on the other hand, seemed to be holding tight to a family grudge that had lasted centuries.

One-handed, Harris poured a measure of what looked like brandy into a snifter. If not for the barrel of the gun pointed in his direction, Danny might have rolled his eyes at the scene the man had crafted. It was straight out of one of the movies that might have starred his ancestor—the hero trapped while the villain takes his time sipping spirits and preparing to deliver a monologue that explains the intricacies of his evil plot.

Danny might as well play along.

"I don't understand how your business relationship with my father relates to the painting, which is the reason I'm here."

"Ah, yes" the man said. "The grand gesture behind your thievery—to steal back the prize for your lady love. To right the wrong you perpetrated against her. To protect her family from the scandal of her grandmother's naughty notoriety. To restore her faith in you, even though you're a man in whom faith is usually wasted."

Clearly, this guy kept his ear to a lot of keyholes.

"Did you practice that speech? It was good. Really. A little old-world. Maybe missing a cackle at the end, but still very effective. I'm impressed."

Harris bent his head in a slight bow, unabashed by Danny's backhanded compliments. "I confess, I've run a few of these conversations through my mind prior to our meeting again."

"That's a hell of a hobby."

"More like a family legacy. Your great-great-great-great-great grandfather might have been the bandit who inspired Zorro, but my ancestor was famous, as well. Captain Harrison Love."

"Who?"

"Captain Harrison Love," he repeated, his tone measured. "Surely you've learned enough about Joaquin to have heard about his nemesis, as well. He was the army officer who caught your dirty, thieving forebear, cut off his head and displayed it in a jar to remind other would-be heroes what would happen if they challenged his authority."

Danny's brain clicked. Harris Liebe. Captain Harrison Love. *Liebe* meant *love* in German. This couldn't be a coincidence that the man who was about to expose Abby's painting was tied to some distant relative of the man who'd reportedly been Danny's ancestor's personal pain in the ass.

He didn't know much about Joaquin Murrieta, but he knew about the head-in-the-jar story. Some parts of the legend were kind of hard to ignore.

"So what? You want to cut my head off and keep it in a jar?"

Harris Liebe sipped his brandy. "Don't be ridiculous. If I'd wanted to cut your head off, I would have done so in Mexico. You wouldn't have felt a thing and no one would have looked twice."

"I assume we didn't meet accidentally in that cantina, then."

"Hardly. I've wanted the Murrieta ring for many years. Took me a while to track it down and ingratiate myself into Ramon's life. Unfortunately, no matter how many trinkets I purchased from his auction house, he wouldn't part with it. I would have stolen it from him, but the man never took it off, and unlike the notorious captain, I find the removal of appendages disgusting."

Danny breathed a little easier. The thought had crossed his mind that this whack-job might try to slice off a digit if he learned that Danny had the ring on underneath his gloves.

"That's very human of you," Danny said. "But you realize that Captain Love cut off the wrong guy's head, right? That's fairly embarrassing."

Harris's eyes flared and he slammed his hand onto the desk. "The captain's mistake cost him his career. He captured a man wearing Joaquin's ring and assumed it was the bandit. He only found out he was wrong when Joaquin stole it back. Though he continued to proclaim he had the bandit's head in the jar, his superiors knew better. He was reduced to running a virtual sideshow."

"That sucked for him, but what does it have to do with you hundreds of years later? You're clearly doing well for yourself. Money. Connections. Exquisite taste in art. I don't get why you want some piece of crap ring with a scratch on the emerald."

"So you've seen it?"

The hunger in the man's gaze was a little more than unnerving.

"Yeah," Danny said with a shrug. "Michael has it. And I guarantee, he's not going to give it up."

"He has to."

"Why?"

Harris poked his free hand into his pocket and pulled out a wallet. He tossed it to Danny, who caught it. Inside were several platinum credit cards under various names, a healthy amount of cash and a picture.

One picture. The old man standing at the entrance to

the University of Chicago with a teenage boy who had the same piercing blue eyes as his grandfather.

"This is about your grandson?"

"Charles Harris Love, the fourth. He has a brilliant mind, but he can't stay out of trouble. Five boarding schools," he complained, his voice rising with indignation. "Not that I should be surprised. His father got kicked out of seven before he went wildcatting in Texas and ended up dying in a rig explosion just a couple of months after the boy was born."

Danny winced. Though he hadn't had any family ties until recently, he was starting to understand the power they possessed.

"I don't get it," Danny said. "The ring never belonged to your family. Why would you want it now?"

"It's the symbol of our greatest error, our greatest shame. It set in motion generations of men who have struggled to succeed at leading good, decent lives. My grandson is already on that path to destruction. Ramon believed that ring had properties—the ability to keep his progeny on the straight and narrow. I want it for my grandson and you're going to get it for me."

Danny resisted any urge to look down at his hand, flex his fingers.

"It's just a hunk of metal and stones."

"Maybe," Harris said, his voice wavering slightly, as if he knew he sounded more than a little mad. "But there is power in symbolism."

"Maybe, but you've gone to a lot of trouble for symbolism," Danny challenged.

"I'll do whatever it takes for my family," Liebe said evenly. "Just like your lady love. She's invited you back into her life to save her family from scandal. I'm no different."

Danny had hoped the conversation would lead back to the portrait, but he'd had no idea it would take such a circuitous route.

"You can have it," Liebe said dismissively.

"The painting? Just like that?"

"Of course not," he said. "An exchange, just as I wanted before. This time, the painting for the ring."

Danny pushed aside all his anger over the man's scheming and focused on the situation at hand. His arrest, after all, had netted him contact with Abby again, and for that, Danny couldn't help but be weirdly grateful. Still, he wasn't going to promise something that wasn't his to give. Not even for Abby.

"You should be talking to Michael, then."

Liebe raised his eyebrows. "He's an FBI. I doubt he'll negotiate."

"But I will?"

"Won't you? Your sense of right and wrong isn't nearly as…well formed. And you, my friend, have a weakness."

Abby.

"I talked about her in Mexico?"

"You rambled on about nothing else. For the price of a couple of bottles of booze, I learned that you didn't give a crap about your family history. I knew then that you put no sentimental value on the ring, which works in my favor. But as the black sheep of the family, they weren't exactly going to hand the thing over to you, either. My trip was nearly wasted, but then you confessed what you'd done to Ms. Albertini—about your regrets. About your promise to get the painting back for her, whatever it took. That's when I started looking for it, hoping I might use it to manipulate you into helping me. Unfortunately, it was not easy to find. After

Ramon's death, I decided to orchestrate your arrest to get you to help me."

"I couldn't do much from a jail cell."

"But you improvised well. Using your adopted sister? A nice touch."

"But she didn't get the ring back."

"She succumbed to the infamous Murrieta charm, which I confess, wasn't unexpected. I met Lucienne, you know. Under another of my aliases. To her, I was one of Ramon's many reliable clients. She played her role very well, but I had the opportunity to see her and Alejandro together during a pre-auction meeting. They tried to fight their shared attraction, but even I could see what would happen if they were left alone long enough. That's when I employed Mr. Rim to do what she obviously couldn't."

Danny pulled off the knit cap he'd worn that was now making his skull hot and itchy. He'd been here a hell of a lot longer than he'd intended. Abby had to be going out of her mind.

"But Alex stopped Jimmy," Danny said, prouder at that moment than he had been previously. Now that he knew Alex, he realized that tangling with armed thugs was no more his specialty than it was Danny's. But he'd risked his life to keep Lucy safe from the danger Danny had put her in—and for that, he'd be eternally grateful.

"He did, and then, he passed the ring on to Michael. A smart move. Stealing from an FBI agent isn't child's play. And since Lucy influenced your brothers to help you get out of jail, I'd lost my leverage over you. That's when I doubled my efforts to retrieve Ms. Albertini's painting…and here we are."

For the first time since the lights had flashed on and his plan to retrieve the painting quick and easy had evaporated, anger bloomed in Danny's chest. The crazy talk about the ring's powers, the manipulation that had landed him in jail and the way this stranger had invaded the lives of just about everyone tied to the Murrieta family were nothing compared to Harris dragging Abby into this madness.

"You did all that just to get your hands on a ring?"

"On a legacy."

"You've lost your mind."

"Now, you hardly know me," Harris replied, unperturbed. "I hardly think you're in any position to judge the state of my sanity."

Danny rubbed his hand down his face, certain the time had come for him to get the hell out of here. The man had finished off half his drink, but his gun hand, unfortunately, remained steady. Danny might never make it across the room without getting shot. And as he had broken into the guy's house with the intention of stealing his property, the police would call it self-defense and the matter would be over. He'd either be dead or in a hell of a lot of pain and looking at jail time. Abby wouldn't get her painting and Harris would continue to harass his family until he had what he wanted.

A couple of months ago, Danny wouldn't have cared. He might have destroyed the ring himself if he'd had the chance, just to break the last bond tying him to the father he'd never known. But things had changed drastically since Ramon's death. Alejandro had saved him from prison. Michael, albeit reluctantly, had trusted him enough to allow him to help on a case. Add to the fact that Lucy, his best friend, was marrying his older brother, and like it or not, his connection to the Murrieta family was now indestructible.

Then there was Abby. She'd been drawn into this

mess because some nut-job wanted a hunk of gold and scratched stones to keep his grandson on the straight and narrow. The man was insane—but he was also holding a gun and, metaphorically, all the cards.

He glanced at the portrait. There was no denying that Abby's grandmother had been a stunning beauty in her youth. Danny stood, and with a silent gesture, received permission to examine the painting more closely. As he neared, he realized how deeply Abby resembled the woman in the painting. The same sweet curves. The same irresistible lips. And since he'd come back into her life, the same bold, irreverent expression.

But despite how much he wanted to bring the painting back to her, he couldn't just turn over the ring. Even if it came off—which he wasn't sure it would—it wasn't his to relinquish. The ring didn't belong just to him. It belonged to Alex and Michael, too.

Danny turned. "What's your timetable?"

"I'm already spending obscene amounts of money on the masquerade. Bring it to me then and I'll give Ms. Albertini the portrait before anyone sees it."

"What will you tell your guests?"

Harris laughed. "I'll tell them to drink another round of Cristal. I don't care about the party. I want the ring. Do you understand?"

The gun notwithstanding, Danny understood that the man was serious. He might be averse to chopping off the body parts of people who stood in his way, but he'd find other means to make people suffer if Danny didn't come through.

"Fine," he said. "It's a deal."

Harris lowered his gun and flicked on the safety.

"You're going to believe me, just like that?"

Liebe grinned. "I trust that you will not betray Ms.

Albertini again. But I suppose I won't know for sure until the party. That's fine. I may be old, but I still enjoy a challenge."

Danny stalked to the door. He didn't know exactly what he was going to do about the ring, but he knew he wouldn't figure it out here—and he wouldn't figure it out without Abby.

15

ABBY JUMPED AT THE SOUND of the soft knock on her door. Without checking the peephole, she flung it open and this time was greeted by the face she'd been waiting hours for. No more surprises. She couldn't take any more surprises.

Danny's grin nearly melted her insides. "I'm like a bad habit, Abby. Hard to get rid of."

With a burst of laughter, she slapped him on the shoulder, then locked her hands on either side of his face and kissed him soundly. Though he chuckled underneath her passionate assault, she could feel the tension in his muscles and in the rigid grasp of his hands on her waist. Something had gone wrong. He had not retrieved the painting.

And she didn't care. He was back. He was safe. And he could now deal with the unexpected visitors who'd shown up at her apartment an hour ago and turned her and Danny's private plan into a family affair.

"Come inside," she said, glancing up and down the hall. He was still wearing his work clothes—an all-black ensemble of pants, turtleneck and leather jacket. He hadn't even taken off his gloves, though he had at least stored the other tools of his felonious trade in a dark shoulder bag. "There are people here to see you."

"People?"

Not just any people.

His family.

Though it was nearly midnight, Abby's living room was more crowded than it had been since she moved in. Alejandro Aguilar, the oldest Murrieta brother, stood near the floor-to-ceiling windows, the Chicago skyscrapers outside looking miniscule compared to his proud stance and intense stare. Abby had mingled with more than a few corporate giants in her life, but she'd been unprepared for this living, breathing brick wall. Add the Spanish accent to the mix and she'd had no defenses when he'd invited himself, his fiancé, Lucienne, his youngest brother, Michael, and his girlfriend, Claire Lécuyer, into her apartment and demanded information about Danny's location.

Erica, who'd come home with her to make sure she didn't wear a hole in the floor pacing until Danny returned, had kept the unexpected invasion cocktail-party polite. She'd moderated the volley of introductions, sent Abby into the kitchen for drinks—which was really just a chance for her to get her head together—and then asked all the right questions to discover that Lucienne had been the one to alert the family that Danny might be in trouble. Michael, who'd been an FBI special agent until he'd taken an indefinite leave of absence, had tracked their wayward brother to Chicago with the help of Claire, a private investigator from New Orleans.

Concerned, they'd descended onto the city like any family should—though from the stunned look on Danny's face, he neither expected nor appreciated their presence. Without saying a word to any of them, he pulled Abby into the hall and rudely shut the door.

"Danny, you can't do that," Abby objected, every bone in her body screaming at the sheer rudeness of him abandoning his family after they'd come so far to check up on him.

"Did you call them?"

"What? No. How would I know how to reach them? Until Alejandro convinced my doorman to escort them upstairs personally, all I knew about your brothers was what you told me—which wasn't much. You don't even have the same last names."

"Then why are they here?"

"Lucienne said you called her a couple of days ago and asked her some questions that made her believe you were here and you were in trouble. After you contacted Michael to ask for access to the auction-house safes, they decided that they needed to help."

He snickered. "Help? One of my brothers is FBI. The other is the poster boy for good citizenship. They are going to go insane if they find out I came to Chicago to steal your painting."

Abby pressed her lips together tightly.

"They already know," she muttered.

"What? I thought you didn't want anyone to know about the painting or your family history or anything."

"I didn't, but I also didn't want to lie to them. They're your family. And besides, I need to get used to the idea that the secrets are going to get out. I told them everything. Alex was really sympathetic."

Danny looked at her as if she'd lost her mind. "Alex? My brother Alex. Alejandro Aguilar of the House of Aguilar was sympathetic to the fact that you asked me to break into someone's house and take back a painting that would reveal to the public at large that your grandmother cheated on your grandfather with an unknown artist who immortalized their indiscretion in oil on canvas?"

Abby frowned. When he put it that way, maybe his brother hadn't been so much sympathetic as pitying.

"Okay, maybe *sympathize* isn't the right word. But his mother's family is a lot like mine. He told me how they survived her marriage to your father and all the scandal when Ramon left without a word. After some things Erica said tonight at dinner, I realized that maybe my family can weather whatever pain the painting dredges up."

"Maybe, but you're not taking into consideration that the Aguilars erased Ramon from their lives. Alex doesn't even have the Murrieta name. His situation is entirely different from yours."

"But he dropped everything in his life to go to San Francisco when Michael called. And even though you are an international art thief who makes no apologies for his career, he still hired you a really great lawyer when you were set up for attempted murder. His belief in family was stronger than any scandal. And you know what? My family survived my grandmother's affair, and to be honest, we survived mine. If the public has to know all about it now, so be it. Life can't always be perfect. It's an impossible standard."

Danny scanned her face for any sign that she was overstating her courage. But she wasn't. Between her conversation about mobsters and bootlegging with Erica and her confessional with Danny's family, Abby had decided that it was time to stop running from the sins of her past. Her grandmother, always a free spirit caged by the Albertinis' quest for respectability, had to be spinning in her grave to see her granddaughter sacrificing so much to avoid something as insignificant as a scandal. Abby had to believe that even Marshall, who'd spent the four years of their marriage convincing her that he'd forgiven her transgression, would be disappointed in her hiding from her true self.

Abby no longer cared what other people thought—she just wanted to be happy.

She deserved to be.

But she was no fool. Happiness wasn't something gifted on a person from someone else. If she wanted happiness, she was going to have to take it, and if the struggle resulted in some pain and bruising, she'd survive. And in the end, thrive.

After a long minute, Danny's mouth curved into a grin. His intense gaze softened around the edges in a way that made her want to drag him into her bedroom and have her way with him.

"If this is what you want," he said. "Because I didn't get the painting."

"I figured," she said, patting his clearly portrait-less shoulder bag. "Besides, you said if you got it, you'd leave right away. And you're here. And damn it, Danny, I'm glad."

This time when she kissed him, the act didn't feel as desperate. The press of their mouths was comforting and calm, a complete contrast to the emotions ricocheting through her. Just because he agreed to stay long enough to help her weather the upcoming storm didn't mean he'd stay forever. In fact, she wasn't sure he'd stay long enough to deal with his family.

"Ready to go inside?" she asked.

"It's going to be a bloodbath," he joked.

Despite his dire warning, he reentered the apartment

with a grin on his face. He stored his shoulder bag beside the door and Abby tried not to read too much into it, though she couldn't help but wonder if he was preparing for a getaway. She couldn't blame him. They both had some serious issues to work through—with their families and with each other—before they could have any kind of future together. A future she now knew she desperately wanted.

But the big questions would have to wait.

"So what is this, a Murrieta intervention?" Danny asked once back inside.

"Nah, bro," Michael said, turning from his relaxed position on the couch. "We just thought we'd fly halfway across the country to make sure we didn't have to bail you out of jail again. Alex has better things to spend his money on, and frankly, I'm tired of picking up after your messes."

Danny sputtered and released Abby, who shut the door behind them and engaged the locks. She wished Erica hadn't already left on the optimistic assumption that since everyone there had come together to help Danny—and by extension, Abby—she was in the way. She might have made a good referee.

"You? Picking up after me?" Danny asked. "I'll take that from Alex, but wasn't it just last week that my expertise helped save your girlfriend here from a serial rapist?"

Claire stood and gave Danny a hug—a move he was entirely unprepared for. Abby's heart twanged with jealousy as the exotic beauty, a masterpiece of milk-and-coffee skin, thick dark hair and muted green eyes, wrapped her arms around Danny's waist and pressed close to his chest.

"Don't listen to your brother, Danny," Claire said,

her southern Louisiana accent tipping her over from stunning to irresistible. "He's just trying to piss you off, which apparently is what brothers do."

"Then we must have been born experts at being brothers, despite the fact that we've only just met," Alex assessed.

Danny unfolded himself from Claire's embrace.

"Okay, then," he said. "Now that we've established that we're all one happy family and that you cared enough to ride to my rescue, you can leave. I'm fine and I don't need your help."

"But you didn't get the painting," Abby said.

She hadn't meant to say that out loud. She swallowed deeply when everyone turned to face her, but it wasn't like Danny to not complete a job. Not unless something had happened.

"I mean, it doesn't matter," she insisted, "but I would like to know what happened."

Lucienne slid back in her chair, Lady curled on her lap. "Yes, Danny, let's hear the story. You're not exactly known for coming back empty-handed."

"How about if I bring some drinks?" Abby offered as the tension in the room rose to combustible levels. "Wine this time, maybe?"

"Hell, screw the wine," said Claire, who stood up from the couch and collected the water bottles Abby had offered them when they'd first arrived. "Where's your rum? Give me a fifth and open access to your fridge and I'll whip something together that will liven this crowd right up."

For all her stunning beauty and hands-on approach to saying hello to Danny, Abby liked Claire. Like her, she was still a bit of an outsider to this increasingly close-knit family. Danny was connected to Lucienne through his adoption and to his brothers by blood. She and Claire were just girlfriends—though in reality, Abby wasn't even that. She was just Danny's lover…and if they stuck to their original plan, she wouldn't even be that for much longer.

While Claire mined Abby's refrigerator and pantry for ingredients that produced a delicious pitcher of hurricanes, the others remained in the living room, talking in hushed tones. Their voices rose here and there, but not enough for Abby to hear what was going on. She filled an ice bucket while Claire cut oranges and speared them and maraschino cherries with toothpicks for fancy and wholly unnecessary garnishes.

"You don't need to go to that much trouble," Abby said.

"I'm just giving them some time," Claire replied. "I'm an only child, but I know when siblings need some time on their own."

Abby grabbed a cherry and popped it into her mouth. "It's so weird for me to see Danny with his family. When we, um, had our relationship before, I never thought of him as related to anyone."

"At the time, I doubt he did, either, *chère,*" Claire said. "Except Lucienne. But from what I gather, he kept his relationship with her very quiet so that she wouldn't get caught up in his trouble. And she says she's a very different person now from who she used to be. Falling in love does that to a woman, doesn't it?"

Abby groaned. Was she in love? Was she willing to change who she was—who'd she become—to fit into Danny's world? That went against everything she'd tried to accomplish within herself since Marshall's death. She'd sought Danny out not so she could change for

him, but so she could put that part of her past to rest
and move on.

So far, nothing of her original plan had gone as she'd
expected and she still wasn't sure if that was good or
bad.

"I'm sorry I dragged all of you into this," Abby said.
"I didn't mean to disrupt everyone's lives. I just wanted
my painting back."

"Is that really what you wanted?"

Abby lined the iced glasses of fruity alcoholic punch
onto a tray. "I thought so."

"But now?"

Abby glared at Claire. Was everyone in this family
so relentless?

"I want Danny, too."

"And how exactly is that going to work? I mean, you
are a...wealthy socialite."

Abby wanted to argue with her, but she couldn't. Her
life was her life. She was raised completely differently
from Danny. He'd been a foster kid who'd learned to
steal and scam to survive. She was an educated trust-
fund baby who worked a nice, respectable job that rarely
came with any surprises or excitement. With or without the painting—scandal and family embarrassment
aside—he didn't fit into her world and vice versa.

"I'm not sure yet," she confessed.

Claire took one of the hurricane glasses off the tray,
filled it with her sweet rum concoction and handed it
to Abby. "At least you're being straight up with yourself. Then you and Danny need to be straight with each
other. Because I could be totally wrong, but I'm guessing that up until now, you haven't been."

Abby took the tray into the other room. She and
Danny hadn't been honest with each other. They'd meant

to be. They'd tried to be. They'd laid their cards out on the table as best they could, agreeing that their relationship couldn't possibly last beyond the moment he retrieved the painting for her. At the time, they'd thought this event would bring their affair full circle. But no matter what had kept Danny from retrieving the portrait, Abby knew she wasn't yet ready to let him go.

DANNY GLANCED OVER his shoulder, wanting Abby to finish whatever small talk she was making in the kitchen so he could get this conversation over with. He wasn't about to have it twice. Instead of spending the past fifteen minutes explaining to his brothers about what had happened tonight with Harris Liebe, he'd been recounting the events of five years ago, when he'd first met Abby and had broken her heart.

Lucienne sat back in the chair, her disapproving eyes boring into him. "Wow, I never realized how delusional I've been about you all these years."

"Delusional? You know what I did for a living, Luce. You were part of it!"

"I knew you were a thief, but not a dog. How could you do that to her? She was engaged!"

Danny growled in frustration. He didn't need this shit. He'd just blown a job—a job that was crucial in finally putting his past mistake to rest. He didn't need Lucy judging him. He didn't need anyone judging him. He'd already judged himself and the verdict wasn't pretty.

"Why do you think I came with her when she asked? This was my chance to make it right."

"I get how stealing the painting back for her leads toward that goal," Michael said. "But you're involved with her again, too. How's that going to work when you disappear?"

Danny scrunched his lips together, refusing to answer the question. This wasn't a conversation he needed to have with his brothers. He and Abby had a lot to discuss, but he wouldn't allow them to have an audience when they did.

"I've haven't exactly planned that far," he said.

Alex, who'd hardly spoken during Danny's confession, stood behind his soon-to-be wife, his head bowed in either disappointment or deep thought—or both. When he finally spoke, a hint of amusement played in his voice.

"I guess the ring's magic isn't infallible."

"How do you figure?" Danny asked, yanking off the leather gloves he'd kept on since his return to Abby's apartment. "I probably never would have come to Chicago without this hunk of gold giving me some enhanced sense of right and wrong. And look how great that's turned out."

"Excuse me?"

Danny looked up to see Abby holding a half-empty glass of bright red rum punch, which he had a feeling was going to get dumped on his head if he didn't make a clarification. "I'm talking about the painting, Abby. Not you."

He stood so that Abby could take his place on the couch with Claire and Michael.

"So what went wrong?" Lucy asked.

"The guy was waiting for me."

"Harris Liebe?" Abby's mouth had dropped open. "How did he even know you were coming?"

"Because he set the whole thing up."

For the next twenty minutes, Danny retold everything he'd learned from Harris Liebe, going all the way back to his professional connection with Ramon and his tracking down Abby's painting and planning to display it simply as a means to get to Danny and the ring for his wayward grandson. The retelling did not make the logic any easier to follow, but as Claire pointed out, they didn't need to agree with the guy's motives. They just had to come up with a way to beat him.

"So the bottom line is that he wants to trade the ring for the painting," Alejandro said.

"I won't allow it." Abby shook her head. "I'll call the police first. I'll report the painting stolen."

"Can you even prove it was yours to begin with?" Lucy asked. "Your family kept the story very well hidden. It wasn't even insured. And since you didn't report it stolen when Danny took it, the police aren't going to listen to you. You'll expose your family for nothing."

Abby leaned her head against his shoulder, and though every eye was on him, Danny slipped his arm around her waist and pulled her closer, loving the smell of her hair and the feel of her warm against him. He glanced down at the ring and wondered about the legend Ramon had told Michael. The ring was supposed to give the wearer a heightened sense of justice, an attraction to adventure and a jacked-up sense of romance. For his part, Danny thought the whole thing was bullshit. What the damned thing did was make a man fall in love at the absolute worst time in his life.

"Then what are we going to do?" Abby asked. "If he shows the painting, he'll have lost his leverage against Danny and then he'll just move on to some other scheme. We have to stop him."

Alex smiled. "This is a smart woman you've chosen, *mi hermano.*"

"She'd be smarter if she just stayed away from me," Danny muttered.

"Maybe," Abby agreed. "But I sure as hell wouldn't be any happier."

Michael made an exaggerated retching noise. "Okay, we get it, we get it. You're in love. Blah, blah, blah. It's getting late and you'll have the bedroom all to your-selves in a minute. For now, can we please stay focused on the situation at hand? When is this big reveal party Liebe is planning?"

"Day after tomorrow," Abby said.

"And it's a masquerade?" Claire asked, her eyes light-ing up.

Danny rolled his. Those New Orleans natives loved an excuse to get dressed up and wear a mask.

Abby nodded.

"Then I suggest we get some sleep tonight and re-convene in the morning to come up with a new plan of attack," Alex said. "Perhaps one that won't land us in jail if it fails." As if his word settled the matter entirely, Alex stood.

Michael joined him. "Agreed. If this Harris Liebe joker wants to destroy the Murrieta legacy, then I think we need to give him a fair chance." He grinned. "Times three, of course."

Danny looked up, halfway expecting his brothers to have their arms stretched out while they waited for him to pile on the third hand so they could shout "All for one and one for all."

That was, of course, the wrong story. Danny stood, shaking his head in pity for the man who'd dared to mess with the Murrieta brothers. Liebe might have been better off with the Three Musketeers because the three Zorros were going to kick his ass.

16

ABBY SHUT THE DOOR behind Danny's family as they headed off to a nearby hotel. She turned to find Danny sitting in the chair Lucy had claimed earlier. Lady had jumped up onto his lap and Black Jack, who'd made himself somewhat scarce while the apartment was filled with people, now sat at his feet meowing to join his partner. With a groan of resignation, Danny leaned back and stretched his legs, creating more lap for the cat, who leaped up and rubbed his face against Danny's chest.

A couple of days ago, Black Jack wouldn't go near Danny and Lady only curled around his ankles to annoy him. Now they were both completely in love.

She knew the feeling.

The truth had hit her first during her conversation with Erica at dinner, then while she helped Claire mix the fruity rum drinks and again when Michael had teased them so like a brother would. She loved Danny. For the first time, she truly and deeply loved him.

She didn't think she had before—how could she when the man who'd seduced her had not been real, but a fantasy lover created with the express purpose of coercing her into giving up the location of her grandmother's precious portrait? But over the course of their affair, Danny had come to truly care for her. He'd said so the night before her wedding, and though she had not believed him then, she did now.

But that didn't mean he still loved her. Yes, he was attracted to her. Yes, he felt a strong sense of obligation to make up for the sins of his past. But if she was going to spill her true feelings, she had to know that he wouldn't reject her. She'd gotten stronger over the past five years, but every woman had a breaking point.

"You're becoming quite the cat lover," she whispered, enjoying the return of silence to her normally quiet space.

Danny gave Black Jack such a generous scratch behind the ear, the cat nearly toppled off his lap in ecstasy. Man, did she know that feeling.

"They're not so bad," he said. "Definitely keep you from being lonely."

"Sometimes," she confessed. "But not all the time."

She grabbed the tray she'd stored beside the couch and started collecting the glasses from the coasters around the coffee table. With a gentleness that tightened her chest, Danny placed the cats on the floor and joined her. They moved with unrehearsed synchronicity, across the table, through the kitchen and, finally, into her bedroom. Together, they stripped off their clothes, but they didn't touch or kiss until he extended a gallant hand in invitation to the shower stall.

But they didn't make love. Their conversation was limited to the sweet moans that came from the simple pleasure of having someone to soap up the sponge and run the foamy ball over your back, to rinse the shampoo out of your hair and bring you a fluffy, rack-warmed towel before you stepped out onto the chilly tile. Only when Abby sat down in front of her bathroom mirror to brush out her hair did Danny finally say the words she'd hoped he'd wait until morning to say.

"I can't stay, Abby."

"Danny, please—" She spun around on her stool and grabbed his hands. He couldn't leave. Not now. Not yet.

"I don't want to hurt you again."

"You'll hurt me if you leave."

"I'll hurt you worse if I stay. I'm a thief, Abby. It's all I've ever been. It's all I know. You deserve better."

"I had better," she quipped. Marshall had been the best man she'd ever met—understanding, forgiving, righteous, kind and generous. She'd loved him fiercely, but he was gone and wasn't coming back. "Now I want you."

Danny knelt down in front of her, raised her hands to his lips and kissed her knuckles passionately.

"You'll have me. For a couple more days, until we stop this joker from harassing you and my brothers. But then I have to go and try to figure out what the hell I'm going to do with the rest of my life. It's time to reboot, but I'm not sure I can do anything differently."

"I know," she said, pulling his face closer to hers. "I know more than anyone what it's like to start over— first after I cheated on Marshall with you and lost the painting, and again after Marshall died. I've reinvented myself twice, but I haven't quite gotten the combination right. I'm still working on me, but that doesn't mean I don't want you in my life."

"You're perfect." He placed two sweet kisses on her face, one at the top of each cheekbone.

"I'm not," she insisted. "And I've got to stop trying to be. My whole life, I've been the perfect daughter, the perfect student, the perfect socialite with her charity work and her education in art history. Then I morphed into the perfect wife, and I loved every minute of it, but it wasn't me—it wasn't all of me. It's a lot of work to be good all the time, Danny."

"I really wouldn't know," he cracked.

"That's why we'd be great for each other. I can show you how to be good and you can give me lessons on how to be bad."

He nuzzled the area just beneath her earlobe and chuckled. "Now that's a job I'm suited for."

He flicked the spot where she'd tucked in her towel tight, releasing the material so that it fell away in a warm, soft rush. He nibbled a path down to her collarbone, then lower, to the sensitive crests of her breasts. His hands slid down her waist and outer thighs, his fingers kneading and needful.

"Danny," she managed, her focus breaking under the intensity of his pleasurable assault. "Tell me you'll stay."

He flicked her nipple with his tongue. "Believe me, sweetheart. I'm not going anywhere."

She shivered when he drew the sensitive tip between his lips. His sucking was tight and intense—pure concentrated pleasure that sent spires of need straight to her sex. She wanted him to promise. She wanted him to stay. But more than anything, she wanted him to make love to her—something she knew he wouldn't do if she insisted on asking for more than he could give.

Instead, she surrendered. He slid his hands across her thighs, spreading them wide so that her exposed flesh quivered. He did not make her wait, but slipped his fingers between her labia, then eased her natural moisture into every needful crevice while he alternated his mouth from breast to breast, each time sucking longer and harder until the pleasure came at the cost of exquisite bites of pain.

He buried his face in her softness. He murmured against her skin, sweet assurances she couldn't understand and didn't want to. Instead, she filled in her own fantasies—Danny giving up his criminal lifestyle, pledging to find a new path, all because of her. He dropped down low, spread her thighs farther and continued his sweet litany with his lips against her sexual center. He licked and nipped and explored the full depths of her while she tangled her hands in his delicious hair and allowed the sensual inferno to smoke, stoke, spark and flame. Just when she was on the edge of ecstasy, he lifted her from the chair, carried her to the bed and slid inside her. No pretext. No protection. Just his skin to her skin. His soul to hers.

Nothing between them but a million different reasons why this lovemaking might be their last.

His thrusts were deep, but slow. He pressed into her as far as he could, then eased out with infinitesimal slowness, dragging the sensations, swallowing her cries of frustration with kisses that were just as deep, just as powerful, just as long. When she attempted to wrap her legs around his waist to accelerate the tempo, he shifted so that his powerful thighs trapped hers. The shift in position made her squeal in surprise.

"Oh, yeah," he said. "You're so tight. How does this feel? Right here?"

He couldn't go as deep, but with her legs trapped between his, her body tightened and every thrust squeezed maximum pleasure from minimum space. Her clit ignited so that she lost herself in sensations within seconds. She moaned and cried out for mercy, but he gave her none, milking her body until her orgasm consumed her. She clawed at his chest and back while he bathed her in kisses. Only when she shouted out his name in release did he untrap her, bury himself to the hilt and join her in her mindless pleasure.

Exhausted, she wondered if she'd ever move again—if she'd ever want to move if the promise of this kind of pleasure on a nightly basis was not in her future.

After a few minutes, he rolled away from her, retrieved a discarded towel and used it to clean her, the soft sensations of the damp towel against her hot center renewing her lust. When he finally lay down beside her, she turned and flung her thigh over his hip, ensuring that he wasn't going anywhere—at least not yet.

"I think we forgot something," he said sheepishly. "I couldn't wait another minute."

She smiled, her body flooded with a kind of warmth that seesawed between love and lust. Five years ago, she had not loved him. Not like this. This was new and powerful and addictive. She wouldn't be able to go without him, no matter what he might believe about his inability to stay.

"It's okay," she said. "I've been on birth control for years. I almost stopped when…" She cut herself off, not wanting to talk about Marshall again when she was wrapped in the arms of the man who'd nearly stolen her from him.

"When Marshall died? You can talk about him, Abby. He's a part of you. I'm not jealous."

"Not even a little?" she said with a pout.

"Yeah, maybe a little. Obviously, you had a good life with him. You'd still be having that good life if not for a cruel twist of fate. I want that for you again, I really do."

"Do you believe in fate?"

He shrugged and drew his fingers, including the one that wore the family ring, up and down her arm. "I believe that the world works against us. That you have to grab whatever happiness you can get your hands on for as long as you can, because it won't last."

"Wow," she said, genuinely caught off guard by his utterly fatalistic outlook. "That's a sad way to look at things."

"Sad? Not at all. It makes you appreciate times like these. It makes you hold them close and milk every amazing minute from them because tomorrow it could all be over. Look at your husband. Do you think he knew how happy he'd made you by forgiving you?"

She didn't have to think hard to answer his question. She and Marshall had had this conversation. Once she'd cheated on her soon-to-be spouse, the rules about what they could or couldn't discuss had flown out the window. They'd talked openly and honestly about everything—including the thrill she'd gotten from Danny's bold and voracious interest in her that had ultimately caused her to stray. From that moment on, Marshall had stopped trying to hide his emotions, from deep love to untamable lust. The man who hadn't kissed her until their fourth date and who hadn't pressured her to go to bed with him until shortly before he'd offered her an engagement ring unleashed his true desires. Every inch of her, body and soul, had felt not only loved and cherished, but also wanted.

Marshall had raised the bar damned high—but she had no doubt that Danny could surpass him, if only he gave himself the chance.

"Yes, he knew. And I know he'd want me to have that with someone else. You can't use him as an excuse not to stay with me, Danny. In fact, I don't think an excuse exists that I'm going to accept. So," she said, pressing close and tilting her bottom so that she could feel a hint of a renewed erection against her, "you're going to have to think of something else. Because I'm not ready to let you go, and if there's one thing you've taught me, it's that when you want something, you have to take it— whether it's the right thing to do or not."

DANNY FELT LIKE AN IDIOT. In all the disguises and personas he'd adopted over the course of his criminal career, he'd never dressed up like this. Other than a few vague memories of store-bought, glorified garbage-bag Halloween costumes with plastic masks whose eyeholes were either too far apart or too close together, he'd never worn anything this outlandish. But since both of his brothers had sucked it up in order to help Abby and put an end to an old family vendetta, he figured he'd survive. Especially when Abby came around the corner bedecked in a sparkly confection of a dress that made his body yearn for a little more time before they had to leave.

"Oh, my," he said on a husky breath.

The spangles on her dress shimmered in the lights from the hall. She'd decided, in honor of her grandmother, to wear a thirties-style gown that dipped low in the front and lower in the back. Pure Hollywood glamour. The gold silk clung to her skin, precluding the need for undergarments, and as she stared at him from across the room, her nipples puckered beneath the fabric.

"I hope you have something to wear with that," he said, hoping she'd pull out a thick down coat or massive fur. Instead, she held up a pearl-white, feathered half-jacket, along with a handheld gilded mask and a glittery purse that dangled on a string of crystals.

"Will this do?"

"It will," he said, unable to stay away from her. He slid his black-gloved hands over her hips and tugged her close. "It definitely will. You might solve all our problems, you know, without a lick of trouble. One glance at you and the old man is going to keel over from a heart attack."

"Oh, great, one more thing for me to feel guilty about," she quipped.

He moved to kiss her, but the bright red hue of her lips was too perfect to smudge. Instead, he pressed against the small of her back until she arched her body and gave him instant and glorious access to her neck and throat.

"You can't help it if you're beautiful, can you?"

"I can change into that wicked-witch costume I wore to the children's charity event four Halloweens ago," she threatened, but he knew her vanity wouldn't allow it. He almost called her bluff, but decided they didn't have the time. Michael and Claire had mapped out a strict schedule, and when it came to work, Danny was nothing if not punctual.

"No time," he said, peeling his lips away from the delicious skin between her breasts. "Just put that jacket thing on and let's go."

"Aren't you forgetting something?"

She leaned down and snagged the black mask, cape and flat-brimmed Spanish gaucho hat he'd tossed onto the corner of the bed. Putting down her accessories, she made a show of circling the cape around his shoulders, tying the mask over his eyes and then topping the whole look with the hat. When he glanced in the mirror again, he'd transformed into the perfect representation of the fictional character his family legend had inspired.

"This is crazy," he said.

"He'll expect it," Abby assured him.

"I don't owe the old man anything," he argued. "He almost got Lucy and Alex killed. He nearly had me put away in prison for the one crime I didn't commit."

"But in the end, he's just a deluded old man desperate to help his grandson. And you have a chance to put this bad blood aside and start fresh. If you have to a wear a sexy costume to do it, I think it'll be worth it, don't you?"

Abby slid her hand hungrily up his chest. The lust glittering in her amber eyes made him forget every objection he had to this plan to end the feud with Harris Liebe. Danny would have given up every ill-gotten dime he had if he could stay here with Abby just a few more minutes.

But minutes would turn into hours and hours into days and days into forever. No matter how deeply she believed that he could somehow stay with her and make a relationship work, Danny knew better. He wasn't the settling-down type. He wasn't the marrying type. He was the love-them-and-leave-them type.

So now that he loved Abby to the very depths of his soul, it was time to leave.

"Okay, let's get this party started."

"Definitely," she said, picking up her accessories. "The sooner we put this mess to rest, the sooner we can get back here and you can show me precisely how talented with the ladies your famous ancestor was."

He laughed and crooked his arm to Abby, deciding not to destroy her fantasy just yet. First, he'd get that painting back for her. Then and only then would he break the news that no matter how much he wanted to stay and spend the rest of the night showing her just how much he cared for her, he was leaving with Alex and Lucy on their midnight flight to Madrid.

While Abby had gone with Claire to troll the Chicago costume shops for the pieces they needed to pull off this scheme, he and Lucy had discussed his options for the future. With her getting out of the fence business for good, he'd lost his desire to continue the cottage industry they'd created together. Truth was, the whole thing hadn't felt right since his arrest. Sitting in a six-by-six cell with no windows had given him plenty of time to think.

But as much as he could change his career, he couldn't change his past. Abby's life was too high-profile, her good name too important for him to risk her happiness. So instead, he'd accepted Lucy's invitation to go with them to Europe, and from there, he could decide what he wanted to do with the rest of his life. Alex had suggested he take over the security at the House of Aguilar. No one knew better how to keep thieves out than a thief himself.

The only thing he'd have to learn was how to keep Abby out of his heart.

_17_

THE MINUTE THEY STEPPED OFF the elevator, Danny stopped dead. Abby grabbed him by the hand and pulled him forward, folding her lips inward to keep from dissolving into giggles. Reluctant didn't begin to describe Danny's attitude toward wearing the costume, but Michael, standing just inside the door of her building's lobby, seemed to be having a grand time.

At the sight of his brother, he'd extended his black cape to its full width, then folded the fabric across his masked face. He looked like a crazy cross between Zorro and Dracula. Claire, standing beside him in a low-cut, hooped-skirt gown that could not have looked any better had it been worn by Vivien Leigh in _Gone with the Wind,_ laughed behind a frilly lace fan.

Alejandro, whose dark skin and penetrating eyes best portrayed their legendary ancestor, stood with his arms crossed, but a grin tugged at the corners of his mouth and his intense black eyes sparkled within the confines of his mask. When the expression turned predatory, Abby realized Alex wasn't grinning at Michael's shenanigans. Lucienne had emerged from the lobby ladies' room looking every bit the femme fatale—sequined red dress, elbow-length blue satin gloves, her long red hair swirled over her left eye, Veronica Lake–style. Her slim thigh peeked through the hip-height slit in her skirt as she moved across the marble lobby with a slinky sashay that would make the animated Jessica Rabbit damned proud.

The women were gorgeous. The men were painfully handsome. And though they'd been a family for only a couple of months, the warmth the sons of Ramon Murrieta exuded matched the emotions Abby shared with her parents after nearly thirty years. Maybe it was because they had no secrets from each other. Their strengths, weaknesses, foibles and follies had been exposed for each of them to see.

And they hadn't abandoned each other—hadn't allowed old resentments, fear or past hurts to take apart their haphazard family. Even women as different as Lucienne, with her criminal past, and Claire, who used to be a cop, had been folded into the Murrieta legacy. Abby had no doubt they'd take her in, too, judging by the warm smiles and compliments she received as she and Danny joined them.

She'd dragged their brother into a boatload of trouble, but no one blamed her or thought less of her. They accepted her, no questions asked.

"Well, we're quite a trio," Michael said, shoving Danny next to Alex. "The three amigos."

"The three idiots," Danny muttered. "Why are we wearing the same costume again?"

Alex cleared his throat. "Liebe is living under a delusion, which is a weakness we can exploit. If he sees all three of us, united in homage to our ancestor, he'll believe we're serious about handing over the ring. Did you find out if his grandson is going to be there tonight?" he asked Abby.

She shook her head. "According to my contact at the caterer's, he's not on the guest list."

"I did a little digging of my own, though," Claire said. "Liebe used his ill-gotten gains to get the kid into Northwestern. So he is here in Chicago."

"God," Danny said. "I hope he doesn't show up tonight. If he realizes how wacked out his grandfather is, his whole future could be a lost cause."

Abby stared at Danny, speechless.

"Don't look at me like I sprang a new head," he said wearily, though the corner of his mouth tweaked up in a reluctant grin. "I'm not completely heartless."

She slid her hand up his arm and pressed her cheek to his, not caring that his brothers were groaning about this intimate, yet public display of affection. "You're not heartless at all."

"Okay, loverboy, let's get this party started," Michael said, pushing his brother toward the door. They roughhoused for a second before Alex put a stop to it, leaving the women to exchange stares that said, *Boys will be boys.*

They might not have been brothers three months ago, but they were now—and they had a lot of time to make up for. And damn it if Abby didn't want to be there every step of the way.

As they headed out into the frigid October air, Abby tried not to think about the fact that in less than an hour or so, Danny would try to leave.

Emphasis on the word *try,* because she fully intended to stop him. He'd convinced himself that he could never fit into her world. And a week ago, she would have agreed with him. Maybe she still did. But the fact re-

mained that she refused to let him go. Maybe it was ir-
rational. Maybe it was crazy. Maybe it was desperate
and pathetic and unbecoming to a woman of her beauty,
intelligence and social standing.

So, consequently, she couldn't think of a better reason
to hold on tight.

But first, they had to put this mess with Harris Liebe
to rest.

Alejandro had hired a limousine to transport them
to the party, but so had everyone else on the guest list
judging by the long line of cars crawling up the street in
front of Harris Liebe's rented Lake Shore house, a stunning stone building that had an impressive front portico
and rose up at least three stories. Abby no longer thought
it was an accident that Liebe had leased a house in her
parents' neighborhood. The man was a master manip-
ulator. He was counting on her need to keep her dirty
laundry under wraps to force Danny and his brothers to
give him what he wanted. Clearly, he knew a lot about
the Murrieta family history, but he didn't know nearly
enough about this new generation. Or about her.

By the time they piled out of the car, the men were
restless. The couples split up immediately, entering a
few minutes apart so they didn't draw quite as much
attention to the fact that all three men were dressed the
same, a tactic Michael had suggested to throw Liebe off.
Abby spotted their host as they strode through the foyer,
but did not make eye contact. It helped that the man in-
furiated her. He'd used her to get what he wanted—and
she'd never even met him.

But if she'd resisted calling Danny when the news
about her painting had come out—then what? Liebe
would have tried something else, hooked someone else
into bringing Danny out of hiding. In a twisted way, she

supposed she should be glad for the man's vendetta. If not for his determination to end the blood feud between the Loves and the Murrietas, Danny would never have come back into her life.

As they crossed into a large living room on the ground floor, she caught sight of Erica. She couldn't miss her. Black feathered wings sprouted from her shoulders, as perfect an accessory as the halo, crusted with equally dark sparkles, that she'd perched at a jaunty angle on her head. Her inky and slinky goddess dress clung to her curves in ways that had the people standing around her staring, openmouthed, even as she laughed and sipped from a flute of champagne.

When Abby registered who those open mouths belonged to, she stumbled over the train of her dress. Danny caught her by the arm and hoisted her upright.

"You okay?"

"Oh, my…word."

Danny followed the direction of her stare and grinned. "She looks hot."

"I agree, but my parents obviously think a little differently. My in-laws, too."

Erica had, at Abby's instruction, contacted Abby's parents and asked them to come home for this important social event, but seeing them standing with Gennie and Doug Chamberlain, Marshall's parents, knocked her for a loop. She'd intended to introduce Danny to her parents before he escaped—but she hadn't expected to expose him to her in-laws, too.

Well, if she was going to go down, she might as well do it in flames.

"Maybe we should get out of here before they—"

"Abigail!"

Abby took a deep breath and held so tight to Danny's

arm, she nearly popped off one of her artificial nails. She pasted on a serene smile, then took a step toward Erica, who'd called out. Danny held steady, but she turned and pierced him with her determination.

"The least you can do before you disappear off the face of the earth is to meet my parents."

"Why would you want me to?"

"Don't they deserve to meet the man their daughter is in love with, particularly right before he breaks her heart again?"

His mouth was grim, but his eyes, so green and hypnotic, flashed with shock.

"You're going to introduce me? The real me?"

"That's the only you I know. Come on, you'll charm the pants off them."

And he did. Abby couldn't contain the smile that illuminated her whole body after Danny shook her father's hand firmly, gave her mother a sweet little bow and then bestowed the same courtesies on her former in-laws. She proudly introduced Danny as Daniel Murrieta, because honestly, that's who he was to her.

A man of mystery—a man with a shady past that he'd turned into a present he could be proud of. Whether he was ready to acknowledge his sacrifices to himself or not, she knew how hard it must have been for him to come back to Chicago and relive the one relationship that had nearly torn both of them apart. But somehow, together, they'd twisted their dishonest, manipulative affair into a real love story. They trusted each other. They sacrificed for each other. They loved each other. Did anything else matter?

"And what do you do, Mr. Murrieta?" Doug Chamberlain asked, a frown tilting the corner of his mouth and

accentuating the sternness of the costume he wore—
that of a five-star Army general.

"I'm a security specialist," Danny replied. "My
brother owns an auction house in Madrid and I'm about
to join him there to work on upgrading his systems."

Abby's eyes widened. This was new. She'd known
he was leaving—but she hadn't realized he had such a
definitive plan.

Her father, shockingly, had dressed in a wide-
shouldered, pin-striped suit with a glossy fedora and
cigar. He looked like a mobster. And her mother, in a
flashy blue flapper outfit, fit the perfect bill as his moll.

"That sounds interesting," Tony Albertini commented. "Been doing this long?"

"In a manner of speaking," Danny replied.

Abby couldn't tear her gaze away from her parents.
Of all the costumes they could have chosen, these were
the last ones she would have imagined they'd go for in
a million years. Her shock must have shown because
Erica tugged on Tony's lapel and said, "Don't your mom
and dad look spiffy? Since they had to get back on such
short notice, I took care of ordering their costumes for
them. I think your dad looks hot."

And so the conversation dissolved into a surreal suc-
cession of flirtations, compliments and small talk that
Abby would never in a million years have expected from
anyone in their social circle. Her in-laws, who had never
learned about the affair that had nearly wrecked her
marriage to their son, seemed utterly taken with Danny.
Gennie, who'd recently encouraged Abby to move on
and be happy, pinched her on the arm and winked in
silent approval. Her mother, on the other hand, wasn't as
subtle. She made an announcement that she needed an

immediate refill to her champagne and grabbed Abby
to accompany her on her quest.

In a semiprivate corner near the dining room, Lourdes
Albertini speared her daughter with an intense look.
"This is what you want?"

Abby couldn't run circles around her mother, even
if she wanted to—which she didn't. "Yes, mom. I love
him."

"Like you did before?"

"No," Abby said, her heart cracking in her chest as
the truth burst through. "Not at all like before. I know
everything about him now, warts and criminal offenses
and everything. I know I'm taking a big risk with my
heart, but I did that with Marshall, too, after what happened. And that turned out to be wonderful. How lucky
am I to have a second chance?"

"Lucky? That remains to be seen. But you need to
trust your instincts, baby. If this is what you want, then
I'm here for you. But he's signing a prenup."

Abby laughed. "One step at a time. First I have to
convince him to stay in the country."

Her mother shrugged her spangled shoulders. "I
don't know—I've been to Madrid. It's lovely this time
of year."

"I can't believe you and dad came home," Abby said.
"I mean, you know what could happen tonight, right?"

Lourdes nodded. "Erica filled us in, and frankly,
sweetie, it's time your father stopped taking his family's
past so seriously. His mother was a fabulous woman.
She would have been brokenhearted to know you spent
so much time trying to mold yourself into a perfectly
proper young lady. In fact, I wouldn't be surprised if
that's not why she willed the painting to you in the first
place. She wanted you to have it on your eighteenth

birthday so you'd see that sometimes, going a little wild isn't so bad."

"I can't believe you're telling me all this now," Abby said.

"Yes, well, as you get older, you realize that putting up appearances all the time isn't as important as living a good life. You're a good girl, sweetie. You always will be, no matter who you sleep with. We're the sum total of our past, present and future, and right now, I'm more concerned about your future than anything else. Your father is, too."

"Well, don't worry about me," Abby said. "Because I think I've finally found my future. And there's someone else who needs to know that."

"Daniel Murrieta?" her mother asked.

"Him, too, but no. Harris Liebe."

Abby gave her mother a kiss on the cheek, then hurried around the growing crowd of guests to the room she'd just seen Liebe disappear into. A very official, bulky-looking guy stood in front of the door. With his dark glasses and twisty earpiece, she figured he was security, which meant the painting was probably inside the room, too.

She turned and caught Alejandro's eye. He was standing nearby with Lucienne. Several gestures later and Michael and Claire drifted into view. She hadn't spotted Danny, but she trusted he'd come through as planned.

Didn't he always?

"I need to speak to Mr. Liebe," she said to the guard.

"And you are?" the man questioned.

"Abigail Albertini. He has something of mine that I believe he wishes to return."

He turned and spoke into the cuff of his jacket. After a moment, he stood back and opened the door. Unlike the study Danny had described on the third floor, this room was a spacious parlor. Most of the furniture had been shifted near the walls and in the center of the room was an easel covered with a square of blue satin.

"Ms. Albertini," Liebe said, toddering toward her, his gnarled hand extended politely. He was, not surprisingly, dressed in the bright cadet blues of a cavalry commander, complete with gold epaulets on the shoulders and a hat with dual crossed swords. "I have to confess I'm surprised to meet you alone."

"I wanted to deal with our business separately," she said. "May I?"

She gestured toward the covered painting, and after a short hesitation, he nodded his approval. She walked to the easel and drew off the shiny covering. Squinting, she lifted the easel and moved it a couple of inches back so that it got the full benefit of the light hanging above it.

"She was beautiful, wasn't she?"

"If you go for that sort of thing," he said with a grumble.

Abby laughed. Most people weren't half as prudish as they pretended to be—she was a prime example.

"Her name was Viviana Goletti. She married my grandfather, Gianni Albertini, when she was only sixteen years old."

"And when did she meet her lover, the artist?" he asked boldly.

Abby threw him a coy glance over her shoulder, glad he'd cut to the chase. "She was twenty-four. By all accounts, she'd tried very hard to conform to the expectations of her new family, but she was a wild child. Her mother had been a flapper. Her father a bootlegger from New York City. That's how the marriage to my grandfather was arranged—a business arrangement between rivals. But my grandfather had started phasing out the illegal side of his business. Prohibition was coming to an end and he intended to be ready for the transition. He was a smart man, my grandfather."

"Not smart enough to keep his wife at home with her clothes on."

She spun around and crossed her arms indignantly over her chest. "I find it fascinating that someone dealing in stolen goods can be so self-righteous and judgmental. This painting is rightfully mine and you know it."

A short scuffle sounded outside the door, but Harris Liebe didn't seem to notice.

"And you'll have it back," he promised. "Once your boyfriend gives me what I want."

She smiled, liking the idea of having Danny as a *boyfriend.*

"Fine," she said, turning back to the painting and admiring the expression on the woman's face. Abby had only known her grandmother when she was in her eighties, so it wasn't hard to look at the nude young woman draped sensuously across an elegant chaise longue and see not a relative, but a woman so completely comfortable with her nudity and her sexuality. A couple of months ago, Abby might not have been able to admire the sensual representation of her high cheekbones, buoyant breasts and curved belly, hips and mons, but now, she found the whole painting stunning.

"Shall I cancel the unveiling, then?" he asked.

"No," she said immediately. "The light in here is lovely and the party is well attended. I say it's time to allow the art lovers of Chicago to see what they've been missing."

The man was stunned to silence, and he staggered a little when the door opened and Alejandro strode inside.

He shut the door behind him. A heartbeat later, Michael emerged from behind a drape. She swirled to find Danny, then gasped, when his gloved hand slid across the bare skin at the small of her back.

He kissed her, dipping her backward with a romantic sweep that made her sigh. She could get used to this. She could get very, very used to this.

He took off his mask, and one by one, Michael and Alejandro did the same.

Harris Liebe spluttered and moved toward the door, but Alex blocked his path. "You'll find, Captain," Alex said with a wry glance at the old man's costume, "that you are not paying your security guards nearly enough to keep them on the job once they've received a better offer."

"What are you doing here?" he asked.

"Well, you wanted me to give up something that was important to our family," Danny answered. "You didn't expect me to do it behind my brother's backs, did you?"

18

APPARENTLY, THE OLD MAN HAD. A couple of months ago—hell, a couple of *days* ago—Danny would have gone to great lengths to avoid including Alejandro and Michael in anything he thought, said, did or planned. But now, even in their ridiculous matching costumes, they felt like a team.

Like brothers.

And at the same time, the weight and warmth of Abby's body pressed against his felt just as natural, perfectly suited not to the man he'd been, but to the one he wanted to become. She was so damned beautiful, inside and out, that he couldn't imagine going five minutes without touching her, much less the rest of his life.

But he'd deal with that change of plans later.

"You want to end the Murrieta-Love blood feud, so I figured I should bring all the Murrietas with me. To make it official."

Michael and Alejandro removed their hats and masks, so Danny did the same.

"You're going to hand over the ring?" the old man questioned. "But the young lady doesn't care if I show her portrait to the world."

"That's you?" Michael asked, his brow arched provocatively.

"It's her grandmother," Danny said, moving his body between Michael and the revealing portrait. "Show some respect."

Abby pulled him out of the way. "I think she's beautiful. And I'd also like to think there's a little bit of a family resemblance."

She winked at him, and if he'd had the time, he might have kissed her again just to stop her teasing.

"Be that as it may," Alejandro commanded, "it's become quite clear to my brothers and me that this matter between our families needs to be concluded. As our ancestor was, clearly, on the wrong side of the law, it only makes sense that we make the sacrifice."

Alex nodded to Michael, who pulled off the glove on his right hand and revealed the emerald-centered ring with the distinctive Z-shaped scratch. With reluctant nods from both his brothers, Michael removed the ring and handed it to Liebe, who cupped it in his own gloved hand.

He wandered to a lamp, turned on the bulb and held the ring underneath. "It's beat-up, that's for sure."

"It's had a big job, keeping the Murrieta boys out of trouble," Danny said.

"Is that what it does?"

Danny spread his hands and shook his head. "How else do you think you'd get a guy like me to do the honorable thing here? It's certainly not in my nature. Must have been the ring's influence."

"But you quit your job at the FBI," Liebe said, pointing his finger at Michael.

"Only so I could dedicate myself to helping people even if it means going outside the confines of the law,"

Michael replied. "Just like Joaquin did, though I'm sure you don't believe all those stories."

Liebe frowned. His ancestor might have only seen Joaquin Murrieta as a thug and a thief, but nearly a hundred years of legends and stories had to have played on the old man's psyche. And the costumes didn't hurt, either.

"What about you?" Harris asked Alejandro. "You had the ring for a while. What did it do for you?"

Alejandro frowned, but not with anger so much as a dose of much-needed humility. "Made me take greater risks for the right reasons. That's what our father said the ring did for him. It gave him focus and a legacy to live up to. He was not an honorable man in his youth, but once he reclaimed the ring, he embraced the sense of justice, the hunger for adventure and the desire for love that Joaquin embodied. It was a grand transformation. One you witnessed yourself, yes?"

Liebe moved away from the lamp. He turned the ring over in his hand a few times, then closed his eyes and gulped in a few steadying breaths.

"If this hunk of metal put Ramon and the three of you on the straight and narrow path, maybe it'll do the same for my grandson. This will be the end. You give me this ring, and the feud between our families will be over."

Danny looked first to Alejandro and then to Michael. Their expressions were serious and dour, but after a moment, they each nodded.

"Then the matter is done," Alejandro clarified.

The old man shuffled toward the door. "I'm going to give the kid a call right now and have him come on over. I'll stop paying for his schooling if he refuses to wear the thing."

Michael walked over and clapped the man gently on the shoulder. "You just show him the women we came in with and he'll do whatever you ask."

Alejandro and Michael helped Harris Liebe out of the room, and with a suggestive waggle of his brow, Michael closed the door behind them. Danny turned to find Abby staring at the portrait, the tip of her moist, pink tongue running softly over her bold, red lips.

"I do look like her, don't I?"

Danny slipped his hands around her middle and pressed up close behind her so that the netting holding the length of her hair scratched his chin. Naughtily, she shimmied her backside against his sex, spawning the start of an erection.

He groaned. "You are a very wicked woman."

Her laughter rumbled beneath his hands. "I wasn't until you came into my life."

"But you had it in you," he said, leaning her toward the painting. "It's obviously in your blood."

She twisted so she could look at him over her deliciously bare shoulder. "Just like being a good guy is in your blood."

"Only because this damned thing still won't come off."

With his teeth, Danny removed the glove from his right hand. The original Murrieta ring sparkled from his finger. Nothing short of cutting the gold was getting it off his hand, and since his brothers had had no plan to give up or do any harm to their family heirloom, they'd opted instead to keep the ring under Danny's glove while Michael surrendered an amazingly accurate replica that Alex had commissioned—and paid handsomely—to be made quickly.

Michael had suggested that the reason for the ring's

stubborn adherence to Danny's finger was because without it, Danny would never manage to stay on the straight and narrow long enough to keep Abby in his life. Alex had concurred. Neither one was swayed by Danny's relentless arguments that ring or not, Abby would be better off without him—but truth was, he didn't believe it, either. Not anymore.

He wanted to be with Abby more than he wanted any priceless piece of art. He needed to have her at his side, no matter what he had to change about himself to keep her there. To make a real relationship work with Abby, he needed all the help he could get. And if that meant keeping the ring on, he would do it—for as long as it took.

Perhaps forever.

"Were you serious about that job in Spain?" she asked.

"Why not?" he said. "Alex has an uncle running security now and he's getting up there in years. I thought it might be a gas to shore up the House of Aguilar and then maybe contract myself out to other outfits who need to stop guys like me."

She turned around in his arms so that her nose touched the tip of his chin. He tugged her close and she melded into the curves of his body with utter perfection. He'd be lost without this woman. Totally, completely, pathetically and undeniably lost.

"Come with me," he begged.

She looked up and flashed her fake eyelashes at him. "Come with you where?"

She was milking this. She was making him work for it. Well, he deserved it—and worse. He'd probably be paying for the rest of his life.

Lucky dog that he was.

"To Spain, first. To the ends of the universe and any-where in between. I can't live without you, Abby. I love you. God help you, but I love every glorious inch of you."

Sliding her hands up his cheeks, she pulled his face down and kissed him so deeply, he was certain his lips would soon be as stained red as hers. His brothers would have a grand time tormenting him about it, but he didn't care. He didn't care about anything as long as he had Abby.

"I love you, Danny. I didn't before, but I do now. God help me, I do now."

Behind him, he heard someone open the doors to the parlor and soon they were surrounded by people ad-miring the painting that Abby had once gone to great lengths to keep under wraps. Danny took Abby by the hand and wove through the crowd until they found a quiet corner beside the coat closet. With a girlish giggle, Abby tore open the door and tugged him inside.

"Abby, what you are doing?"

"Stealing what I want," she said. "A moment or two alone with the man I love. Think you can handle this wicked woman you've coaxed out of hiding?"

Danny pulled them deeper into the coats and tore away the cape that threatened to strangle him around the neck. "If any guy was perfect for this job, it's me."

"Prove it," she challenged.

And so, while the rest of the house oohed and aahed over the recently discovered scandalous art deco nude, he did.

* * * * *

Harlequin Blaze

COMING NEXT MONTH

Available October 25, 2011

You can find more information on upcoming
Harlequin® titles, free excerpts and more at
www.HarlequinInsideRomance.com.

HBCNM1011

REQUEST YOUR FREE BOOKS!
2 FREE NOVELS PLUS 2 FREE GIFTS!

Harlequin Blaze

red-hot reads!

YES! Please send me 2 FREE Harlequin® Blaze™ novels and my 2 FREE gifts (gifts are worth about $10). After receiving them, if I don't wish to receive any more books, I can return the shipping statement marked "cancel." If I don't cancel, I will receive 6 brand-new novels every month and be billed just $4.49 per book in the U.S. or $4.96 per book in Canada. That's a saving of at least 14% off the cover price. It's quite a bargain. Shipping and handling is just 50¢ per book in the U.S. and 75¢ per book in Canada.* I understand that accepting the 2 free books and gifts places me under no obligation to buy anything. I can always return a shipment and cancel at any time. Even if I never buy another book, the two free books and gifts are mine to keep forever.

151/351 HDN FEQE

Name	(PLEASE PRINT)

Address	Apt. #

City	State/Prov.	Zip/Postal Code

Signature (if under 18, a parent or guardian must sign)

Mail to the Reader Service:
IN U.S.A.: P.O. Box 1867, Buffalo, NY 14240-1867
IN CANADA: P.O. Box 609, Fort Erie, Ontario L2A 5X3

Not valid for current subscribers to Harlequin Blaze books.

**Want to try two free books from another line?
Call 1-800-873-8635 or visit www.ReaderService.com.**

* Terms and prices subject to change without notice. Prices do not include applicable taxes. Sales tax applicable in N.Y. Canadian residents will be charged applicable taxes. Offer not valid in Quebec. This offer is limited to one order per household. All orders subject to credit approval. Credit or debit balances in a customer's account(s) may be offset by any other outstanding balance owed by or to the customer. Please allow 4 to 6 weeks for delivery. Offer available while quantities last.

Your Privacy—The Reader Service is committed to protecting your privacy. Our Privacy Policy is available online at www.ReaderService.com or upon request from the Reader Service.

We make a portion of our mailing list available to reputable third parties that offer products we believe may interest you. If you prefer that we not exchange your name with third parties, or if you wish to clarify or modify your communication preferences, please visit us at www.ReaderService.com/consumerschoice or write to us at Reader Service Preference Service, P.O. Box 9062, Buffalo, NY 14269. Include your complete name and address.

HB11B

Harlequin® Special Edition® is thrilled to present a new installment in USA TODAY bestselling author RaeAnne Thayne's reader-favorite miniseries, THE COWBOYS OF COLD CREEK.

Join the excitement as we meet the Bowmans—four siblings who lost their parents but keep family ties alive in Pine Gulch. First up is Trace. Only two things get under this rugged lawman's skin: beautiful women and secrets. And in Rebecca Parsons, he finds both!

Read on for a sneak peek of CHRISTMAS IN COLD CREEK. *Available November 2011 from Harlequin® Special Edition®.*

On impulse, he unfolded himself from the bar stool. "Need a hand?"

"Thank you! I…" She lifted her gaze from the floor to his jeans and then raised her eyes. When she identified him her hazel eyes turned from grateful to unfriendly and cold, as if he'd somehow thrown the broken glasses at her head.

He also thought he saw a glimmer of panic in those interesting depths, which instantly stirred his curiosity like cream swirling through coffee.

"I've got it, Officer. Thank you." Her voice was several degrees colder than the whirl of sleet outside the windows.

Despite her protests, he knelt down beside her and began to pick up shards of broken glass. "No problem. Those trays can be slippery."

This close, he picked up the scent of her, something fresh and flowery that made him think of a mountain meadow on a July afternoon. She had a soft, lush mouth and for one brief, insane moment, he wanted to push aside that stray lock of hair slipping from her ponytail and taste her. Apparently he needed to spend a lot less time working and a great deal *more* time recreating with the opposite sex if he could have sudden random fantasies about a woman he wasn't even inclined to like, pretty or not.

"I'm Trace Bowman. You must be new in town."

She didn't answer immediately and he could almost see the wheels turning in her head. Why the hesitancy? And why that little hint of unease he could see clouding the edge of her gaze? His presence was obviously making her uncomfortable and Trace couldn't help wondering why.

"Yes. We've been here a few weeks."

"Well, I'm just up the road about four lots, in the white house with the cedar shake roof, if you or your daughter need anything." He smiled at her as he picked up the last shard of glass and set it on her tray.

Definitely a story there, he thought as she hurried away. He just might need to dig a little into her background to find out why someone with fine clothes and nice jewelry, and who so obviously didn't have experience as a waitress, would be here slinging hash at The Gulch. Was she running away from someone? A bad marriage?

So…Rebecca Parsons. Not Becky. An intriguing woman. It had been a long time since one of those had crossed his path here in Pine Gulch.

Trace won't rest until he finds out Rebecca's secret, but will he still have that same attraction to her once he does? Find out in CHRISTMAS IN COLD CREEK. Available November 2011 from Harlequin® Special Edition®.

ALWAYS POWERFUL, PASSIONATE AND PROVOCATIVE.

NEW YORK TIMES AND USA TODAY BESTSELLING AUTHOR

BRENDA JACKSON

PRESENTS A BRAND-NEW TALE OF SEDUCTION

TEMPTATION

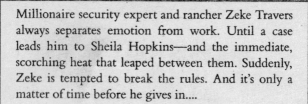

Millionaire security expert and rancher Zeke Travers always separates emotion from work. Until a case leads him to Sheila Hopkins—and the immediate, scorching heat that leaped between them. Suddenly, Zeke is tempted to break the rules. And it's only a matter of time before he gives in....

Available November wherever books are sold.